TEACHER'S ANNOTATED EDITION

Vocabulary Workshop
New Edition

W9-AZJ-148

Level B

Jerome Shostak

Series Consultants

Sylvia A. Rendón, Ph.D.
Coord., Secondary Reading
Cypress-Fairbanks I.S.D.
Houston, Texas

Mel H. Farberman
Director of English
  Language Arts, K–12
Bay Shore U.F.S.D.
Bay Shore, New York

John Heath, Ph.D.
Department of Classics
Santa Clara University
Santa Clara, California

Sadlier-Oxford
A Division of William H. Sadlier, Inc.

Reviewers

The publisher wishes to thank for their comments and suggestions the following teachers and administrators, who read portions of the series prior to publication.

Anne S. Crane
Clinician, English Education
Georgia State University
Atlanta, GA

Arlene A. Oraby
Dept. Chair (Ret.), English 6–12
Briarcliff Public Schools
Briarcliff Manor, NY

Patricia M. Stack
English Teacher
South Park School District
South Park, PA

Susan W. Keogh
Curriculum Coordinator
Lake Highland Preparatory
Orlando, FL

Susan Cotter McDonough
English Department Chair
Wakefield High School
Wakefield, MA

Joy Vander Vliet
English Teacher
Council Rock High School
Newtown, PA

Mary Louise Ellena-Wygonik
English Teacher
Hampton High School
Allison Park, PA

Sr. M. Francis Regis Trojano
Sisters of St. Joseph (CSJ)
Educational Consultant
Boston, MA

Karen Christine Solheim
English Teacher
Jefferson High School
Jefferson, GA

Lisa Anne Pomi
Language Arts Chairperson
Woodside High School
Woodside, CA

Keith Yost
Director of Humanities
Tomball Ind. School District
Tomball, TX

Printed in the United States of America.
ISBN: 0-8215-7117-6
123456789/09 08 07 06 05

CONTENTS

INTRODUCTION

VOCABULARY WORKSHOP has for more than five decades been the leading program for systematic vocabulary development for grades 6–12. It has been proven a highly successful tool in helping students expand their vocabularies, improve their vocabulary skills, and prepare for the vocabulary strands of standardized tests.

This New Edition of VOCABULARY WORKSHOP preserves and improves upon those key elements of the program that have made it so effective *and* introduces important new features that make the series more comprehensive in scope and current in approach to vocabulary instruction, especially with respect to standardized testing.

Key Elements

- At each Level, a **word list** of 300 main entries, plus hundreds of synonyms, antonyms, and other related words

- Proven and effective **five-step approach to instruction**, leading students to mastery of word meanings and usage

- Excellent **preparation for the SAT** and other standardized tests with strong correlations between word lists and words that frequently appear on the SAT, as well as practice in types and formats of exercises found on the SAT

- Frequent **review and assessment** both in Student Text and in supplementary programs

---

New Features

To address recent changes in such standardized tests as the SAT and the ACT, the New Edition of VOCABULARY WORKSHOP introduces two features designed to provide students with further opportunities to prepare for new challenges presented on these standardized tests and, at the same time, to apply and extend their vocabulary, reading, and writing skills. These new features appear in each of the Reviews.

- **Vocabulary for Comprehension**, a two-page feature, consists of a reading passage and a page of exercises that give students practice in the kinds of comprehension and vocabulary questions that appear on such standardized tests as the "new" SAT and the ACT.

- Following the Vocabulary for Comprehension exercises is a new feature called **Grammar in Context**. Referring to a grammar or usage topic illustrated in the preceding reading passage, Grammar in Context provides instruction and practice in a grammar or usage skill tested on the Writing section of the "new" SAT and on other standardized tests.

Other Features

Among the features that were introduced in the previous edition of the VOCABULARY WORKSHOP program and that have been carried over to the New Edition are the following:

- In the Units, an expanded **Definitions** section that includes synonyms, antonyms, and complete illustrative sentences for each part of speech for every taught word

- Also in the Units, **Vocabulary in Context**, a reading passage that provides examples of how Unit words are used in more fully developed contexts than simple sentences

- Instruction in and examples of key vocabulary **strategies**—using context and using word structure—for decoding word meanings

- In the Reviews, the **Building with Classical Roots** section, an exercise that acquaints students with Latin and Greek roots and provides a strategy for finding the meaning of words derived from these roots

- In the Cumulative Reviews, the **Enriching Your Vocabulary** section, designed to broaden and enhance students' understanding of the relationships, history, and origins of the words that make up the English language

- For all Levels, A–H, **interactive online activities** that provide students with engaging word puzzles and games using the vocabulary presented in the Units

- For all Levels, A–H, a **Test Generator CD-ROM** that adds a secure and customizable assessment option to the program, eliminating the risk of "secondhand" tests that may distort assessment results

In the following pages of this Teacher's Edition, you will learn more about the VOCABULARY WORKSHOP program, including these new features and components, as well as how to get the most out of the program for your classroom.

OVERVIEW

"Pure Vocabulary" Approach: Systematic Vocabulary Instruction

The VOCABULARY WORKSHOP program focuses on words themselves, their meanings (both literal and figurative), their ranges of application (or usage), and their relationships to other words.

The approach is systematic in the sense that it begins with and builds upon a word list compiled to provide students with vocabulary they will encounter in their reading both in and out of the classroom. It is designed to provide students with the vocabulary skills they will need in order to achieve higher-level reading proficiency and to succeed at standardized tests.

The VOCABULARY WORKSHOP systematic approach differs from a literature-based approach in that each Unit begins with a thorough consideration of the words themselves rather than with a reading selection featuring words to be studied. (This is not to say that VOCABULARY WORKSHOP cannot be profitably used as a complement to a literature-based approach. See pages T30–T31 for suggestions on how this might be done.)

Rather than in the circumstantial context of literature, VOCABULARY WORKSHOP introduces and exemplifies vocabulary usage in varied and controlled contexts. These range from short phrases to full sentences to the Vocabulary in Context reading passages.

For effective study, the "pure vocabulary" approach also offers these advantages:

- It provides unlimited flexibility in the choice and placement of grade-appropriate material.

- It avoids the problem of trying to deal with a literary passage both as literature and as a vehicle for vocabulary instruction.

- It focuses more directly and completely on the words themselves, their meanings, their usage, and their relationships to other words.

- By economizing space, it allows a greater range of practice, reinforcement, and enhancement.

- It allows maximum coverage of a maximum number of key words.

One of the cornerstones of the VOCABULARY WORKSHOP approach is intensive practice through varied and abundant "hands-on" exercises. This method ensures that students are provided with:

- maximum exposure to different meanings of the key words studied;

- maximum coverage of the range of each key word through its appearance in many different contexts;

• fullest understanding of the key words' relationships to other words.

The aim of the pattern of intensive practice is to include the words in the students' active, daily-use vocabulary. This implies the ability to use a given word not only in its literal, or narrow, sense but also in a figurative way. Furthermore, it means that students will be able to use the word with confidence both as speakers and as writers.

Grade-Level Placements

The chart below shows the suggested grade placement for each Level of VOCABULARY WORKSHOP, depending on the overall ability of the student population involved.

In determining "proper" placement of a particular Level of VOCABULARY WORKSHOP in a given situation, the following considerations should be taken into account:

• Grade placements are based on actual teacher experience and recommendations throughout the long course of VOCABULARY WORKSHOP's history.

• Differences in grade are reflected not only in the "difficulty" of the words presented but also in the "maturity" of the sentences and other contexts in which those words are used.

• Grade levels indicated in the chart should not be taken in too literal or rigorous a sense. A certain amount of experimentation, as well as the use of the diagnostic materials provided in the program, will establish the "correct" placement of a particular Level in a given situation.

• The use of Level H with "above-average" students is designed to enhance preparation for the SAT and other college-entrance examinations.

Grade Placements			
"Average" Students		"Above-Average" Students	
Level	Grade	Level	Grade
A	6	A	5
B	7	B	6
C	8	C	7
D	9	D	8
E	10	E	9
F	11	F	10
G	12	G	11
		H	12

Word Lists

Each Student Text in the VOCABULARY WORKSHOP program for Levels A–H contains 300 words organized in 15 Units.

Criteria for Selection

The selection of words for the VOCABULARY WORKSHOP program is based on four major criteria:

- currency in and usefulness for present-day American oral or written communication;
- frequency on recognized vocabulary lists;
- applicability to standardized tests, especially the SAT;
- current grade-placement research.

General Sources

The lists of key words were developed from many sources:

- traditional, classic, and contemporary literature, including novels, short stories, essays, newspaper and magazine articles, plays, films, videos, and TV programs;
- spelling and vocabulary lists recognized as valid bases for teaching language skills at the middle and secondary levels;
- current subject-area textbooks, glossaries, and ancillary materials (especially for general, nontechnical terms).

Dictionary and Reference Sources

The following were the primary dictionary resources used for word (and definition) selection:

- *Webster's Third International Dictionary of the English Language* (unabridged)
- *Merriam-Webster's Collegiate Dictionary* (Ninth and Tenth editions)

Other supplementary dictionaries consulted included:

- *The American Heritage Dictionary of the English Language* (all four editions)
- *The Random House Dictionary of the English Language* (unabridged; both editions)
- *The Compact Edition of the Oxford English Dictionary*

Standard Word-Frequency Sources

Standard word-frequency studies were employed to evaluate and revise the words on the tentative lists. These included:

- *Primary*
  Dale-O'Rourke: *The Living Word Vocabulary*
  Carroll-Davies-Richman: *Word Frequency Book*

- *Supplementary*
  Harris-Jacobsen: *Basic Reading Vocabularies*
  Thorndike-Lorge: *The Teacher's Word Book of 30,000 Words*
  Zeno-Ivens-Millard-Duvvuri: *The Educator's Word Frequency Guide*

"Sliding-Scale" Placement

Each word list works on a sliding scale based on these principles:

- No word that Dale-O'Rourke indicates as known in a given grade is presented in that grade. Instead, where possible, it is presented 2 or 3 grades earlier.

- Each grade level contains a preponderance of words not known (according to Dale-O'Rourke) 2 or 3 grades later, with an admixture (in decreasing numbers) of words not known 4 or more grades later.

- The higher the grade, the larger the percentage of more difficult words contained on the word list. This was done to accommodate as many "SAT-type" words as possible in the key word lists for Grades 10–12.

PROGRAM COMPONENTS

This New Edition of VOCABULARY WORKSHOP, Levels A–H, consists of the following components:

Components of the VOCABULARY WORKSHOP Program*

- **Student Texts,** 8 Levels (A–H)

- **Teacher's Annotated Editions,** 8 Levels (A–H)

- **Test Booklets**
  - Form A, 8 Levels (A–H)
  - Form B, 8 Levels (A–H)
  - Combined Answer Keys, 8 Levels (A–H)

- **Test Generator CD-ROM,** 8 Levels (A–H)

- SAT-Type **TEST PREP Blackline Masters**
  (answers included), 8 Levels (A–H)

- **Interactive Audio Pronunciation Program,**
  6 Levels (A–F only)

- **Interactive Online Activities,** 8 Levels (A–H)

The components have been designed for use in an integrated year-long vocabulary program, as suggested in the chart on pages T23–T25.

*Note that, in its entirety, the VOCABULARY WORKSHOP program now includes Student Texts, Teacher's Editions, and Supplementary Testing Programs for Grades 2–5 (Levels Purple, Green, Orange, and Blue).

The Student Texts

All eight Student Texts (Levels A–H) present 300 key words and are organized in the same way: 15 Units of 20 words each; 5 Reviews (following Units 3, 6, 9, 12, and 15); and 4 Cumulative Reviews. Preceding the first Unit is a section titled The Vocabulary of Vocabulary and a Diagnostic Test. Concluding each Student Text is a Final Mastery Test.

Vocabulary of Vocabulary (Student Text pages 7–17)

The purpose of this section is to familiarize students with some of the terms, concepts, and strategies that will be introduced and applied in the program. The practice exercises that accompany the discussions are meant to clarify and consolidate the concepts involved.

Some of these terms (for example, *synonyms* and *antonyms*) will already be familiar to most students. However, teachers should not hesitate to review these terms if doing so seems advisable, even at the upper levels of the program. Other, more complex concepts (such as analogies and context), however, may require more instruction and practice, both as preparation for related exercises and as review or reteaching for any students who have difficulty in successfully completing those exercises.

This is particularly true of analogies, which many students find especially challenging. One page of Vocabulary of Vocabulary is devoted to this important critical-thinking exercise so often found on standardized tests.

Diagnostic Test (Student Text pages 18–20)

A Diagnostic Test has been provided at the beginning of each Level as a means of assessing the students' overall vocabulary and test-taking skills. The Test covers a selection of key words introduced in the Level in question and is presented in the form of 50 synonym and antonym items.

Although the Diagnostic Test may be presented as a timed speed test, with the specific aim of determining how many items students can answer in 10 or 15 minutes, it is better used as an informal assessment and/or motivational device. Speed will come when confidence and vocabulary fluency have developed.

The Units

At the heart of the Student Texts—and of the VOCABULARY WORKSHOP program—are the 15 Units in which the 300 key words are introduced.

The work of each Unit is divided into a unique 5-part structure designed to give maximum coverage to each of the key words within the space available.

Structure of the Unit
(20 words)
1. Definitions
2. Completing the Sentence
3. Synonyms and Antonyms
4. Choosing the Right Word
5. Vocabulary in Context

The following descriptions of the individual exercises in a typical Unit of Levels A–H are designed to aid the teacher in using the text to maximum effect in the classroom.

1. DEFINITIONS

The first section of each Unit provides definitions, parts of speech, pronunciation, synonyms, antonyms, and illustrative sentences.

DEFINITIONS

The definitions provided are not of the dictionary type. They are, for the most part, relatively brief and simple. The intent is to give students a reasonably good "core" idea of what each word means, without extensive detail or secondary connotations.

Generally, only a single meaning of maximum usefulness is given the student. However, several meanings may be indicated if they are distinct, if they appear to be more or less equally useful, or if they will enable students to prepare for the vocabulary-in-context strand of the Critical Reading section of the new SAT.

PART OF SPEECH

The part of speech of each word is indicated at the beginning of the definition, using a simple set of abbreviations. When a word functions as several parts of speech, the appropriate abbreviation appears before the corresponding definition. (An explanation of the abbreviations used can be found on page 6 of each Student Text.)

PRONUNCIATION

With each word listing, the pronunciation is indicated by means of a simple set of diacritical marks presented at the beginning of every Student Text (page 6).

The practice has been to indicate only one pronunciation, even where alternate pronunciations are sanctioned by the dictionary. There are only a few exceptions to this—for example, when a word changes its pronunciation in accordance with its use as different parts of speech (ob´ ject and ob ject´).

Note that once they have completed the first section of each Unit, students may utilize the **Interactive Audio Pronunciation Program** (Levels A–F only) for that Unit. This program provides about four hours of spoken material per Student Text, including pronunciations, parts of speech, definitions, and illustrative sentences. For further details about the use of the Audio Program in this and other ways, see page T21.

SYNONYMS AND ANTONYMS

A list of synonyms and/or antonyms is given for each key word for which there is one or more of either. Some of these synonyms and antonyms will reappear in the Synonyms and Antonyms section (see page T13). By studying the given synonyms and antonyms, students will better understand the denotational family of words of which each key word is part; and by comparing specific usages of key words and their synonyms, students can better appreciate appropriate contexts for, and nuances in meaning and connotation represented by, these words.

Note that the lists of synonyms and antonyms are not meant to be exhaustive. Grade-level parameters have been taken into account; and obscure, archaic, and slang synonyms and antonyms have generally been avoided.

ILLUSTRATIVE SENTENCE

Concluding each key entry is an illustrative sentence including a blank space in which students must write the taught word. These sentences, although necessarily brief, provide a context that clarifies the meaning of each word and points up its idiomatic usage. By writing the word in such contextual settings, students begin to see how it can be used effectively in their own writing. Furthermore, the act of writing is in itself a form of reinforcement; and by writing the word, the student must focus attention on its spelling as well.

2. COMPLETING THE SENTENCE

The next activity, Completing the Sentence, is a simple completion exercise in which students are asked to choose and write the word that logically and meaningfully fits into a blank in a given sentence.

When using this activity in the classroom, the teacher should bear in mind the following considerations:

- The sentences in this activity call for the literal or direct (as opposed to the metaphorical or extended) meaning of the words involved. This is an easier usage for students to grasp and provides a good foundation for the more sophisticated contexts that appear in Choosing the Right Word.

- The sentences are designed so that one and only one of the words fits in the given blank. Selection of the proper word has been facilitated by the incorporation of context clues in each sentence.

- The words are to be used as the part of speech given in Definitions. The only exceptions are: Nouns given in the singular in Definitions may be plural in the sentences; verbs given in the base form in Definitions may be used in any tense or form (including participial) required by the sentence.

3. SYNONYMS AND ANTONYMS

In this section students are given phrases that include synonyms or antonyms as presented in the Definitions section and must choose the appropriate key word for each phrase. Each of the 20 key Unit words is covered once in either the Synonyms or the Antonyms part of the section. Besides reinforcing meanings, this exercise provides students with further examples of usage and context.

4. Choosing the Right Word

The fourth activity in each Unit is called Choosing the Right Word. In it students are asked to choose the member of a pair of words that more satisfactorily completes the sentence. At first appearance this exercise may seem an easier activity than Completing the Sentence. In fact, however:

- sentences in this activity are more mature linguistically and in subject matter;

- in many cases the words covered are used in a more figurative, extended, or abstract meaning;

- the part of speech or form of the key word has been changed (for example, from an adjective to an adverb) whenever convenient.

Accordingly, this activity is in reality more difficult than Completing the Sentence and requires real effort and a thorough understanding of the range of a word to complete successfully.

5. Vocabulary in Context

The fifth, and last, section of each Unit is an activity titled Vocabulary in Context. The activity is presented in the form of a reading passage, approximating a standardized-test format, into which a number of the key Unit words have been woven. Its purpose is threefold:

- to give further examples of usage for the selected words;

- to offer an opportunity to derive meaning from context;

- to provide practice in the sort of vocabulary exercises found on standardized tests.

With this activity, it may prove helpful to refer students, if necessary, to the section of Vocabulary of Vocabulary (see Student Text pages 7–17) that serves as an introduction to the strategies involved in studying vocabulary in context.

Follow-Up Activities

Once the work of the Unit is completed, you may find it useful to give a writing exercise in which students may apply and illustrate what they have learned about the words introduced in the Unit.

Writing Essays or Stories

Students might be invited to create their own brief essays or short stories and encouraged to use as many of the Unit's key words as is practical. (Students should, however, be discouraged from trying to "force" key words into their essays or stories indiscriminately, just for the sake of number alone. It is essential that students get in the habit of using these words correctly.) If they are to write essays, students might refer to the Vocabulary in Context passages as models.

WRITING SENTENCES

Depending on the ability level of individual students or of classes, you may prefer instead to administer a short writing exercise (5–10 items) such as the one shown below. This exercise is not so challenging as writing a story or essay but will give students an opportunity to "try out" some of the words they have learned and will provide the teacher with a means of assessing how well students have mastered the meaning and usage of these words.

Sample Writing Exercise (Level D)

Framing Sentences   *On the lines provided, write an **original** sentence that illustrates the meaning and use of each of the following words. Do **not** merely copy one of the sentences given in the Student Text.*

1. dilemma

_____

_____

_____

2. relinquish

_____

_____

_____

3. breach

_____

_____

_____

4. circumspect

_____

_____

_____

5. opinionated

_____

_____

_____

The Reviews

A Review follows every three Units. Every effort has been made to include all of the 60 key words at least once in the Review for the three corresponding Units.

Structure of the Review
1. Vocabulary for Comprehension
2. Grammer in Context
3. Two-Word Completions
4. Choosing the Right Meaning
5. Antonyms
6. Word Families
7. Word Associations
8. Building with Classical Roots

SAT SECTIONS

The first four parts of each Review have been specially designed to meet the needs of students seriously preparing for the verbal part of the SAT and similar standardized tests.

VOCABULARY FOR COMPREHENSION (PART 1)

This new feature is modeled on, and designed to help students prepare for, the Reading sections of standardized tests. Students first read a passage of expository or informational text and then answer vocabulary-in-context and comprehension questions relating to that text. An introduction to this feature may be found on pages 13–15 of the Student Text. It is recommended that students read this introduction and discuss it with their teacher before they undertake the Vocabulary for Comprehension exercises in the Reviews.

GRAMMAR IN CONTEXT (PART 2)

Also a new feature, Grammar in Context aims to provide review and practice in those grammar and usage skills most commonly tested on standardized tests. The grammar skill or skills covered in any given Review are linked to the Vocabulary for Comprehension passage that precedes it. A list of the skills covered in this Level, together with an introduction to the Grammar in Context feature, appears on page 16 of the Student Text.

Two-Word Completions (Part 3)

This part of the Review has been designed to familiarize students with the type of word-omission (cloze) exercise that appears on typical standardized tests, including the SAT. Again the aim here is to refine students' critical-thinking skills. Context clues are embedded within the passages to guide students to the correct choice.

Note: Explanations for the correct answers to the Two-Word Completions exercises can be found in the supplemental answer key on pages T38–T48.

Choosing the Right Meaning (Part 4)

Focusing on usage-discrimination skills, this part of the Review challenges students to choose, from among two or more taught meanings of a word, the only one that the specific context will reasonably allow. This activity gives students useful practice in determining a word's meaning by careful attention to the context in which it appears, a skill assessed in the critical reading section of the SAT.

Note: Explanations for the correct answers to the Choosing the Right Meaning exercises can be found in the supplemental answer key on pages T38–T48.

OTHER SECTIONS OF THE REVIEW

Antonyms (Part 5)

As it requires of students that they recall the meaning of a key word in order to determine its opposite, this activity helps students "situate" a word within the cluster of words of related meanings.

Word Families (Part 6)

This part extends the work of the Units by showing students that by learning one English word they often are acquiring a whole family of related words. It also provides practice in classifying words by part of speech.

Word Associations (Part 7)

The purpose of this activity is to reinforce and extend understanding of the meanings of key words with brief definitions or examples, situations, or allusions that in some way suggest key words.

Building with Classical Roots (Part 8)

Building on the foundation laid down in the Vocabulary of Vocabulary section titled Vocabulary Strategy: Word Structure (Student Text pages 11–12), this part of the Review introduces students to English words derived from common Latin and Greek stems and gives practice in the strategy of finding meaning by analyzing the parts of a word.

The Cumulative Reviews

Once students have completed the Reviews (and any follow-up activities), they may turn to the Cumulative Reviews.

Of the four parts of the Cumulative Reviews, two mirror activities presented in the Reviews: Choosing the Right Meaning and Two-Word Completions. These are presented in the same format and serve the same purpose as their counterparts in the Reviews, primarily to give students practice in types of questions they will encounter on the SAT and other standardized tests.

Each of the Cumulative Reviews begins with a set of analogy exercises. Analogies are valuable and revealing, not merely as a kind of mental gymnastics, but also as a means of pinning down the exact meanings of words and of remedying misconceptions or uncertainties about how those words are used. They also provide an excellent means of testing and refining the critical-thinking skills used on the college level. Furthermore, words that receive the attention necessary to complete an analogy successfully are much more likely to become part of the student's active daily-use vocabulary.

An introduction to the structure of analogies and strategies with which to solve them is provided in "Working with Analogies" on page 17 of the Student Text. It is recommended that students read this introduction and discuss it with their teacher before they undertake the analogies exercises in the Cumulative Reviews.

The fourth part of the Cumulative Review, Enriching Your Vocabulary, is designed to broaden and enhance student knowledge of the interesting origins, history, and relationships of the words that make up the English language.

The Final Mastery Test

The Final Mastery Test in the Student Text of Levels A–H is designed as a practice test of 100 items that gives students and teachers reasonably good insight into how much progress has been made during the year and what kind of additional work is in order.

The purpose of the Final Mastery Test is fourfold.

- It can serve as a dry run in preparation for the more formal (and "secure") tests available as optional components of this program.

- It can serve as an informal evaluation of achievement to date.

- It can serve as a reinforcement activity.

- It can serve as a before-and-after comparison when used in conjunction with the Diagnostic Test.

For whichever purpose the test is used, it is both a testing and a teaching device, the culminating step in a process involving many class periods and, therefore, should be given careful attention.

Supplemental Assessment Components (Optional)

Test Generator CD-ROM (Levels A–H)

The VOCABULARY WORKSHOP Test Generator CD-ROM provides an array of secure student tests that support the Student Texts for Levels A–H. With the Test Generator, teachers may create countless unique vocabulary tests with a variety of question formats, all within seconds. With a database of more than 3,000 questions per Level, teachers never have to administer the same test twice.

The Test Generator CD-ROM provides:

- new and secure Unit Tests, Mastery Tests, Cumulative Tests, Diagnostic Tests, Mid-Year Tests, and Final Mastery Tests

- a wide assortment of question types to choose from: pronunciation, part of speech, spelling, definitions, synonyms and antonyms, sentence completions, sentence framing

- the ability to customize tests to include any number of questions and to assess any Unit in the Student Text

- a method of flagging questions so that they will not appear on other tests

- the option to save a test for future use

- an on-screen Help program

- a printed Teacher's Manual

- technical support

The Test Generator provides a convenient and secure source of assessment and/or extra practice. With the Test Generator CD-ROM, teachers may tailor tests to suit the specific needs of either individual students or an entire class.

The flexibility of the Test Generator makes it easy to use either as needed or more systematically, as an integral part of the VOCABULARY WORKSHOP series. See pages T22–29 for recommendations on how it may be used in conjunction with the Student Text and other components of the program.

Test Booklets (Levels A–H)

Two Test Booklets (Form A and Form B) are available for each of Levels A–H. These Test Booklets have been designed to be used in alternating years, thereby reducing the risk of answers being passed on. Each Test Booklet contains a full set of testing materials and is designed to cover the work of one entire Level of the Student Text. Though the formats of the Test Booklets are the same, the items tested in any given section are completely different. The contents of the Test Booklets have been organized to reflect that of the Student Text and include the following:

- preparatory test-taking tips for students

- a Warm-Up Test (corresponding to the Diagnostic Test in the Student Text)

- 15 Unit Tests, each consisting of 25 items focusing on pronunciation, part of speech, spelling, definitions, synonyms, antonyms, and sentence completions

- 5 Cumulative Tests of 50 items each (plus 2 optional items)

The Warm-Up Test may serve either as an introduction to the Test Booklet as a whole or as an effective follow-up to the Diagnostic Test in the Student Text.

Each Unit Test has been designed for use as soon as the students have completed work on the Unit to which it corresponds or at any point thereafter.

Each Cumulative Test, including the Final Cumulative Test, covers all the work of the Student Text to the point at which it occurs and is designed to be used after the corresponding Review in the Student Text.

Note that these tests may also serve as effective "lead-ins" to the SAT-oriented Cumulative Reviews in the Student Texts and to the SAT-oriented PREP Worksheets in the corresponding TEST PREP Blackline Masters.

For recommendations on how to employ the Test Booklets as part of the complete VOCABULARY WORKSHOP program, see pages T22–T29.

TEST PREP Blackline Masters (Levels A–H)

For further assessment options, a booklet of reproducible TEST PREP Blackline Masters is available for each Level A–H. The TEST PREP component is designed to provide both practice in working with SAT-type test questions and formats *and* review tests covering the entire content of the corresponding Student Text.

- Prep Tests approximate as closely as possible, given the vocabulary that is to be covered, the analogy and word-omission sections of the SAT and provide practice in the vocabulary-in-context strand with brief reading passages as well.

- Answer sheets provide an SAT-type test format to develop student ease and familiarity with standardized testing materials.

- Mastery Tests are meant to be used when students have completed the corresponding group of three Units in the Student Text. Each test covers basic meanings, synonyms, antonyms, sentence completions, and analogies.

- Answer keys, including selected answer rationales, are provided for all tests.

For recommendations on the implementation of the TEST PREP Blackline Masters as part of the complete VOCABULARY WORKSHOP program, see pages T22–T25.

Interactive Audio Pronunciation Program (Levels A–F)

Available in CD format as well as cassette, the Interactive Audio Pronunciation Program provides a convenient and effective means of teaching and learning the recommended pronunciations of all key words introduced in the Student Texts for Levels A–F. It is designed to be used either by the teacher in a classroom setting or by the student in a language laboratory or at home.

- The audio program is ideal for English Language Learners of all cultures and backgrounds and for use in ESL classrooms.

- Students hear the recommended pronunciation of each word at least 6 times, both alone and in context.

- Students are provided with two opportunities to pronounce each word themselves.

- Pronunciations are followed by brief definitions.

- Usage examples in complete-sentence form extend student knowledge of how to use a word correctly in their speech and writing.

- Teacher's notes for the program are provided in Spanish as well as English.

For recommendations on when to use the program, see pages T22–T27.

Interactive Online Vocabulary Activities (Levels A – H)

For each Level, students are provided interactive word games using the vocabulary presented in the Units. These activities, which include crossword puzzles, word searches, "hangman," matching games, and others, are designed to reinforce and enrich student understanding of word meanings and usage. The activities are available free through the Sadlier-Oxford website (www.sadlier-oxford.com).

IMPLEMENTING THE PROGRAM

The format of the VOCABULARY WORKSHOP program allows for great flexibility. The teacher can easily adjust the activity assignments to conform to the special needs of an entire class, of groups within the class, or of individual students.

Schedule for the Year (28 Weeks)

The chart on pages T23–T25 shows how the various components of the VOCABULARY WORKSHOP program for Levels A–H can be scheduled effectively over an academic year lasting 28 weeks.

The following notes should prove helpful when adapting the chart to individual needs:

- Though the chart shows a disposition of material over 28 weeks, the time period can be extended to as many as 34 weeks simply by increasing to two weeks the time allotment for the items under weeks 6, 11, 16, 21, 26, and 28.

- It is not to be supposed that every item listed under Follow-Up Activities is meant to be covered during the week specified. The listings here are designed to offer the teacher options from which to choose in order to tailor the VOCABULARY WORKSHOP program to the specific needs of a particular class. This is also true of the sections or subsections into which some of the Follow-Up components are divided.

KEY

IAPP = Interactive Audio Pronunciation Program, Levels A–F only

BLM = TEST PREP Blackline Masters

TB A/B = Test Booklet Form A/Form B

TG = Test Generator CD-ROM

Using the Program Over the Year (28 Weeks)

Note: "Framing Sentences" and "Story/Essay Writing" are to be supplied by the teacher.

Week	Student Text	Follow-Up Activities
1	Vocabulary of Vocabulary	
2	Diagnostic Test	Warm-Up Test (TB A/B) Warm-Up Prep Test (BLM)
3	Unit 1 IAPP	Framing Sentences Story/Essay Writing Unit Test 1 (TB A/B) Unit Test 1 (TG)
4	Unit 2 IAPP	Framing Sentences Story/Essay Writing Unit Test 2 (TB A/B) Unit Test 2 (TG)
5	Unit 3 IAPP	Framing Sentences Story/Essay Writing Unit Test 3 (TB A/B) Unit Test 3 (TG)
6	Review 1-3	Mastery Test 1–3 (BLM) Mastery Test (TG)
7	—	Cumulative Test 1–3 (TB A/B) Prep Worksheet 1–3 (BLM)
8	Unit 4 IAPP	Framing Sentences Story/Essay Writing Unit Test 4 (TB A/B) Unit Test 4 (TG)
9	Unit 5 IAPP	Framing Sentences Story/Essay Writing Unit Test 5 (TB A/B) Unit Test 5 (TG)

(Continued on pg. T24)

(Continued from pg. T23)

Week	Student Text	Follow-Up Activities
10	Unit 6 IAPP	Framing Sentences Story/Essay Writing Unit Test 6 (TB A/B) Unit Test 6 (TG)
11	Review 4–6	Mastery Test 4–6 (BLM) Mastery Test (TG)
12	Cumulative Review 1–6	Cumulative Test 1–6 (TB A/B) Prep Worksheet 4–6 (BLM)
13	Unit 7 IAPP	Framing Sentences Story/Essay Writing Unit Test 7 (TB A/B) Unit Test 7 (TG)
14	Unit 8 IAPP	Framing Sentences Story/Essay Writing Unit Test 8 (TB A/B) Unit Test 8 (TG)
15	Unit 9 IAPP	Framing Sentences Story/Essay Writing Unit Test 9 (TB A/B) Unit Test 9 (TG)
16	Review 7–9	Mastery Test 7–9 (BLM) Mastery Test (TG) Mid-Year Test (TG)
17	Cumulative Review 1–9	Cumulative Test 1–9 (TB A/B) Prep Worksheet 7–9 (BLM) Cumulative Test (TG)
18	Unit 10 IAPP	Framing Sentences Story/Essay Writing Unit Test 10 (TB A/B) Unit Test 10 (TG)
19	Unit 11 IAPP	Framing Sentences Story/Essay Writing Unit Test 11 (TB A/B) Unit Test 11 (TG)

Week	Student Text	Follow-Up Activities
20	Unit 12 IAPP	Framing Sentences Story/Essay Writing Unit Test 12 (TB A/B) Unit Test 12 (TG)
21	Review 10–12	Mastery Test 10–12 (BLM) Mastery Test (TG)
22	Cumulative Review 1–12	Cumulative Test 1–12 (TB A/B) Prep Worksheet 10–12 (BLM) Cumulative Test (TG)
23	Unit 13 IAPP	Framing Sentences Story/Essay Writing Unit Test 13 (TB A/B) Unit Test 13 (TG)
24	Unit Test 14 IAPP	Framing Sentences Story/Essay Writing Unit Test 14 (TB A/B) Unit Test 14 (TG)
25	Unit 15 IAPP	Framing Sentences Story/Essay Writing Unit Test 15 (TB A/B) Unit Test 15 (TG)
26	Review 13–15	Mastery Test 13–15 (BLM) Mastery Test (TG)
27	Cumulative Review 1–15	Cumulative Test 1–15 (TB A/B) Prep Worksheet 13–15 (BLM) Cumulative Test (TG)
28	Final Mastery Test	Cumulative Mastery Test (BLM) Cumulative Prep Test (BLM) Final Test (TG)

Using the Units

On the top of these 2 pages the teacher will find 2 models for using the Units effectively on a weekly basis. Though there is no single formula or plan that will be sure to yield optimum results all the time, the models presented here and on the next 2 pages are designed to get the teacher thinking about how best to adapt the program to the needs of individual classes.

KEY: IAPP = Interactive Audio Pronunciation Program

TB = Test Booklet Form A or Form B

TG = Test Generator CD-ROM

** Item to be supplied by teacher/student

Assignment
Classwork
Homework

MODEL B: 5 Sessions/Periods (20 Minutes)		
Assignment	**Day 1**	**Day 2**
Classwork	**1.** Collect Framing Sentences** **2.** Review Unit Test **3.** Present Definitions	Review Completing the Sentences
Homework	**1.** Completing the Sentence **2.** IAPP	Synonyms and Antonyms

Using the Reviews

On the bottom of these 2 pages the teacher will find 2 models for using the Reviews effectively on a weekly basis.

Assignment
Classwork
Homework

MODEL B: 5 Sessions/Periods (20 Minutes)		
Assignment	**Day 1**	**Day 2**
Classwork	Present Vocaulary for Comprehension	**1.** Review homework **2.** Grammer in Context
Homework	**1.** Word Associations **2.** Antonyms	Choosing the Right Meaning

Weekly Lesson Plans

MODEL A: 3 Sessions/Periods (35–40 Minutes)

Day 1	Day 2	Day 3
1. Collect Framing Sentences** **2.** Present Definitions	**1.** Review Completing the Sentence, Synonyms and Antonyms **2.** Present Choosing the Right Word and Vocabulary in Context	**1.** Unit Test (TB or TG) **2.** Review last week's Framing Sentences**
1. Completing the Sentence, Synonyms and Antonyms **2.** IAPP	Test Study	Framing Sentences**

Day 3	Day 4	Day 5
Review Synonyms and Antonyms	**1.** Review Choosing the Right Word **2.** Present Vocabulary in Context	**1.** Unit Test (TB or TG) **2.** Review last week's Framing Sentences**
Choosing the Right Word	Test Study	Framing Sentences**

MODEL A: 3 Sessions/Periods (35–40 Minutes)

Day 1	Day 2	Day 3
Present Vocabulary for Comprehension, Antonyms Word Families	**1.** Review homework **2.** Present Grammer in Context Two-Word Completions Word Associations	**1.** Mastery Test (TB or TG) **2.** Review homework
Choosing the Right Meaning	**1.** Test Study **2.** Building with Classical Roots	Remedial work as required

Day 3	Day 4	Day 5
1. Review homework **2.** Present Two-Word Completions	Mastery Test (TB or TG)	**1.** Review Mastery Test **2.** Review homework
1. Test Study **2.** Word Families	Building with Classical Roots	Remedial work as required

Using the Cumulative Reviews

On the top of these 2 pages the teacher will find 2 models for using the Cumulative Reviews effectively on a weekly basis.

Assignment
Classwork
Homework

MODEL B: 5 Sessions/Periods (20 Minutes)		
Assignment	**Day 1**	**Day 2**
Classwork	Present Cumulative Review	Cumulative Test Parts 1–4 (TB)
Homework	Test Study	Test Study

Implementing the Weekly Schedules

The following may prove helpful when adapting the foregoing schedules to specific situations.

- The models shown are, as their designation suggests, purely models—that is, starting points. Accordingly, the teacher is expected to adapt them to the particular situation at hand.

- The models make only minimal use of the Follow-Up Activities suggested earlier and no use whatsoever of the Alternative Approaches to Using the Program suggested on the following pages. The teacher should in all cases feel free to introduce such alternative approaches as are convenient.

- Place assignments and timings are to some extent hypothetical. Teachers should switch items around and adjust timings as needed. Similarly, items may be modified or deleted and new items inserted as the teacher sees fit.

- Multiple listings in a Day's entry for either Classwork or Homework are to be seen as options from which the teacher should select appropriate material. It is unlikely that the teacher could cover all the suggested material in the indicated time allotment.

- With some adjustment, the allotments for each Day can accommodate a 2- or 4-day arrangement. There is usually too much material to cover in 1 day, and a 1-day approach is, therefore, not suggested.

MODEL A: 3 Sessions/Periods (35–40 Minutes)		
Day 1	**Day 2**	**Day 3**
Present Cumulative Review	Cumulative Test (TB or TG)	**1.** Review Cumulative Test **2.** Review Prep Worksheet
Test Study	Prep Worksheet	Remedial work as required

Day 3	**Day 4**	**Day 5**
Cumulative Test Parts 5–6 (TB)	Review Cumulative Test	Review Prep Worksheet
—	Prep Worksheet	Remedial work as required

Alternative Approaches to Using the Program

Writing Approach

Research has shown that vocabulary acquisition is maximized when learning is authentically contextualized—when learners have a "real-life" purpose for acquiring and using a new word. Activities such as the following can provide these authentic contexts.

- Students can create journals or logs in which they use the key words to express experiences, thoughts, or feelings that are personally meaningful. They are free to keep these entries for their eyes only or to share them with others.

- Students can use the key words in personal letters to friends and relatives or in letters to the editor of the school or local newspaper. Students should write about subjects of real interest and concern to them.

- Students can use the key words to write descriptions of people they know or characters they are interested in. These character sketches or personality profiles may be written for a class yearbook, for a book report, or as a reference for a friend.

Literature-Based Approach

The VOCABULARY WORKSHOP program can be combined with some of the items listed below to form a *literature-based* approach to vocabulary study. Each of the items listed has been surveyed for use of some of the key words presented in the specified level of VOCABULARY WORKSHOP. Seeing the words they are studying in classic world literature will reinforce student appreciation of the value of possessing a good active-use vocabulary.

Classic Literature To Use With The Program

Levels A–C

Lloyd Alexander
The Book of Three

Laurie Halse Anderson *Speak*

William H. Armstrong *Sounder*

Natalie Babbit *Tuck Everlasting*

Ray Bradbury *Dandelion Wine*

Pearl S. Buck
The Good Earth

Sheila Bumford
The Incredible Journey

Frances Hodgson Burnett
The Secret Garden

Sandra Cisneros
The House on Mango Street

Sook Nyul Choi
The Year of Impossible Good-byes

Robert Cornier
The Chocolate War

Karen Cushman
The Midwife's Apprentice

Daniel Defoe *Robinson Crusoe*

Elizabeth B. De Trevino
I, Juan de Pareja

Arthur Conan Doyle
The Hound of the Baskervilles

Esther Forbes *Johnny Tremain*

Paul Gallico
The Snow Goose

Jean Craighead George
Julie of the Wolves

William Goldman
The Princess Bride

Rosa Guy *The Friends*

Virginia Hamilton
The House of Dies Drear
M.C. Higgins, the Great

Jean Wakatrsuki Houston and
James D. Houston
Farewell to Manzanar

Norton Juster
The Phantom Tollboth

Rudyard Kipling
Just So Stories

E.L. Konigsburg
The View from Saturday

Harper Lee
To Kill a Mockingbird

Madeline L'Engle
A Wrinkle in Time

Julius Lester
Long Journey Home

Lois Lowry
The Giver
Gathering Blue

Daniel P. Mannix
The Fox and the Hound

Nicholasa Mohr *Going Home*

Walter Dean Myers *Hoops*

Mary Norton *The Borrowers*

George Orwell *Animal Farm*

Katherine Paterson
   Jacob Have I Loved

Anne Petry
   *Harriet Tubman: Conductor on the
   Underground Railroad*

Marjorie Kinnan Rawlings *The Yearling*

Jack Schaefer *Shane*

George Selden
   The Cricket in Times Square

Antoine de Saint-Exupéry
   The Little Prince

Elizabeth George Speare
   The Sign of the Beaver

Rex Stout *Fer-de-Lance*
   The Golden Spiders

Yoshido Uchida *Journey Home*

H.G. Wells
   War of the Worlds

Laura Ingalls Wilder
   Little House on the Prairie

Laurence Yep *Dragon's Gate*

Additional Titles and Enrichment

Louisa May Alcott *Little Women*

Lewis Carroll *Alice's Adventures in
   Wonderland*

Willa Cather *My Antonia*

James Fenimore Cooper *The Deerslayer*

Charles Dickens
   Oliver Twist
   A Tale of Two Cities
   A Christmas Carol

Carson McCullers
   Member of the Wedding

To coordinate reading and vocabulary study, the following may prove helpful:

- Instruct students to devote a special notebook to vocabulary. As they come across key words in their reading, they should head a page of the notebook with the word; copy the title of the work; and then indicate (a) the definition of the word used in that sentence, (b) its part of speech, and (c) whether it is used in a literal or figurative sense.

- Students may then be instructed to check *Bartlett's Familiar Quotations* for other famous examples of the use of the key word in question. These may be copied into the notebook and shared with others in the class.

Content-Area Approach

VOCABULARY WORKSHOP can be used to enhance student understanding and use of vocabulary in subjects such as social studies and history, science and health, and other curriculum areas.

In the following list of nonfiction print and video titles you will find works that relate in content to Vocabulary in Context exercises appearing in specific Units and Reviews of the VOCABULARY WORKSHOP Student Texts for Levels D–H. Students may wish to read or view some of these works and report on the topics and issues that they treat. In their reports, whether oral or written, students should be encouraged to use words they have come to know through their Student Texts.

Literature and Media to Use with the Program

Middle Grades Nonfiction

Author	Title	Level & Unit
Alcott, Louisa May	*Hospital Sketches*	Level B, Unit 8
Asimov, Isaac	"Dial Versus Digital," from *American Way* magazine, (1985)	Level C, Unit 10
Ballard, Robert D.	*Exploring the Titanic*	Level C, Unit 15
Bean, Alan	*Apollo: An Eyewitness Account*	Level B, Unit 7
Chesnut, Mary	*Mary Chesnut's Civil War*	Level B, Unit 8
Dobie, J. Frank	*The Longhorns*	Level B, Unit 2
Freedman, Russell	*Lincoln: A Photography*	Level B, Unit 3
King, Martin Luther, Jr.	"I Have a Dream" speech (Aug. 28, 1963)	Level B, Review 10-12
Knight, Theodore	*The Olympic Games*	A, U 5; B, Rev. 13-15
Lauber, Patricia	*The News About Dinosaurs*	A, U 11; C, U8
Laycock, George	*Famous Caves Worldwide*	Level B, Unit 1
Levine, Ellen	*If Your Name Was Changed at Ellis Island*	Level A, Unit 3
Lindbergh, Anne Morrow	"Morning—'The Bird Perched for Flight'" from *Earth Shine*	Level B, Unit 7
McKissack, Frederick, Jr., and Patricia C. McKissack	*Black Diamond: The Story of the Negro Baseball Leagues*	Level C, Unit 2
Sandburg, Carl	*Abe Lincoln Grows Up*	Level B, Unit 3
Sills, Leslie	"Mary Cassatt" from *Visions About Women Artists*	Level A, Unit 13
Steger, Will, and Jon Bowermaster	*Over the Top of the World*	Level A, Review 10-12
Young, Donald	*Our National Parks*	Level B, Units 1, 6

Middle Grades Fiction

Author	Title	Genre	Level & Unit
Allen, Samuel	"To Satch"	Poem	Level C, Unit 2
Bradbury, Ray	"All Summer in a Day"	Short Story	Level B, Unit 7
Cisneros, Sandra	"Good Hot Dogs"	Poem	Level B, Unit 15
Sherwood, Robert	*Abe Lincoln in Illinois*	Play	Level B, Unit 3
Whitman, Walt	"O Captain! My Captain!"	Poem	Level B, Unit 3
Whittier, John Greenleaf	"Barbara Frietchie"	Poem	Level B, Unit 8

Middle Grades Videos

Title	Distributor	Level & Unit
America's Endangered Species	National Geographic Video	Level A, Review 7-9
The Bicycle Corps	PBS Home Video	Level C, Unit 4
Biographies of U.S. Presidents	Discovery Channel Video	Level B, Unit 13
The Gilbert & Sullivan Collection	PBS Home Video	Level C, Unit 1
Hoover Dam	PBS Home Video	Level C, Unit 13
The Incas	PBS Home Video	Level C, Review 13-15
Lewis and Clark	PBS Home Video	Level A, Unit 9
Lions of the African Night	National Geographic Video	Level B, Unit 4
River of Stone	Discovery Channel Video	Level B, Unit 6
Mary Cassatt from Artists' Specials	Discovery Channel Video	Level A, Unit 13
Mummies: Frozen in Time	Learning Channel Video	Level C, Review 13-15
Mysteries Underground	National Geographic Video	Level B, Unit 1
Rain Forest: Heroes of High Frontier	National Geographic Video	Level C, Unit 3

Other content-related activities to which students might apply vocabulary study are:

- Working in pairs or small groups, they can choose sentences from Completing the Sentence or Choosing the Right Word and discuss a larger context in which these sentences could have appeared, such as a history or mathematics textbook, a daily newspaper, a book review, a personal letter, or a scientific article.

- Students can work together to link individual vocabulary words to a particular content area. Then working in pairs, they can find "real-world" examples of the words used in context in that content area.

- Students can work cooperatively to create sentence and paragraph contexts that illustrate the meaning of the content-area words that they have identified.

Useful Classroom Techniques

Classroom experience and research have shown that some students learn more readily when they can exercise a great deal of personal choice and can interact with others. VOCABULARY WORKSHOP can be adapted in the following ways to accommodate such students.

Cooperative Activities

Working cooperatively does not just mean working in proximity to other students or dividing an assignment or project into discrete tasks. Rather it means that students take individual and collective responsibility for the learning of all members of the group and for the successful completion of the group goal. Students who cooperate to develop their vocabulary should maintain an ongoing dialogue to monitor the comprehension of all group members.

Oral and Kinesthetic

- One student can write the key words in a given unit on the chalkboard while the rest of the class is divided into pairs or small groups. A member of each group will read a numbered item from the Unit aloud. The rest of the group will confer and then supply the required vocabulary word. The student reader will evaluate each answer and give reasons why it is correct or incorrect based on the word's definition and any context clues.

- Students in groups can discuss the shades of meaning or connotations among selected synonyms and antonyms for a given Unit and among the alternative answers in Choosing the Right Meaning.

- Students can work together to create puns, riddles, Tom Swifties, and limericks to illustrate the multiple meanings of appropriate vocabulary words. They may want to collect and publish their creations in illustrated books or an audio-anthology.

- Members of a group can work together to improvise stories, skits, or pantomimes that illustrate the meaning of a key word in a given Unit, while other group members guess the word being illustrated.

Written

- Students can work cooperatively to brainstorm their own vocabulary word lists based on their current reading and writing in all areas of the curriculum and on their personal reading and writing experiences.

- The class can collaborate to create their own Unit, covering vocabulary words they have chosen. Different groups can be assigned to develop each of the unit activities.

- Students may want to create their own minidictionaries, based on the word lists in VOCABULARY WORKSHOP or on categories of words that are especially meaningful or useful to them, such as sports, fashion, music, and career terms.

- Students can make use of semantic mapping and other graphic devices, such as flowcharts, to generate new vocabulary or to demonstrate understanding of word relationships. Semantic mapping, or webbing, can be used to illustrate word families, synonyms, and antonyms. Flowcharts can illustrate etymological and grammatical relationships.

Alternative Types of Assessment

The following types of assessment may be used in addition to or in lieu of the objective-scoring materials provided in the VOCABULARY WORKSHOP, Levels A–H. The emphasis here is on monitoring understanding rather than on ranking students.

Self-Evaluation

Students can use their journals to reflect on their own process of learning and use of new words. They may consider, for example, which words from VOCABULARY WORKSHOP they understood quickly and used frequently and why. They may want to use these insights to design their own vocabulary-acquisition strategies.

Teacher-Student Conferencing

Meetings take place at every stage of the vocabulary-acquisition process. Meeting over time allows teachers to assess students' developing understanding of words as used in specific contexts.

Observation

Using a checklist of 2 or 3 important criteria, the teacher can observe and evaluate students while they are interacting in groups or engaging in other oral activities. Teachers can also probe for deeper levels of comprehension by asking students to clarify or give reasons for their choice of word or context.

Peer Evaluation

Students meet in pairs or small groups to develop standards or criteria to evaluate their vocabulary acquisition. They then apply their standards to their peers' oral or written expression, giving positive feedback and concrete suggestions for improvement.

Portfolio Assessment

By having students collect and save self-selected samples of their writing over a period of time, teachers have an ongoing record of students' vocabulary development and of their facility in using words in context.

Multimodal Assessment

Students with strong nonverbal competencies can be given the opportunity to demonstrate in nonverbal media their understanding of new vocabulary. For example, they can draw, paint, model, dance, compose music, or construct objects to communicate their comprehension of a word and its definition.

TEACHER RESOURCES

The following lists have been compiled to assist the teacher in the effective presentation of the VOCABULARY WORKSHOP program, Levels A–H.

I. DICTIONARIES

Recommended

Merriam-Webster *Collegiate Dictionary* [Eleventh Edition] (Springfield, MA: Merriam-Webster, 2003)

Webster's Third New International Dictionary (Springfield, MA: G. & C. Merriam, 1993)

American Heritage Dictionary (Boston: Houghton Mifflin, 2000)

Oxford English Dictionary [Compact Edition] (Oxford: Oxford University Press, 1971)

Skeat, W.W. *A Concise Etymological Dictionary of the English Language* (NY: G.P. Putnam, 1980)

Supplemental

12,000 Words [A Supplement to Webster's *Third International Dictionary*] (Springfield, MA: Merriam-Webster, 1993)

The Random House Dictionary of the English Language [Unabridged Edition] (NY: Random House, 1987)

II. THESAURI

Recommended

Roget's II The New Thesaurus (Boston: Houghton Mifflin, 1995)

Random House Roget's Thesaurus (NY: Random House, 2001)

Rodale, J. [Revised by Urdang, L. and La Roche, N.] *The Synonym Finder* (Emmaus, PA: Rodale Press, 1979)

Supplemental

Chapman, R.L. (Ed.). *Roget A to Z* (NY: Harper Perennial, 1994)

Laird, C. *Webster's New World Thesaurus* (NY: Warner Books, 1990)

Roget's International Thesaurus [Fifth Edition] (NY: HarperCollins, 1992)

Abate, F. *The Oxford Dictionary and Thesaurus: The Ultimate Language Reference for American Readers* (NY: Oxford University Press, 1996)

III. OTHER REFERENCE WORKS

Recommended

Carroll, J., Davies, P., and Richman, B. *Word Frequency Book* (Boston: Houghton Mifflin, 1971)

Dale, E. and O'Rourke, J. *The Living Word Vocabulary* (Chicago: Scott & Fetzer, 1981)

Supplemental

Harris, A. and Jackson, M. *Basic Reading Vocabularies* (NY: Macmillan, 1982)

Thorndike, E. and Lorge, I. *The Teacher's Book of 30,000 Words* (NY: Teachers College Press, Columbia University, 1968)

IV. HISTORY

General

Baugh, A.C. and Cable, T. *A History of the English Language* [Third Edition] (Englewood Cliffs, NJ: Prentice-Hall, 1992)

Carver, C. *A History of English in Its Own Words* (NY: HarperCollins, 1991)

Jespersen, O. *Growth and Structure of the English Language* (Chicago: University of Chicago Press, 1982)

McCrum, R., Cran, W., and MacNeil, R. *The Story of English* (NY: Penguin, 1993)

Myers, L.M. *The Roots of Modern English* (Boston: Little, Brown, 1961)

Pyles, T. *The Origins and Development of the English Language* [Fourth Edition] (NY: Harcourt, Brace, Jovanovich, 1993)

Robinson, O. *Old English and Its Closest Relatives* (Stanford, CA: Stanford University Press, 1993)

American English

Dillard, J.L. *All-American English* (NY: Random House, 1975)

Dillard, J.L. *American Talk* (NY: Random House, 1976)

Flexner, S.B. *I Hear America Talking* (NY: Simon & Schuster, 1976)

Mencken, H.L. *The American Language* (NY: Alfred A. Knopf, 1979)

V. OTHER USEFUL RESOURCES

A Dictionary of American Idioms (Woodbury, NY: Barron's Educational Series, Inc., 1995)

Bryson, B. *A Dictionary of Troublesome Words* (NY: Viking Penguin, 1988)

Carroll, D. *Dictionary of Foreign Terms in the English Language* (NY: Hawthorn Books, 1973)

Dixson, R. *Essential Idioms in English* (Englewood Cliffs, NJ: Pearson ESL, 1993)

Evans, I.H. (Ed.) *Brewer's Dictionary of Phrase & Fable* (NY: Harper & Row, 2000)

Harrison, G. *Vocabulary Dynamics* (NY: Warner Books, 1992)

Hendrickson, R. *The Dictionary of Eponyms* (NY: Stein and Day, 1985)

Morris, W. and M. *Morris Dictionary of Word & Phrase Origins* (NY: Harper & Row, 1988)

Orgel, J.R. *Building an Enriched Vocabulary* (NY: William H. Sadlier, Inc., 1999)

Paxson, W. *New American Dictionary of Confusing Words* (NY: NAL-Dutton, 1990)

Room, A. *Dictionary of Contrasting Pairs* (NY: Routledge Educational Series Inc., 1988)

Room, A. *The Penguin Dictionary of Confusibles* (NY: Penguin Books, 1989)

Shipley, J. *Dictionary of Word Origins* (Glenville, IL: Greenwood Press, 1988)

Smith, R. *Dictionary of English Word-Roots* (Totowa, NJ: Littlefield, Adams & Co., 1980)

Spears, R. *Slang and Euphemisms* (NY: NAL-Dutton, 1991)

Webster's Word Histories (Springfield, MA: Merriam-Webster, 1989)

ANSWERS TO EXERCISES IN REVIEWS AND CUMULATIVE REVIEWS

Two-Word Completions (page 45)

1. (b) yearned for (Contrast clue: "I'm . . . with") . . . humdrum (Contrast clue: "of . . . danger")

2. (a) pelt (Situational clue: What does an irate hockey crowd often do to show its displeasure with the officiating?) . . . hurtled (Situational clue: How would you describe programs, paper cups, and even a dead fish moving through the air?; Contrast clue: "landed at his feet")

3. (d) hazards (Restatement clue: "traps for the unwary") . . . unscathed (Situational clue: How would a President *not* be likely to leave office when his job is so full of hazards?)

4. (d) regime (Restatement clue: "administration") . . . truce (Situational clue: What would a government seek to arrange with rebel forces in order to pacify a country?)

5. (c) ingredients (Situational clue: What does one call the various things, such as crabmeat, that go into a fish stew?) . . . available (Restatement clue: "in season")

6. (b) adjacent (Situational clue: Which buildings would be affected first by a fire fanned by high winds?) . . . retard (Situational clue: What would firefighters try to do to the progress of a fire that appeared to be moving quickly?)

Choosing the Right Meaning (page 46)

1. (b) (Clue: What attitude would the world exhibit if it were "on the brink of war"?) (a), (c), (d): wrong sense of word for context (ws).

2. (a) (Clue: Sense is restated in "frankness.") (b), (c), (d): ws.

3. (d) (Clue: How might one characterize a headache?) (a), (b), (c): ws.

4. (c) (Clue: How would geographic isolation affect the distribution of a species?) (a), (b), (d): ws.

5. (a) (Clues: What trait is a mule known for? (Context indicates contrast with "meek.") (b), (c), (d): ws.

Two-Word Completions (page 75)

1. (d) prominent (Restatement clue: "famous") . . . anecdotes (Restatement clue: "amusing stories involving many people")

2. (c) orthodox (Contrast clue: "more traditional") . . . substantial (Restatement clue: "they . . . results")

3. (a) inflict (Situational clue: What *doesn't* the actual injection of novocaine usually do in regard to pain?) . . . wince (Situational clue: What might a person do physically when imagining something unpleasant?)

4. (b) controversy (Situational clue: What would a new economic program be likely to stir up on Capitol Hill?) . . . hostile (Contrast clue: "in favor of")

5. (d) disheartened (Situational clue: What would a setback do to someone who wasn't determined?) . . . utmost (Situational clue: What kind of an effort do you make when you give something your "very best shot"?)

6. (c) fugitives (Restatement clue: "convicts [who] escaped") . . . fruitless (Contrast clue: "managed to recapture")

Choosing the Right Meaning (page 76)

1. (c) (Clue: A weary cast might give what kind of performance?) (a), (d): ws; (b): irrelevant to meaning of word (ir).

2. (b) (Clue: What would probably be the purpose of fasting and suffering pain?) (a), (c): ws; (d): ir.

3. (b) (Clue: How would one generally characterize "tract houses"?) (a), (c): ws; (d): ir.

4. (a) (Clue: Context indicates meaning relating to structure and analysis.) (b), (c), (d): ws.

5. (a) (Clue: What would be the likely effect of three straight victories in a political race?) (b), (c), (d): ws.

Analogies (page 81)

1. (d) Something that is A is full of B.
2. (c) A means the same as B.
3. (d) It is easy to A someone who is B.
4. (d) A means the same as B.
5. (b) You would use an A to B someone.
6. (d) An A is shorter than a B.
7. (a) It is difficult to A someone who is B.
8. (a) It is easy to A someone who is B.
9. (c) A life that is A lacks B.
10. (a) Someone who was A would be difficult to B.

Choosing the Right Meaning (pages 81–82)

1. (c) (Clue: To what sort of world are we "accustomed"? Context indicates contrast to "fantastical, topsy-turvy.") (a), (b): ws; (d): ir.

2. (d) (Clue: What sort of behavior might prompt Alice to chase a rabbit?) (a), (c): ir; (b): ws.

3. (c) (Clue: Context implies a quality that virtual reality, like a dream, lacks.) (a), (b): ws; (d): ir.

4. (b) (Clue: How would one characterize such a notion as time?) (a), (c): ws; (d): ir.

5. (d) (Clue: How might machines sketched by an "accomplished inventor" be described?) (a), (b), (c): ws. (An "accomplished inventor" would not conceive "old-fashioned" machines; nor, similarly, "picturesque" ones.)

Two-Word Completions (page 82)

1. (d) malignant (Situational clue: What kind of tumor would a surgeon remove?) . . . eradicate (Restatement clue" "remove")

2. (c) plagued (Situational clue: What would ill health and financial worries do to a person?) . . . customary (Situational clue: How would one describe the frame of mind that a person usually has?)

3. (b) dissuaded (Situational clue: What would a person who quotes the given passage from the Bible probably be attempting to do?) . . . vengeance (Situational clue: If you retaliate for a wrong, what are you seeking?)

4. (b) alliance (Situational clue: What did Caesar, Pompey, and Crassus form?) . . . dominate (Situational clue: If you become the undisputed master of something, what is your relationship to it?)

5. (a) luster (Situational clue: What would something have if it shines brightly?) . . . oration (Situational clue: What would the foremost public speaker of his day be famous for?)

Two-Word Completions (page 108)

1. (c) swerved (Situational clue: What would one do to avoid rocks or other hazards that suddenly appeared in one's path?) . . . capsized (Situational clue: If you were suddenly pitched headlong into a river, what must have happened to the canoe you were riding in?)

2. (a) momentum (Contrast clue: "stop") . . . accelerator (Contrast clue: "brakes")

3. (b) decreases (Situational clue: What happens to the value of the dollar when prices go up?) . . . erodes (Situational clue: What effect does inflation have on the purchasing power of the dollar?)

4. (c) parched (Situational clue: What would a long trek over dusty roads on the hottest day of summer do to one's throat?) . . . quench (Situational clue: What does one always want to do to thirst?)

5. (b) proficiency (Situational clue: With what might an experienced worker be expected to handle a job?) . . . flounder (Situational clue: What, on the other hand, might be expected to happen to a beginner before he/she learns the ropes?)

6. (d) prudent (Contrast clue: "only a fool") . . . outstrip (Restatement clue: "spend . . . make")

Choosing the Right Meaning (page 109)

1. (b) (Clue: What might an air force desperate for pilots send into battle?) (a): ws; (c), (d): ir.

2. (d) (Clue: Correct meaning is suggested in "Destiny.") (a), (b), (c): ws.

3. (b) (Clue: One might feel the victim of an injustice if one's contribution were "dismissed" as what?) (a), (c): ws; (d): ir.

4. (a) (Clue: Context indicates contrast with "secretly in cahoots.") (b): ir. (c), (d): ws.

5. (c) (Clue: What would diplomats be likely to do with a proposal before responding to it?) (a), (b), (d): ws.

Analogies (page 114)

1. (a) A means the same as B.
2. (d) An A would be likely to B a person to/from some action.
3. (a) An A would make land B.
4. (d) An A would be likely to B a person.
5. (c) An A is a type of B.
6. (d) You have committed A if you B.
7. (a) Something that is A by definition has a great deal of B to it.
8. (b) You cannot A something that is B.
9. (c) A means the opposite of B.
10. (b) A means the same as B.

Choosing the Right Meaning (pages 114–115)

1. (c) (Clue: What might hard feelings do for generations?) (a): ws; (b), (d): ir.

2. (d) (Clue: The arrival of royalty is often "announced" by what?) (a), (b), (c): ws.

3. (b) (Clue: What would one be doing with a boss's patience if one repeatedly asked for an explanation?) (a), (c): ws; (d): ir.

4. (b) (Clue: At what might a missile be fired?) (a), (c), (d): ws.

5. (a) (Clue: What kind of parties would have "differences" and resist the efforts of "negotiators"?) (b): ws; (c), (d): ir.

Two-Word Completions (page 115)

1. (c) melancholy (Restatement clue: "mournful") . . . yearned (Situational clue: How might a sad little camper feel about home after some time away from it?)

2. (a) fickle (Restatement clue: "unpredictable") . . . detested (Contrast clue: "the darling of the crowd")

3. (b) onslaught (Situational clue: What must the enemy have made if what they did caused such havoc in your ranks?) . . . inflicted (Situational clue: What would you do with a defeat?)

4. (d) interrogated (Situational clue: What do the police do with a suspect in a crime?) . . . verify (Situational clue: What must be done to an alibi before a person can be removed from the list of suspects in a crime?)

5. (b) erode (Situational clue: What might laziness and indifference do to one's liberties?) . . . vigilant (Situational clue: What *wouldn't* people who were lazy and indifferent be likely to be in regard to defending their rights and liberties?)

Two-Word Completions (page 141)

1. (c) hearth (Situational clue: In what would a fire be likely to be lit?) . . . narrative (Situational clue: With what might an old sailor be likely to entertain children?)

2. (a) abundance (Situational clue: How would crops be likely to grow in soil that is remarkably rich and fertile?) . . . surplus (Situational clue: If you grow more produce than you need for yourself, what do you have?)

3. (b) dilapidated (Situational clue: Why would you want to renovate an old house?) . . . clutter (Situational clue: What might be strewn around the rooms of a dilapidated old house and blocking the entrances?)

4. (c) mulling (Contrast clue: "reached a decision") . . . veto (Contrast clue: "sign the bill")

5. (a) nomadic (Restatement clue: "were . . . moving") . . . quest (Restatement clue: "pursuit")

Choosing the Right Meaning (page 142)

1. (c) (Clue: Finding a test not as difficult as one feared might prompt what kind of smile?) (a), (b): ws; (d): ir.

2. (a) (Clue: Where would one "wall up" an animal one has killed?) (c): ws; (b), (d): ir.

3. (b) (Clue: On what would a "curtain" be drawn?) (a), (c): ws; (d): ir.

4. (d) (Clue: How would jackals probably take their leave at the approach of men?) (a), (b), (c): ws.

5. (b) (Clue: "Conspicuous consumption" is, by definition, acquisition for the sake of prestige.) (c), (d): ws; (a): ir.

Analogies (page 147)

1. (b) A means the opposite of B.
2. (b) A is a kind of B.
3. (d) A means the opposite of B.
4. (a) A means the same as B.
5. (c) An A is a kind of performer usually found in a B.
6. (c) If something is A, a person cannot B it.
7. (d) Someone who was A would feel B.
8. (a) A means the same as B.
9. (a) A means the same as B, or an A is the result of a B.
10. (c) A suggests that one ends up with B of something than one had originally.

Choosing the Right Meaning (page 147–148)

1. (a) (Clue: What would be the most likely response to a "predictable," "dull" show?) (b): ws; (c), (d): ir.

2. (d) (Clue: How might packing material be molded to improve its protective function?) (a), (b), (c): ws.

3. (c) (Clue: What might no one be "able to fill" in the ranks of officers?) (a), (b): ws; (d): ir.

4. (c) (Clue: What might be done to a beverage served to guests?) (a): ws; (b), (d): ir.

5. (b) (Clue: Context indicates contrast with "swift.") (a), (c), (d): ws.

Two-Word Completions (page 148)

1. (a) prescribe (Situational clue: What does modern medicine do in regard to remedies for common illnesses?) . . . maladies (Inference clue: What is cancer an example of?)

2. (b) drone (Situational clue: What word describes the sound airplanes make when they pass overhead?) . . . scurrying (Situational clue: What would you do when you heard an air-raid siren go off?)

3. (c) cluttered (Situational clue: What would all kinds of junk lying around do to staircases and hallways?) . . . hazard (Situational clue: What would all kinds of junk constitute in respect to a fire?)

4. (b) snare (Situational clue: For what purpose do hunters set traps?) . . . quest (Situational clue: Why would an animal leave its lair?)

5. (d) parched (Situational clue: What would happen to land during a "dry season"?) . . . trickle (Situational clue: What might happen to a mighty river during a "dry season"?)

Two-Word Completions (page 174)

1. (d) feuds (Contrast clue: "united front") . . . heed (Contrast clue: "ignore")

2. (d) pall (Situational clue: What would tragic news do to the atmosphere of a friendly little gathering?) . . . mirth (Contrast clue: "tears")

3. (a) officiates (Restatement clue: "presiding") . . . impartial (Contrast clue: "show any favoritism")

4. (b) reputable (Contrast clue: "who . . . me") . . . patronize (Restatement clue: "shop at")

5. (b) hoard (Situational clue: What does a miser do with his or her money?) . . . bankrupt (Situational clue: If you throw your money around freely, what is likely to happen to you?)

6. (a) haggle (Situational clue: What might a fussy person properly be accused of?) . . . nutritious (Restatement clue: "nourishing")

Choosing the Right Meaning (page 175)

1. (a) (Clue: What would allies plan for offensives in order to put maximum pressure on the enemy?) (b): ws; (c), (d): ir.

2. (c) (Clue: What "types" would be expected to speak in "witty, glittering epigrams"?) (a), (d): ws; (b): ir.

3. (a) (Clue: What might cause a laboratory mixture to explode?) (b), (c), (d): ws.

4. (d) (Clue: One would probably not feel sorry for someone who does what with respect to self-pity?) (a), (b), (c): ws.

5. (d) (Clue: Context indicates crime was not of spur-of-the-moment nature ["of opportunity"].) (a): ws; (b), (c): ir.

Analogies (page 180)

1. (d) An A is by definition B.
2. (a) An A is a person who is by definition B.
3. (b) A means the same as B.
4. (b) Someone who is A would be looking for B.
5. (c) A is an example of a B.
6. (c) A means the opposite of B.
7. (d) A person would A with his or her B.
8. (b) The person to whom an A is given is the B.
9. (a) Something that is A is easy to B.
10. (c) An A is an animal that is proverbially B.

Choosing the Right Meaning (pages 180–181)

1. (c) (Clue: How might figs be characterized?) (a), (b), (d): ws.

2. (b) (Clue: What is a friar's role at a wedding?) (a), (c), (d): ws. [Answer: Friar Laurence]

3. (b) (Clue: How might a poet feel toward a form in which he has had success?) (c): ws; (a), (d): ir.

4. (c) (Clue: How might one describe skyscrapers in relation to the city over which they rise?) (a): ws; (b), (d): ir.

5. (a) (Clue: How would one characterize taxes ["levies"] imposed arbitrarily by a ruling government?) (b), (d): ws; (c): ir.

Two-Word Completions (page 181)

1. (d) interrogating (Situational clue: What do police officers do to the eyewitnesses of an accident?) . . . bystanders (Situational clue: What usually collects at the scene of any accident?; Contrast clue: "eyewitnesses")

2. (a) dissuade (Situational clue: What would you try to do in regard to people who were pursuing a dangerous course of action?) . . . futile (Contrast clues: "did everything I could," "but," "unfortunately")

3. (b) hazard (Situational clue: What would an intrepid daredevil be likely to do in regard to life and limb?) . . . timid (Contrast clue: "intrepid")

4. (b) browsed (Situational clue: How would you describe the way in which someone was looking at a book if he or she were doing it idly?) . . . rural (Situational clue: In what kind of setting would you be likely to find scenes of haying and plowing?)

5. (c) plague (Situational clue: What was the "Black Death" an example of?) . . . disrupting (Situational clue: What did the "Black Death" do to the social and economic life of Europe?; Restatement clue: "or even paralyzing")

Notes

Vocabulary Workshop
New Edition

Jerome Shostak

Series Consultants

Sylvia A. Rendón, Ph.D.
Coord., Secondary Reading
Cypress-Fairbanks I.S.D.
Houston, Texas

Mel H. Farberman
Director of English
 Language Arts, K–12
Bay Shore U.F.S.D.
Bay Shore, New York

John Heath, Ph.D.
Department of Classics
Santa Clara University
Santa Clara, California

Sadlier-Oxford
A Division of William H. Sadlier, Inc.

Reviewers

The publisher wishes to thank for their comments and suggestions the following teachers and administrators, who read portions of the series prior to publication.

Anne S. Crane
Clinician, English Education
Georgia State University
Atlanta, GA

Susan W. Keogh
Curriculum Coordinator
Lake Highland Preparatory
Orlando, FL

Mary Louise Ellena-Wygonik
English Teacher
Hampton High School
Allison Park, PA

Lisa Anne Pomi
Language Arts Chairperson
Woodside High School
Woodside, CA

Arlene A. Oraby
Dept. Chair (Ret.), English 6–12
Briarcliff Public Schools
Briarcliff Manor, NY

Susan Cotter McDonough
English Department Chair
Wakefield High School
Wakefield, MA

Sr. M. Francis Regis Trojano
Sisters of St. Joseph (CSJ)
Educational Consultant
Boston, MA

Keith Yost
Director of Humanities
Tomball Ind. School District
Tomball, TX

Patricia M. Stack
English Teacher
South Park School District
South Park, PA

Joy Vander Vliet
English Teacher
Council Rock High School
Newtown, PA

Karen Christine Solheim
English Teacher
Jefferson High School
Jefferson, GA

Photo Credits

Art Resource, NY/National Portrait Gallery, Smithsonian Institution: 156. *Photo Courtesy of Steve Brown*: 163. *Corbis*/Bettmann: 41, 57, 97, 123; Bill Varie: 71; Raymond Gehman: 83; Steve Kaufman: 104; Reuters: 130; Free Agents Limited: 149. *Getty Images*/Stone/John Lund: 34. *Index Stock Imagery*/Matthew Borkoski: 116. *Adam Jones*: 27. *Major League Baseball Photos*/Rich Pilling: 170. *Mid America Science Museum*: 137. *NASA*: 90, 182. *New York State Historical Society*: 64.

PREFACE

For over five decades, VOCABULARY WORKSHOP has proven a highly successful tool for guiding systematic vocabulary growth and developing vocabulary skills. It has also been shown to be a valuable help to students preparing for standardized tests. This New Edition of VOCABULARY WORKSHOP has been prepared in recognition of important changes to these tests, with the introduction of two features designed to address the new emphasis on writing skills, including grammar, and reading skills on those tests.

A new **Vocabulary for Comprehension** section appears in each of the five Reviews. This two-page feature is modeled on the reading sections of standardized tests, and as in those tests, presents reading comprehension questions, including specific vocabulary-related ones, based on a reading passage. (For more on Vocabulary for Comprehension, see page 13.)

Following Vocabulary for Comprehension in each of the Reviews is another new feature called **Grammar in Context**. This one-page exercise is linked to the reading passage that precedes it, referring to a grammar or usage topic illustrated in the passage and then reviewing that topic with a brief explanation and practice questions. (For more on Grammar in Context, see page 16.)

The 15 Units that form the core of VOCABULARY WORKSHOP remain unchanged. Each of the Units comprises a five-part lesson consisting of **Definitions**, **Completing the Sentence**, **Synonyms and Antonyms**, **Choosing the Right Word**, and **Vocabulary in Context**. Together, these exercises provide multiple and varied exposures to the taught words, an approach that has been shown to be consistent with and supportive of research-based findings in vocabulary instruction.

Enrichment and vocabulary-building exercises also remain in the form of **Building with Classical Roots**, **Word Associations**, and **Word Families** in the Reviews, and **Analogies** and **Enriching Your Vocabulary** in the Cumulative Reviews.

In this Level of Vocabulary Workshop you will study 300 key words. The words in this Level, as well as all of the other Levels of this series, have been selected on the following bases: currency and general usefulness; frequency of appearance on recognized vocabulary lists; applicability to, and appearance on, standardized tests; and current grade-level research. In addition to the 300 key words, you will be introduced to hundreds of other words in the form of synonyms, antonyms, and other relatives. Mastery of these words will make you a better reader, a better writer and speaker, and better prepared for the challenges of standardized tests.

CONTENTS

PRONUNCIATION KEY

The pronunciation is indicated for every basic word introduced in this book. The symbols used for this purpose, as listed below, are similar to those appearing in most standard dictionaries of recent vintage. (Pronunciation keys and given pronunciations sometimes differ from dictionary to dictionary.) The author has consulted a large number of dictionaries for this purpose but has relied primarily on *Webster's Third New International Dictionary* and *The Random House Dictionary of the English Language (Unabridged)*.

There are, of course, many English words for which two (or more) pronunciations are commonly accepted. In virtually all cases where such words occur in this book, the author has sought to make things easier for the student by giving just one pronunciation. The only significant exception occurs when the pronunciation changes in accordance with a shift in the part of speech. Thus we would indicate that *project* in the verb form is pronounced prə jekt', and in the noun form, präj' ekt.

It is believed that these relatively simple pronunciation guides will be readily usable by the student. It should be emphasized, however, that the *best* way to learn the pronunciation of a word is to listen to and imitate an educated speaker.

Vowels	ā	lake	e	stress	ü	loot, new
	a	mat	ī	knife	u̇	foot, pull
	â	care	i	sit	ə	jumping, broken
	ä	bark, bottle	ō	flow	ər	bird, better
	au̇	doubt	ô	all, cord		
	ē	beat, wordy	oi	oil		

Consonants	ch	child, lecture	s	cellar	wh	what
	g	give	sh	shun	y	yearn
	j	gentle, bridge	th	thank	z	is
	ŋ	sing	th̲	those	zh	measure

All other consonants are sounded as in the alphabet.

Stress	The accent mark *follows* the syllable receiving the major stress: en rich'

Abbreviations	*adj.* adjective	*n.* noun	*prep.* preposition
	adv. adverb	*part.* participle	*v.* verb
	int. interjection	*pl.* plural	

See page T21 for information about the Interactive Audio Pronunciation Program.

THE VOCABULARY OF VOCABULARY

There are some interesting and useful words that are employed to describe and identify words. The exercises that follow will help you to check and strengthen your knowledge of this "vocabulary of vocabulary."

Denotation and Connotation

The **denotation** of a word is its specific dictionary meaning. Here are a few examples:

Word	Denotation
eminent	distinguished or noteworthy
cumbersome	hard to handle or manage
remember	call to mind

The **connotation** of a word is its **tone**—that is, the emotions or associations it normally arouses in people using, hearing, or reading it. Depending on what these feelings are, the connotation of a word may be *favorable* (*positive*) or *unfavorable* (*negative, pejorative*). A word that does not normally arouse strong feelings of any kind has a *neutral* connotation. Here are some examples of words with different connotations:

Word	Connotation
eminent	favorable
cumbersome	unfavorable
remember	neutral

Exercises *In the space provided, label the connotation of each of the following words* **F** *for "favorable,"* **U** *for "unfavorable," or* **N** *for "neutral."*

<u>U</u> **1.** unfit   <u>F</u> **3.** effective   <u>F</u> **5.** festive

<u>U</u> **2.** absurd   <u>N</u> **4.** ration   <u>U</u> **6.** sinister

Literal and Figurative Usage

When a word is used in a **literal** sense, it is being employed in its strict (or primary) dictionary meaning in a situation (or context) that "makes sense" from a purely logical or realistic point of view. For example:

> Yesterday I read an old tale about a knight who slew a *fire-breathing* dragon.

In this sentence, *fire-breathing* is employed literally. The dragon is pictured as breathing real fire.

Sometimes words are used in a symbolic or nonliteral way in situations that do not "make sense" from a purely logical or realistic point of view. We call this nonliteral application of a word a **figurative** or **metaphorical** usage. For example:

> Suddenly my boss rushed into my office, *breathing fire*.

In this sentence *breathing fire* is not being used in a literal sense. That is, the boss was not actually breathing fire out of his nostrils. Rather, the expression is intended to convey graphically that the boss was very angry.

Exercises   *In the space provided, write **L** for "literal" or **F** for "figurative" next to each of the following sentences to show how the italicized expression is being used.*

   __L__   **1.** The carpenter *pried* the nails out of the wall.

   __F__   **2.** The police officer tried to *pry* information from the accused.

   __F__   **3.** She walked *at a snail's pace* through the mall.

Synonyms

A **synonym** is a word that has *the same* or *almost the same* meaning as another word. Here are some examples:

eat—consume   clash—conflict
hurt—injure   fire—discharge
big—large   slim—slender

Exercises   *In each of the following groups, circle the word that is most nearly the **synonym** of the word in **boldface** type.*

1. resign	**2. origin**	**3. prevent**	**4. confirm**
a. quit	a. model	a. roar	a. destroy
b. restore	b. field	b. mumble	b. prove
c. remove	c. beginning	c. sing	c. amaze
d. install	d. ending	d. stop	d. hate

Antonyms

An **antonym** is a word that means *the opposite* of or *almost the opposite* of another word. Here are some examples:

enter—leave   happy—sad
wild—tame   leader—follower
buy—sell   war—peace

Exercises   *In each of the following groups, circle the word that is most nearly the **antonym** of the word in **boldface** type.*

1. consent	**2. denounce**	**3. variety**	**4. hardship**
a. guarantee	a. recall	a. sameness	a. scholarship
b. arrange	b. ignore	b.scarcity	b. strength
c. remove	c. praise	c. speed	c. distance
d. refuse	d. forget	d. annoyance	d. ease

VOCABULARY STRATEGY: USING CONTEXT

How do you go about finding the meaning of an unknown or unfamiliar word that you come across in your reading? You might look the word up in a dictionary, of course, provided one is at hand. But there are two other useful strategies that you might employ to find the meaning of a word that you do not know at all or that is used in a way that you do not recognize. One strategy is to analyze the **structure** or parts of the word. (See pages 15 and 16 for more on this strategy.) The other strategy is to try to figure out the meaning of the word by reference to context.

When we speak of the **context** of a word, we mean the words that are near to or modify that word. By studying the context, we may find **clues** that lead us to its meaning. We might find a clue in the immediate sentence or phrase in which the word appears (and sometimes in adjoining sentences or phrases, too); or we might find a clue in the topic or subject matter of the passage in which the word appears; or we might even find a clue in other parts of a page itself. (Photographs, illustrations, charts, graphs, captions, and headings are some examples of such features.)

One way to use context as a strategy is to ask yourself what you know already about the topic or subject matter in question. By applying what you have learned before about deserts, for example, you would probably be able to figure out that the word *arid* in the phrase "the arid climate of the desert" means "dry."

The **Vocabulary in Context** exercises that appear in the Units and the **Vocabulary for Comprehension** and the **Choosing the Right Meaning** exercises that appear in the Reviews and Cumulative Reviews provide practice in using subject matter or topic to determine the meaning of given words.

When you do the various word-omission exercises in this book, look for **context clues** built into the sentence or passage to guide you to the correct answer. Three types of context clues appear in the exercises in this book.

A **restatement clue** consists of a *synonym* for, or a *definition* of, the missing word. For example:

"I'm willing to <u>tell</u> what I know about the matter," the reporter said, "but I can't _____ my sources."
a. conceal   b. defend   c. find   (d. reveal)

In this sentence, *tell* is a synonym of the missing word, *reveal*, and acts as a restatement clue for it.

A **contrast clue** consists of an *antonym* for, or a phrase that means the *opposite* of, the missing word. For example:

"I'm trying to <u>help</u> you, <u>not</u> (**assist,** (**hinder**))you!" she exclaimed in annoyance.

In this sentence, *help* is an antonym of the missing word, *hinder*. This is confirmed by the presence of the word *not*. *Help* thus functions as a contrast clue for *hinder*.

An *inference clue* implies but does not directly state the meaning of the missing word or words. For example:

A <u>utility infielder</u> has to be a very _____
player because he is a veritable <u>jack-of-all-trades</u> on the
_____ diamond.

   a. veteran . . . football   c. experienced . . . hockey
   (b. versatile . . . baseball)   d. energetic . . . golf

In this sentence, there are several inference clues: (a) the term *jack-of-all-trades* suggests the word *versatile* because a jack-of-all-trades is by definition versatile; the word *utility* in the term *utility infielder* suggests the same thing; (b) the words *infielder* and *diamond* suggest *baseball* because they are terms employed regularly in that sport. Accordingly, all these words are inference clues because they suggest or imply, but do not directly state, the missing word or words.

Exercises *Use context clues to choose the word or words that complete each of the following sentences or sets of sentences.*

1. I threw out all my old notes, but made certain not to
_____ the new ones.

   a. understand   c. keep
   b. overrate   (d. discard)

2. The search crew _____ through all the evidence,
and their hard work was rewarded with _____ for all
of them.

   (a. sifted . . . promotions)   c. wandered . . . sentences
   b. rushed . . . grief   d. jumped . . . policies

3. I am looking not for temporary solutions but for a (**permanent,** gallant)
settlement.

VOCABULARY STRATEGY: WORD STRUCTURE

One important way to build your vocabulary is to learn the meaning of word parts that make up many English words. These word parts consist of **prefixes**, **suffixes**, and **roots**, or **bases**. A useful strategy for determining the meaning of an unknown word is to "take apart" the word and think about the parts. For example, when you look at the word parts in the word *invisible,* you find the prefix *in-* ("not") + the root *-vis-* ("see") + the suffix *-ible* ("capable of"). From knowing the meanings of the parts of this word, you can figure out that *invisible* means "not capable of being seen."

Following is a list of common prefixes. Knowing the meaning of a prefix can help you determine the meaning of a word in which the prefix appears.

Prefix	Meaning	Sample Words
bi-	two	bicycle
com-, con-	together, with	compatriot, contact
de-, dis-	lower, opposite	devalue, disloyal
fore-, pre-	before, ahead of time	forewarn, preplan
il-, im-, in-, ir, non-, un-	not	illegal, impossible, inactive, irregular, nonsense, unable
in-, im-	in, into	inhale, import
mid-	middle	midway
mis-	wrongly, badly	mistake, misbehave
re-	again, back	redo, repay
sub-	under, less than	submarine, subzero
super-	above, greater than	superimpose, superstar
tri-	three	triangle

Following is a list of common suffixes. Knowing the meaning and grammatical function of a suffix can help you determine the meaning of a word.

Noun Suffix	Meaning	Sample Nouns
-acy, -ance, -ence, -hood, -ity, -ment, -ness, -ship	state, quality, or condition of, act or process of	adequacy, attendance, persistence, neighborhood, activity, judgment, brightness, friendship
-ant, -eer, -ent, -er, -ian, -ier, -ist, -or	one who does or makes something	contestant, auctioneer, resident, banker, comedian, financier, dentist, doctor
-ation, -ition, -ion	act or result of	organization, imposition, election

Verb Suffix	Meaning	Sample Verbs
-ate	to become, produce, or treat	validate, salivate, chlorinate
-en	to make, cause to be	weaken
-fy, -ify, -ize	to cause, make	liquefy, glorify, legalize

Adjective Suffix	Meaning	Sample Adjectives
-able, -ible	able, capable of	believable, incredible
-al, -ic,	relating to, characteristic of	natural, romantic
-ful, -ive, -ous	full of, given to, marked by	beautiful, protective, poisonous
-ish, -like	like, resembling	foolish, childlike
-less	lacking, without	careless

A **base** or **root** is the main part of a word to which prefixes and suffixes may be added. Many roots come to English from Latin, such as *-socio-,* meaning "society," or from Greek, such as *-logy-,* meaning "the study of." Knowing Greek and Latin roots can help you determine the meaning of a word such as *sociology,* which means "the study of society."

In the **Building with Classical Roots** sections of this book you will learn more about some of these Latin and Greek roots and about English words that derive from them. The lists that follow may help you figure out the meaning of new or unfamiliar words that you encounter in your reading.

Greek Root	Meaning	Sample Word
-astr-, -aster-, -astro-	star	astral, asteroid, astronaut
-auto-	self	autograph
-bio-	life	biography
-chron-, chrono-	time	chronic, chronological
-cosm-, -cosmo-	universe, order	microcosm, cosmopolitan
-cryph-, -crypt-	hidden, secret	apocryphal, cryptographer
-dem-, -demo-	people	epidemic, democracy
-dia-	through, across, between	diameter
-dog-, -dox-	opinion, teaching	dogmatic, orthodox
-gen-	race, kind, origin, birth	generation
-gnos-	know	diagnostic
-graph-, -graphy-, -gram-	write	graphite, autobiography, telegram
-log-, -logue-	speech, word, reasoning	logic, dialogue
-lys-	break down	analysis
-metr-, -meter-	measure	metric, kilometer
-micro-	small	microchip
-morph-	form, shape	amorphous
-naut-	sailor	cosmonaut
-phon-, -phone-, -phono-	sound, voice	phonics, telephone, phonograph
-pol-, -polis-	city, state	police, metropolis
-scop-, -scope-	watch, look at	telescopic, microscope
-tele-	far off, distant	television
-the-	put or place	parentheses

Latin Root	Meaning	Sample Word
-cap-, -capt-, -cept-, -cip-	take	capitulate, captive, concept, recipient
-cede-, -ceed-, -ceas-, -cess-	happen, yield, go	precede, proceed, decease, cessation
-cred-	believe	incredible
-dic-, -dict-	speak, say, tell	indicate, diction
-duc-, -duct-, -duit-	lead, conduct, draw	educate, conduct, conduit
-fac-, -fact-, -fect-, -fic-, -fy-	make	faculty, artifact, defect, beneficial, clarify
-ject-	throw	eject
-mis-, -miss-, -mit-, -mitt-	send	promise, missile, transmit, intermittent
-note-, -not-	know, recognize	denote, notion
-pel-, -puls-	drive	expel, compulsive
-pend-, -pens-	hang, weight, set aside	pendulum, pension
-pon-, -pos-	put, place	component, position
-port-	carry	portable
-rupt-	break	bankrupt
-scrib-, -scribe-, -script-	write	scribble, describe, inscription
-spec-, -spic-	look, see	spectator, conspicuous
-tac-, -tag-, -tang-, -teg-	touch	contact, contagious, tangible, integral
-tain-, -ten-, -tin-	hold, keep	contain, tenure, retinue
-temp-	time	tempo
-ven-, -vent-	come	intervene, convention
-vers-, -vert-	turn	reverse, invert
-voc-, -vok-	call	vocal, invoke

VOCABULARY AND READING

Word knowledge is essential to reading comprehension. Quite simply, the more words you know, the easier it is to make sense of what you read. Your growing knowledge of word meanings combined with an ability to read carefully and think about what you read will help you succeed in school and do well on standardized tests, including the new SAT, the ACT, and the PSAT.

The **Vocabulary for Comprehension** exercises in this book will give you the opportunity to put your vocabulary knowledge and critical reading skills to use. Each exercise consists of a nonfiction reading passage followed by comprehension questions. The passages and questions are similar to those that you are likely to find on standardized tests.

Kinds of Questions

The questions on the reading sections of standardized tests are formulated in many different ways, but they are usually only of a small number of kinds, or types— the same ones that appear most frequently in the Vocabulary for Comprehension exercises in this book.

Main Idea Questions generally ask what the passage as a whole is about. Questions about the main idea may begin like this:

- The primary or main purpose of the passage is
- The primary focus of the passage is on
- The passage is best described as
- The passage is primarily concerned with
- The title that best describes the content of the passage is

Often the main idea is stated in the first paragraph of the passage. Sometimes, however, the first paragraph serves as an introduction and the main idea is included later on. When you answer questions about the main idea, you should make sure that the answers you choose reflect the focus of the entire passage and not just part of it. You may also be asked the main idea of a specific paragraph.

Detail Questions focus on important information that is explicitly stated in the passage. Often, however, the correct answer choices do not use the exact language of the passage. They are instead restatements, or paraphrases, of the text. So, for example, the answer to a question about "trash production and disposal" might use the term "waste management."

Vocabulary-in-Context Questions check your ability to use context to identify a word's meaning. All vocabulary-in-context questions include line references so that you can refer back to the passage to see how and in what context the word is used.

Here are some examples:

- **Condone** (line 6) most nearly means
- **Eminent** (line 8) is best defined as
- The meaning of **diffuse** (line 30) is

It is important to use context to check your answer choices, particularly when the vocabulary word has more than one meaning. Among the choices may be two (or more) correct meanings of the word in question. Your task is to choose the meaning that best fits the context.

Inference Questions ask you to make inferences or draw conclusions from the passage. These questions often begin like this:

- It can be inferred from the passage that
- The author implies that
- The passage suggests that
- Evidently the author feels that

The inferences you make and the conclusions you draw must be based on the information in the passage. Your own knowledge and reasoning come into play in understanding what is implied and in reaching conclusions that are logical.

Questions about Tone show your understanding of the author's attitude toward the subject of the passage. Words that describe tone, or attitude, are "feeling" words, for example, *indifferent, ambivalent, scornful, astonished, respectful*. These are typical questions:

- The author's attitude toward . . . is best described as
- The author's perspective is that of . . .
- Which word best describes the author's tone . . .

To determine the tone, it's important to pay attention to the author's choice of words and note your personal reaction. The author's attitude may be positive *(respectful, astonished)*, negative *(scornful)*, or neutral *(indifferent, ambivalent)*.

Questions about Author's Technique focus on the way a text is organized and the language the author uses. These questions ask you to think about structure and function. For example:

- The final paragraph serves to
- What is the function of the phrase . . . ?
- What does the author mean by . . . ?
- The author cites . . . in order to . . . .

To answer the questions, you must demonstrate an understanding of the way the author presents information and develops ideas.

Strategies

Here are some general strategies to help you in reading each passage and answering the questions.

- Read the introduction first. The introduction will provide a focus for the selection.

- Be an active reader. As you read, ask yourself questions about the passage, for example: What is this paragraph about? What does the writer mean here? Why does the writer include this information?

- Refer back to the passage when you answer the questions. In general, the order of the questions mirrors the organization of the passage, and many of the questions include paragraph or line references. It is often helpful to go back and reread before choosing an answer.

- Read carefully, and be sure to base your answer choices on the passage. There are answer choices that make sense, but are not based on the information in the passage. These may be true statements, but incorrect answers. The correct answers are either restatements of ideas in the text or inferences that can be made from the text.

- Consider each exercise a learning experience. Keep in mind that your ability to answer the questions correctly shows as much about your understanding of the questions as about your understanding of the passage.

GRAMMAR AND WRITING

In order to write well, so that your meaning and your purpose are clearly understood, you must use words correctly; but, more than that, you must also make sure that what you write is grammatically correct. Knowing the rules of grammar, usage, and mechanics—the conventions of standard English—make your writing not just correct but more powerful and persuasive, too.

As a student you are regularly challenged to write effectively and correctly not only in your English classes but in your social studies, science, and history classes, too. Furthermore, high schools and colleges have raised their expectations for graduates. If you have taken a standardized test recently or are preparing to take one, you know this only too well. The writing and grammar sections of these tests have grown more demanding than ever.

On these grammar sections, questions usually appear in one or two multiple-choice formats. In one, you must decide if a mistake has been made in a sentence and, if one has been made, identify it. In another format, you must decide if an identified word or phrase is incorrect and, if it is incorrect, choose from several options the best way to correct it.

The **Grammar in Context** exercise that appears in each of the five Reviews in this book will provide you with opportunity to review and apply grammar and usage rules that are critical to good writing and that are frequently tested on the multiple-choice parts of standardized tests. In Level B, these topics are:

- Run-on sentences, sentence fragments
- Adjectives, adverbs
- Subject-verb agreement
- Who and whom
- Parallel construction

(For the sake of convenience, we sometimes use the term *grammar* to embrace all of the "rules" of English; but it's important to note that grammar, usage, and mechanics represent different aspects of writing. Grammar deals mostly with parts of speech and with parts of sentences and their relations. Usage, as the name suggests, concerns the way that words and phrases are used; usage topics would include, for example, irregular verbs, active and passive voice, subject-verb agreement, and double negatives. Mechanics deals with punctuation, capitalization, and spelling.)

There are many reasons to write and speak correctly other than to score well on standardized tests. You are judged by the way you write and speak. Your use of English is evaluated in the writing you do in school, on college applications, and in many different kinds of careers. You should be able to write and speak correctly when the situation calls for it—in a formal writing assignment, on a test, or in an interview. The more you practice standard English, the more comfortable and confident you will become when you write and speak.

WORKING WITH ANALOGIES

A verbal analogy expresses a relationship or comparison between sets of words. Normally, an analogy contains two pairs of words linked by a word or symbol that stands for an equals (=) sign. A complete analogy compares the two pairs of words and makes a statement about them. It asserts that the relationship between the first pair of words is the same as the relationship between the second pair.

In the **Analogies** exercises that appear in the Cumulative Reviews, you will be asked to complete analogies, that is, to choose the pair of words that best matches or parallels the relationship of the key, or given, pair of words. Here are two examples:

1. maple is to **tree** as
   a. acorn is to oak
   b. hen is to rooster
   c. rose is to flower
   d. shrub is to lilac

2. joyful is to **gloomy** as
   a. cheerful is to happy
   b. strong is to weak
   c. quick is to famous
   d. hungry is to starving

In order to find the correct answer to exercise 1, you must first determine the relationship between the two key words, **maple** and **tree**. In this case, that relationship might be expressed as "a maple is a kind (or type) of tree." The next step is to select from choices a, b, c, and d the pair of words that best reflects the same relationship. Clearly, the correct answer is (c); it is the only choice that parallels the relationship of the key words: a rose is a kind (or type) of flower, just as a maple is a kind (or type) of tree. The other choices do not express the same relationship.

In exercise 2, the relationship between the key words can be expressed as "joyful means the opposite of gloomy." Which of the choices best represents the same relationship? The answer, of course, is (b): "strong" means the opposite of "weak."

Here are examples of some other common analogy relationships:

Analogy	Key Relationship
big is to **large** as **little** is to **small**	**Big** means the same thing as **large**, just as **little** means the same thing as **small**.
brave is to **favorable** as **cowardly** is to **unfavorable**	The tone of **brave** is **favorable**, just as the tone of **cowardly** is **unfavorable**.
busybody is to **nosy** as **klutz** is to **clumsy**	A **busybody** is by definition someone who is **nosy**, just as a **klutz** is by definition someone who is **clumsy**.
cowardly is to **courage** as **awkward** is to **grace**	Someone who is **cowardly** lacks **courage**, just as someone who is **awkward** lacks **grace**.
visible is to **see** as **audible** is to **hear**	If something is **visible**, you can by definition **see** it, just as if something is **audible**, you can by definition **hear** it.
liar is to **truthful** as **bigot** is to **fair-minded**	A **liar** is by definition not likely to be **truthful**, just as a **bigot** is by definition not likely to be **fair-minded**.
eyes are to **see** as **ears** are to **hear**	You use your **eyes** to **see** with, just as you use your **ears** to **hear** with.

There are many different kinds of relationships represented in the analogy questions you will find in this book, but the key to solving any analogy is to find and express the relationship between the two key words.

DIAGNOSTIC TEST

This test contains a sampling of the words that are to be found in the exercises in this Level of VOCABULARY WORKSHOP. It will give you an idea of the types of words to be studied and their level of difficulty. When you have completed all the units, the Final Mastery Test at the end of this book will assess what you have learned. By comparing your results on the Final Mastery Test with your results on the Diagnostic Test below, you will be able to judge your progress.

Synonyms

*In each of the following groups, circle the word or phrase that **most nearly** expresses the meaning of the word in **boldface** type in the given phrase.*

1. an **abnormal** situation
a. typical
b. terrible
c. funny
(d. unusual)

2. **lubricate** the car
a. start
(b. oil)
c. stop
d. repair

3. set **ultimate** goals
a. temporary
b. hasty
c. sincere
(d. final)

4. an act of **vengeance**
a. mercy
(b. revenge)
c. daring
d. fate

5. **proficient** workers
a. inexperienced
b. awkward
c. slow
(d. skillful)

6. become a **fugitive**
a. criminal
(b. runaway)
c. jailer
d. victim

7. without **prior** planning
(a. earlier)
b. intelligent
c. necessary
d. careful

8. **insinuate** that I eat too much
a. claim
b. deny
c. admit
(d. imply)

9. accused of **homicide**
(a. killing)
b. lying
c. stealing
d. cheating

10. **prominent** members of our community
a. shady
b. wealthy
(c. leading)
d. foreign

11. bring down their **wrath**
a. troubles
(b. rage)
c. self-esteem
d. temperature

12. **reluctant** assistants
a. experienced
b. awkward
(c. unwilling)
d. paid

13. a **legitimate** government
(a. lawful)
b. foreign
c. new
d. tyrannical

14. a **legible** report
a. detailed
b. recent
(c. readable)
d. thorough

15. **sagacious** remarks
a. nasty
b. humorous
c. kind
(d. wise)

16. live a **humdrum** life
    a. exciting   b. poor   c. unusual   (d. dull)

17. a highly **disputatious** person
    a. likable   b. annoying   c. logical   (d. argumentative)

18. be ever **vigilant**
    a. careless   b. carefree   c. merciless   (d. alert)

19. **procure** assistance
    a. seek   b. offer   c. reject   (d. obtain)

20. **indulge** the children
    (a. coddle)   b. discipline   c. mistreat   d. feed

21. **miscellaneous** objects
    a. worthless   b. expensive   (c. various)   d. similar

22. **inflict** pain
    (a. deal out)   b. cure   c. study   d. fear

23. **vicious** animals
    a. gentle   b. trained   (c. savage)   d. useful

24. **flourish** their swords
    a. hold   b. seize   c. destroy   (d. wave)

25. a **sodden** pile of leaves
    a. little   (b. wet)   c. huge   d. messy

26. in a **melancholy** mood
    a. typical   b. angry   c. strange   (d. sad)

27. **interrogate** the witness
    (a. question)   b. believe   c. punish   d. listen to

28. nothing more than a **hoax**
    (a. fraud)   b. nobody   c. thief   d. problem

29. **loom** on the horizon
    a. see   b. notice   c. discover   (d. appear)

30. a **customary** procedure
    a. wrong   b. profitable   c. clever   (d. usual)

Antonyms

*In each of the following groups, circle the word or expression that is most nearly opposite in meaning to the word in **boldface** type in the given phrase.*

31. very **hardy** plants
    a. unusual   b. beautiful   (c. fragile)   d. expensive

32. a **cluttered** room
    a. spacious   (b. tidy)   c. carpeted   d. messy

33. a major **catastrophe**
    a. war   b. problem   c. disaster   (d. triumph)

34. **prudent** in her use of money
    (a. foolish)   b. stingy   c. thoughtful   d. wise

35. a **fruitless** effort
   a. costly   b. hurried   (c. successful)   d. halfhearted

36. vital to our well-being
   a. important   b. sympathetic   (c. unnecessary)   d. accustomed

37. very **lax** about discipline
   a. unconcerned   b. happy   (c. strict)   d. forgetful

38. voiced **trivial** objections to the plan
   a. silly   (b. significant)   c. several   d. separate

39. a truly **hospitable** welcome
   a. warm   b. unexpected   (c. cold)   d. fitting

40. a **hilarious** movie
   a. long   (b. sad)   c. profitable   d. foreign

41. feel very **lethargic** today
   (a. energetic)   b. gloomy   c. tired   d. confident

42. ignite a fire
   (a. extinguish)   b. feed   c. ignore   d. report

43. an unexpected **surplus** of wheat
   a. harvest   b. demand   c. use   (d. lack)

44. a **graphic** account
   a. partial   b. vivid   c. long-winded   (d. colorless)

45. a **grim** forecast
   a. detailed   (b. rosy)   c. gloomy   d. recent

46. despondent about his grades
   (a. overjoyed)   b. careful   c. unhappy   d. concerned

47. hostile actions
   a. sensitive   (b. friendly)   c. cheerful   d. unusual

48. a **lavish** gift
   a. costly   b. unusual   c. beautiful   (d. skimpy)

49. gigantic tomatoes
   a. ripe   (b. tiny)   c. poisonous   d. expensive

50. a **clarification** of the issue
   a. discussion   b. avoidance   (c. confusion)   d. explanation

Definitions

Note carefully the spelling, pronunciation, part(s) of speech, and definition(s) of each of the following words. Then write the word in the blank space(s) in the illustrative sentence(s) following. Finally, study the lists of synonyms and antonyms given at the end of each entry.

1. adjacent
(ə jās′ ənt)

(*adj.*) near, next to, adjoining

Boston and its _____**adjacent**_____ suburbs were severely flooded after three days of heavy rain.

SYNONYMS: alongside, nearby, neighboring
ANTONYMS: faraway, distant, remote

2. alight
(ə līt′)

(*v.*) to get down from, step down from; to come down from the air, land; (*adj.*) lighted up

The passengers hurried to _____**alight**_____ from the airplane.

The sky was _____**alight**_____ with a red glow as the fire raged in the distance.

SYNONYMS: (*v.*) dismount, descend, land, touch down
ANTONYMS: (*v.*) mount, ascend, board, take off

3. barren
(bar′ ən)

(*adj.*) not productive, bare

In contrast to the rich land we left behind, the plains appeared to be a _____**barren**_____ landscape.

SYNONYMS: unproductive, sterile, desolate, arid
ANTONYMS: fertile, productive, fruitful

4. disrupt
(dis rəpt′)

(*v.*) to break up, disturb

Even the loud demonstration on the street below was not enough to _____**disrupt**_____ the meeting.

SYNONYMS: upset, displace, disorder
ANTONYMS: organize, arrange

5. dynasty
(dī′ nə stē)

(*n.*) a powerful family or group of rulers that maintains its position or power for some time

The Han _____**Dynasty**_____ of China was in power for about 400 years.

SYNONYMS: ruling house, regime

6. foretaste
(fôr′ tāst)

(*n.*) an advance indication, sample, or warning

The eye-opening first scene of the new play gave the audience a _____**foretaste**_____ of things to come.

SYNONYMS: preview, anticipation

7. germinate
(jər′ mə nāt)

(v.) to begin to grow, come into being

After he interrogated the suspect, suspicion began to
_____germinate_____ in the inspector's mind.

SYNONYMS: sprout, shoot up, grow, burgeon
ANTONYMS: wither, die, stagnate, shrivel up

8. humdrum
(həm′ drəm)

(adj.) ordinary, dull, routine, without variation

All household tasks are _____humdrum_____,
according to my brother, who never helps with them.

SYNONYMS: monotonous, uneventful, prosaic, boring
ANTONYMS: lively, exciting, thrilling, exhilarating

9. hurtle
(hər′ təl)

(v.) to rush violently, dash headlong; to fling or hurl forcefully

After separating from its booster rocket, the capsule began
to _____hurtle_____ through space.

SYNONYMS: speed, fly, race, catapult, fling
ANTONYMS: crawl, creep

10. insinuate
(in sin′ yü āt)

(v.) to suggest or hint slyly; to edge into something indirectly

The attorney attempted to _____insinuate_____ that
the witness's testimony was false.

SYNONYMS: imply, intimate
ANTONYMS: barge in, broadcast

11. interminable
(in tər′ mə nə bəl)

(adj.) endless, so long as to seem endless

We had an _____interminable_____ wait in the hot,
crowded train station.

SYNONYMS: never-ending, ceaseless
ANTONYMS: brief, short, fleeting

12. interrogate
(in ter′ ə gāt)

(v.) to ask questions, examine by questioning

Two detectives helped the young, inexperienced officer to
_____interrogate_____ the suspect.

SYNONYMS: question, query

13. recompense
(rek′ əm pens)

(v.) to pay back; to give a reward; (n.) a payment for loss,
service, or injury

My grandparents were happy to
_____recompense_____ the little girl who found their
lost puppy.
As _____recompense_____, the landlord offered all
tenants a month free of rent.

SYNONYMS: (v.) repay; (n.) compensation

14. renovate
(ren′ ə vāt)

(*v.*) to repair, restore to good condition, make new again

The young couple brought in an architect and a contractor to help them _____ renovate _____ the old house.

SYNONYMS: repair, fix up, recondition

15. résumé
(rez′ ə mā)

(*n.*) a brief summary; a short written account of one's education, working experience, or qualifications for a job

The job applicant gave a copy of her _____ résumé _____ to the person in charge of the employment agency.

SYNONYMS: synopsis, job history

16. sullen
(səl′ ən)

(*adj.*) silent or brooding because of ill humor, anger, or resentment; slow moving, sluggish

The _____ sullen _____ student sat down in the back of the classroom.

SYNONYMS: grumpy, surly, peevish, morose
ANTONYMS: cheerful, blithe, sociable, vivacious

17. trickle
(trik′ əl)

(*v.*) to flow or fall by drops or in a small stream; (*n.*) a small, irregular quantity of anything

The water began to _____ trickle _____ from the rusty old pipe.

The runoff, which is quite heavy in the spring, dwindles to a _____ trickle _____ by late summer.

SYNONYMS: (*v.*) dribble, drizzle, drip; (*n.*) small amount
ANTONYMS: (*v.*) gush, pour, flood; (*n.*) deluge

18. trivial
(triv′ ē əl)

(*adj.*) not important, minor; ordinary, commonplace

The general left all _____ trivial _____ details to subordinates.

SYNONYMS: insignificant, petty, trifling
ANTONYMS: important, weighty, momentous

19. truce
(trüs)

(*n.*) a pause in fighting, temporary peace

After tense negotiations, the warring nations reluctantly agreed to a five-day _____ truce _____ .

SYNONYMS: cease-fire, armistice
ANTONYMS: war, warfare, fighting

20. vicious
(vish′ əs)

(*adj.*) evil, bad; spiteful; having bad habits or an ugly disposition; painfully severe or extreme

The _____ vicious _____ rumor was damaging to their friendship.

SYNONYMS: wicked, malicious, savage
ANTONYMS: good, kind, kindly, mild, harmless

Completing the Sentence

From the words for this unit, choose the one that best completes each of the following sentences. Write the word in the space provided.

1. Many people who lead rather _____**humdrum**_____ lives get a great thrill from watching the exciting adventures of TV and movie superheroes.

2. The "coming attractions" shown before the main feature gave us a distinct _____**foretaste**_____ of what the next film would be like.

3. Although they lived in a house _____**adjacent**_____ to ours, we never really got to know them well.

4. The judge said to the lawyer, "You have a right to _____**interrogate**_____ the witness, but there is no need to bully her."

5. I never would have thought that so bitter and long-lasting a quarrel could result from such a(n) _____**trivial**_____ and unimportant cause.

6. We need large sums of money to keep our school system going, but we are getting only a(n) _____**trickle**_____ of funds from the state.

7. When I applied for the job, I left a(n) _____**résumé**_____ of my previous work experience with the personnel office.

8. Though they didn't say so in so many words, they did _____**insinuate**_____ that I was responsible for the accident.

9. Although the building is old and needs repair, we are convinced that we can _____**renovate**_____ it without spending a lot of money.

10. After the big party, cleaning up, which was supposed to take "just a few minutes," proved to be an almost _____**interminable**_____ job.

11. After the warring nations had agreed to a(n) _____**truce**_____, they faced the far more difficult task of working out a real peace.

12. She was so happy and grateful that I felt more than _____**recompensed**_____ for all that I had tried to do to help her.

13. Though my dog Rover is huge and fierce-looking, children are fond of him because he doesn't have a(n) _____**vicious**_____ disposition.

14. As the drought continued without a letup, the once fertile farmlands of the region slowly became _____**barren**_____ "dust bowls."

15. The suspect's only reaction to the detective's question was a wry smile and _____**sullen**_____ silence.

16. In only a few days, the seeds that I had planted in the fertile soil of the garden began to _____**germinate**_____ and take root.

17. During the exciting chase, the police cars _____**hurtled**_____ through the town.

18. In the 11th century, a foreign warlord invaded the country and set up a(n) _____ **dynasty** _____ that ruled for more than 250 years.

19. As we sat at the side of the lake, we enjoyed watching the wild geese swoop down and _____ **alight** _____ on the surface of the water.

20. Our carefully laid plans were completely _____ **disrupted** _____ by a sudden and totally unexpected turn of events.

Synonyms

*Choose the word from this unit that is **the same** or **most nearly the same** in meaning as the **boldface** word or expression in the given phrase. Write the word on the line provided.*

1. given the day off as **compensation** _____ recompense _____

2. chased by the **savage** dog _____ vicious _____

3. decided to **fix up** the old theater _____ renovate _____

4. **question** the guilty-looking man _____ interrogate _____

5. sit through a seemingly **never-ending** play _____ interminable _____

6. attempt to **touch down** on the ground _____ alight _____

7. **imply** that it was the teacher's fault _____ insinuate _____

8. sent a **job history** to the company _____ résumé _____

9. sign a binding **armistice** to end the fighting _____ truce _____

10. got a **preview** of what was in store _____ foretaste _____

11. **race** through space at an amazing speed _____ hurtle _____

12. is a **petty** matter not worth pursuing _____ trivial _____

13. watch water **drip** from the tap _____ trickle _____

14. begun during the time of the old **regime** _____ dynasty _____

15. started to **sprout** overnight _____ germinate _____

Antonyms

*Choose the word from this unit that is **most nearly opposite** in meaning to the **boldface** word or expression in the given phrase. Write the word on the line provided.*

16. acres of **fertile** soil _____ barren _____

17. was known as a **cheerful** patient _____ sullen _____

18. had a **lively** existence _____ humdrum _____

19. walked to the **remote** building _____ adjacent _____

20. would **organize** the meeting _____ disrupt _____

Choosing the Right Word

*Circle the **boldface** word that more satisfactorily completes each of the following sentences.*

1. He said that he was going to ask only "a few casual questions," but I soon saw that he wanted to (**recompense, interrogate**) me thoroughly.

2. When we are having fun, time rushes by, but even five minutes in the dentist's waiting room may seem (**adjacent, interminable**).

3. The administration had no major scandals, but it was also (**barren, sullen**) of outstanding accomplishments.

4. With flattery and clever half-truths, the newcomers (**insinuated, renovated**) themselves into the inner circle of the organization.

5. The principal asked the students not to hang around in front of the houses and other buildings (**adjacent to, alighting**) the school.

6. "The program the usher handed you contains a brief (**résumé, dynasty**) of the action of the opera you are about to see," I replied.

7. As he grew old, the torrent of beautiful music that he had produced for so many years was reduced to a mere (**foretaste, trickle**).

8. Even the most (**humdrum, vicious**) work can be interesting if you regard it as a challenge to do the very best you can.

9. The flight attendant asked the passengers to make sure that they had all their personal belongings before (**disrupting, alighting**) from the aircraft.

10. Regardless of who started this silly quarrel, isn't it time for us to declare a (**dynasty, truce**) and work together for the best interests of the school?

11. Planted in the fertile soil of her imagination, the seed of a great idea soon (**germinated, disrupted**) into a workable proposal.

12. I am angry not because she criticized me but because she made remarks that were untrue and (**trivial, vicious**).

13. What we want to do is (**recompense, renovate**) the old house without harming its charm and beauty.

14. Only twenty yards from the finish line, the horse stumbled and (**hurtled, insinuated**) its rider to the ground.

15. For three generations their family has formed one of the leading automotive (**truces, dynasties**) of this country.

16. When I saw a big "A" on my term paper in English, I felt that I had been fully (**germinated, recompensed**) for all my hours of hard work.

17. Our team spirit is so high that there is never a (**sullen, trivial**) reaction from players who aren't chosen to start a game.

18. Are we going to allow minor disagreements to (**disrupt, recompense**) the club that we have worked so hard to organize?

19. The way to be successful at a job is to carry out all instructions carefully, even though you think some of them are (**trivial, sullen**) or silly.

20. If the sights we've seen today are a true (**recompense, foretaste**) of what lies ahead, we're in for some real treats.

Vocabulary in Context

*Read the following passage, in which some of the words you have studied in this unit appear in **boldface** type. Then complete each statement given below the passage by circling the letter of the item that is **the same** or **almost the same** in meaning as the highlighted word.*

Underground Majesty

(Line)

The hill country midway between Nashville and Louisville along Interstate 65 looks like much of the land in rural America. Its landforms are typical of vistas you will see in Tennessee, Kentucky, and the surrounding states. Yet there is nothing **humdrum** about what lurks beneath those ridges, bluffs, and streams. For
(5) underneath the old-growth forest of black oak, beech, sugar maple, tulip poplar, and hickory lies the world's longest cave system, Mammoth Cave, with its seemingly **interminable** number of underground passageways and rooms.

Prehistoric hunters were the first to discover, explore, and use Mammoth Cave for shelter. Later, Native Americans
(10) also lived in the cave. About 200 years ago, American settlers came to this region. Unlike Native Americans, these settlers considered the caves to be of **trivial** importance. During the
(15) War of 1812, however, the cave's resources became valuable: saltpeter, used in making gunpowder, was mined there. After the war, with the help of explorer-guides, the cave
(20) gained national attention as a tourist attraction.

Park rangers with visitors to Mammoth Cave

Nowadays, visitors can get a **foretaste** of the cave's history and uses within a few hundred yards of its historic entrance. There they will come to the
(25) Rotunda, a huge chamber that features the remains of the saltpeter mine that was in full operation during the War of 1812.

Today, Mammoth Cave is both a national park and a World Heritage Site. To accommodate its many visitors, hotels and restaurants have been built **adjacent to** the cave's Historic Entrance. As a safety precaution, many miles of its
(30) passageways have handrails that are lit with electric lights. Yet even with these improvements, the cave remains a dangerous place. In fact, all visitors must tour the cave accompanied by a park ranger.

---

1. The meaning of **humdrum** (line 4) is
  a. morose   c. exciting
  b. ordinary   d. disruptive

2. Interminable (line 7) most nearly means
  a. brief   c. internal
  b. fruitful   d. endless

3. Trivial (line 14) is best defined as
  a. minor   c. weighty
  b. important   d. extended

4. The meaning of **foretaste** (line 23) is
  a. payment   c. indication
  b. review   d. gulp

5. Adjacent to (line 28) most nearly means
  a. near   c. distant
  b. similar   d. remote

UNIT 2

Definitions

Note carefully the spelling, pronunciation, part(s) of speech, and definition(s) of each of the following words. Then write the word in the blank space(s) in the illustrative sentence(s) following. Finally, study the lists of synonyms and antonyms given at the end of each entry.

1. available
(ə vā′ lə bəl)

(*adj.*) ready for use, at hand

Bean sprouts and bean curd are _____ **available** _____ in the Chinese market on Main Street.

SYNONYMS: obtainable, on hand
ANTONYMS: unobtainable, not to be had

2. cater
(kā′ tər)

(*v.*) to satisfy the needs of, try to make things easy and pleasant; to supply food and service

Our grandmother cared for the twins all summer, but she refused to _____ **cater** _____ to their every whim.

SYNONYMS: pamper, indulge, gratify, provide
ANTONYMS: frustrate, deny, refuse

3. customary
(kəs′ tə mer ē)

(*adj.*) usual, expected, routine

The _____ **customary** _____ tip given to a waiter for service is 15 percent of the bill.

SYNONYMS: regular, normal, traditional
ANTONYMS: strange, odd, unusual, untraditional

4. dissuade
(dis wād′)

(*v.*) to persuade not to do something

Despite offering big raises and bonuses, the boss was unable to _____ **dissuade** _____ workers from quitting.

SYNONYMS: discourage, talk out of
ANTONYMS: persuade, talk into

5. entrepreneur
(än trə prə nər′)

(*n.*) a person who starts up and takes on the risk of a business

In the first year of business, an _____ **entrepreneur** _____ often assumes losses for the sake of future profits.

SYNONYMS: businessperson, impresario

6. firebrand
(fī′ ər brand)

(*n.*) a piece of burning wood; a troublemaker; an extremely energetic or emotional person

A rash young _____ **firebrand** _____, the new editor of the newspaper strove to expose corruption in the mayor's office.

SYNONYMS: hothead, agitator, rabble-rouser
ANTONYMS: peacemaker, pacifier, conciliator

7. hazard
(haz′ ərd)

(*n.*) risk, peril; (*v.*) to expose to danger or harm; to gamble

Snow tires can help eliminate the

_____ hazards _____ of driving on icy roads.

When asked to predict when the long drought would end,

the meteorologist would not _____ hazard _____ a guess.

SYNONYMS: (*n.*) danger; (*v.*) venture

8. homicide
(hom′ ə sīd)

(*n.*) the killing of one person by another

It did not take the jury very long to find the drifter guilty of

_____ homicide _____ .

SYNONYMS: manslaughter, murder

9. indifference
(in dif′ rəns)

(*n.*) a lack of interest or concern

The outcome of the rugby match between the two teams is

a matter of complete _____ indifference _____ to me.

SYNONYMS: apathy, unconcern
ANTONYMS: interest, concern, enthusiasm

10. indignant
(in dig′ nənt)

(*adj.*) filled with resentment or anger over something unjust, unworthy, or mean

Angered by the editorial in the newspaper, my mother

wrote an _____ indignant _____ letter to the editor.

SYNONYMS: offended, resentful, outraged, exasperated
ANTONYMS: pleased, delighted, overjoyed, elated

11. indispensable
(in di spen′ sə
bəl)

(*adj.*) absolutely necessary, not to be neglected

Oxygen is a gas that is _____ indispensable _____ to life processes.

SYNONYMS: essential, crucial, vital
ANTONYMS: unnecessary, nonessential

12. lubricate
(lü′ brə kāt)

(*v.*) to apply oil or grease; to make smooth, slippery, or easier to use

The workers had to _____ lubricate _____ the equipment regularly so that production would not suffer.

SYNONYMS: oil, grease

13. mutual
(myü′ chü əl)

(*adj.*) shared, felt, or shown equally by two or more

During the course of the summer, the adoring couple

formed a _____ mutual _____ admiration society.

SYNONYMS: two-sided, joint, shared, reciprocal
ANTONYMS: one-sided, unilateral

14. pelt
(pelt)

(*v.*) to throw a stream of things; to strike successively; to hurry

The children resisted the urge to _____**pelt**_____ the cars with snowballs.

SYNONYMS: bombard, shower, pepper

15. plague
(plāg)

(*n.*) an easily spread disease causing a large number of deaths; a widespread evil; (*v.*) to annoy or bother

In the 14th century, a _____**plague**_____ spread by infected rats wiped out about one fourth of the population of Europe.

Mosquitoes will _____**plague**_____ the campers if they forget to wear insect repellent on the hike.

SYNONYMS: (*n.*) epidemic, pestilence; (*v.*) pester, vex
ANTONYMS: (*n.*) boon, blessing

16. poised
(poizd)

(*adj., part.*) balanced, suspended; calm, controlled; ready for action

The captain and other members of the crew were _____**poised**_____ for takeoff.

SYNONYMS: (*adj.*) collected, self-confident, ready
ANTONYMS: (*adj.*) nervous, tense

17. regime
(rā zhēm')

(*n.*) a government in power; a form or system of rule or management; a period of rule

The present _____**regime**_____ in that country came to power through democratic elections.

SYNONYMS: administration, rule

18. retard
(ri tärd')

(*v.*) to make slow, delay, hold back

Nothing will _____**retard**_____ economic progress more than a new tax on imports.

SYNONYMS: slow down, restrain, impede
ANTONYMS: hasten, speed up

19. transparent
(trans par' ənt)

(*adj.*) allowing light to pass through; easily recognized or understood; easily seen through or detected

The students could see the other class through the _____**transparent**_____ glass door.

SYNONYMS: clear, translucent, obvious
ANTONYMS: frosted, sooty, smoky, unclear, indistinct

20. unscathed
(ən skaᵗhd')

(*adj.*) wholly unharmed, not injured

Remarkably, the captain and the entire crew emerged from the wreck _____**unscathed**_____.

SYNONYMS: unhurt, sound, intact, unimpaired
ANTONYMS: injured, damaged, harmed, hurt

Completing the Sentence

From the words for this unit, choose the one that best completes each of the following sentences. Write the word in the space provided.

1. Having spent many years as political opponents, the two senators have developed a(n) _____ **mutual** _____ respect for each other.

2. Though they have done nothing to hasten passage of the bill, they haven't tried to _____ **retard** _____ the process either.

3. It takes a special kind of bravery to face the _____ **hazards** _____ of life in the jungle.

4. Until it was almost too late, the hunters did not see the leopard crouching in a tree, _____ **poised** _____ to leap on them.

5. When the wounded shopkeeper died, the charges against the person who had been arrested were raised from robbery to _____ **homicide** _____ .

6. Eventually, the army toppled the country's democratic _____ **regime** _____ and set up a military dictatorship in its place.

7. It took the authorities quite some time to put down the riot that a few rash _____ **firebrands** _____ had managed to start.

8. Although we arrived at the stadium only a few minutes before the game, we found that many good seats were still _____ **available** _____ .

9. Angry at the call, the crowd began to _____ **pelt** _____ the referee with all kinds of refuse.

10. Since the seat covers in the car were _____ **transparent** _____ , we could see the attractive pattern of the upholstery underneath.

11. Most of the homeowners in this area have tried in vain to overcome the _____ **plague** _____ of crabgrass that threatens to overrun their lawns.

12. At the front desk, a(n) _____ **indignant** _____ guest was angrily complaining about the shabby treatment he had received from the staff of the hotel.

13. Though the habit of taking a siesta in the afternoon may seem strange to a foreigner, it is quite _____ **customary** _____ in this part of the world.

14. With the emergence of market economies in Eastern Europe have come hordes of _____ **entrepreneurs** _____ seeking business opportunities there.

15. No one has ever been able to explain to my satisfaction how Indian holy men can walk _____ **unscathed** _____ across beds of hot coals.

16. Mother prepares wholesome, tasty meals, but she says she is not going to _____ **cater** _____ to the special tastes of six different children.

17. A sense of humor is _____ **indispensable** _____ if you are to cope with all the strains and difficulties of everyday life.

18. Only a really hard-hearted person could show such _____indifference_____ to the plight of the homeless who wander our streets.

19. The guidance counselor tried to _____dissuade_____ me from taking the job because she thought the work would be too pressured for me.

20. When we _____lubricate_____ the engine of a car, we try to cut down the friction at every point.

Synonyms

*Choose the word from this unit that is **the same** or **most nearly the same** in meaning as the **boldface** word or expression in the given phrase. Write the word on the line provided.*

1. met the new **impresario** of sports entertainment	entrepreneur
2. is **vital** to the good of the community	indispensable
3. found guilty of **murder**	homicide
4. entered into a **joint** agreement	mutual
5. began to **bombard** the windshield with hailstones	pelt
6. had a very **obvious** allegiance to the interest group	transparent
7. is considered a **rabble-rouser** by colleagues	firebrand
8. a law that would **vex** the firm for years to come	plague
9. was needed to **grease** the bicycle chain	lubricate
10. hired to **provide** the wedding supper	cater
11. is a **danger** to motorists and pedestrians	hazard
12. thrived under the new **administration**	regime
13. uses any excuse **at hand**	available
14. wants to **discourage** her from taking the job	dissuade
15. is **ready** to serve on the jury	poised

Antonyms

*Choose the word from this unit that is **most nearly opposite** in meaning to the **boldface** word or expression in the given phrase. Write the word on the line provided.*

16. was **overjoyed** when the candidate lost	indignant
17. was **harmed** in the explosion	unscathed
18. became a matter of **concern** to the coach	indifference
19. would **hasten** his recovery	retard
20. used **unusual** healing methods	customary

Choosing the Right Word

*Circle the **boldface** word that more satisfactorily completes each of the following sentences.*

1. The aid that we have (**indignantly, mutually**) given each other during the years has enabled both of us to overcome many problems.

2. All during that nightmarish period, I found myself (**plagued, dissuaded**) by doubts and fears about the future.

3. It seems that only last year she was an awkward child, but now she is a charming and (**poised, unscathed**) young woman.

4. When the new (**hazard, regime**) took power, it canceled or reversed most of the policies of its predecessor.

5. Innocent or guilty, no one involved in a major political scandal ever comes away from it entirely (**dissuaded, unscathed**).

6. The public's (**indifference, hazard**) to government may be measured in the number of citizens who do not bother to vote.

7. The judge explained to the jury that killing someone in self-defense may be considered justifiable, or noncriminal, (**homicide, plague**).

8. When my 8-year-old sister started up a chain of lemonade stands, I knew we had a budding (**entrepreneur, firebrand**) in the family.

9. Unfortunately, nothing any of us said could (**dissuade, cater**) Ned from his plan to quit his job.

10. Your excuse for missing practice was so (**transparent, indispensable**) that even a child would have seen right through it.

11. You cannot ignore me for months on end and then take it for granted that I will be (**available, customary**) whenever you want me.

12. Southern (**firebrands, hazards**) agitating for a complete break with the Union helped speed the coming of the Civil War.

13. A little courtesy can do much to (**dissuade, lubricate**) the machinery of our everyday social life.

14. Do you agree with the criticism that many television programs shamelessly (**cater, retard**) to the lowest tastes?

15. When the salesclerk replied rudely to my polite inquiry about the price of the garment, I became a bit (**transparent, indignant**).

16. Since I am a creature of habit, I find that I can't do anything in the morning without first having my (**customary, mutual**) cup of coffee.

17. In Shakespeare's day, an actor who displeased the audience might find himself (**poised, pelted**) with a barrage of rotten vegetables.

18. On our long camping trip, we learned that we could get along without many things that we had considered (**indispensable, indifferent**).

19. Though I have no means of knowing for sure where they happen to be, may I (**hazard, lubricate**) the guess that they're in the gym?

20. Modern medicine has found that antibiotics are a very effective means of (**catering, retarding**) or arresting the spread of some diseases.

*Read the following passage, in which some of the words you have studied in this unit appear in **boldface** type. Then complete each statement given below the passage by circling the letter of the item that is **the same** or **almost the same** in meaning as the highlighted word.*

Life on the Range

(Line)

Although cowboys have been portrayed as romantic figures in American folklore and film, in reality their life on the trail was anything but romantic. From about 1865 to 1890, cowboys drove approximately 10 million head of cattle from ranches in southern Texas to faraway northern locations. Where the herds went changed during the period. At first, the drives supplied cattle to forts, mining towns, and (5) reservations. Later, with the coming of the railroad, the destinations were railroad towns in Kansas or Nebraska, where the cattle were sold for beef to Eastern buyers. Regardless of the destination, the trip was dangerous and exhausting. In addition to stampedes, cowboys encountered many other **hazards** on the drive.

Along with dangers, almost anything (10) could **retard** the long journey. If the raging rivers they had to cross didn't slow the cowboys down, then the weather would. Cowboys were routinely **pelted** by hail and **plagued** by dust storms. They were also (15) often sickened by the food that was **available** to them.

The majority of the cowboys who drove cattle were Texans. Some were ex-Confederate soldiers. Others were former (20) slaves. Most were young. All were small. Their size made it easier for the horses to carry them over long distances. Cowboys

Herd of longhorn cattle on the move

also had something else in common. All worked long hours for very low pay, for up to four months at a time before resting or returning home. Only teamwork got them (25) through the ordeal. Cowboys soon learned that cattle could be managed most effectively in herds of about 2,500 head, with eight to twelve cowboys for each herd. Cattle drivers worked together to herd, round up, watch, and brand the cattle. This teamwork was **indispensable** to the success of any cattle drive.

---

1. Hazards (line 9) most nearly means
  a. epidemics   c. agitators
  (b.)perils   d. challenges

2. The meaning of **retard** (line 11) is
  (a.)slow down   c. speed up
  b. grease   d. calm

3. Pelted (line 14) most nearly means
  a. offended   c. scalded
  b. pampered   (d.)showered

4. Plagued (line 15) is best defined as
  a. discouraged   (c.)pestered
  b. unhurt   d. oiled

5. The meaning of **available** (line 17) is
  a. usual   c. crucial
  (b.)obtainable   d. intact

6. Indispensable (line 29) most nearly means
  a. unnecessary   (c.)essential
  b. useless   d. useful

Definitions

Note carefully the spelling, pronunciation, part(s) of speech, and definition(s) of each of the following words. Then write the word in the blank space(s) in the illustrative sentence(s) following. Finally, study the lists of synonyms and antonyms given at the end of each entry.

1. animated
(an' ə māt id)

(adj.) full of life, lively, alive; *(part.)* moved to action

After the game the sportscaster found the winning team to be in an _____ **animated** _____ mood.

SYNONYMS: *(adj.)* energetic, vigorous
ANTONYMS: *(adj.)* dull, lifeless, dead, flat

2. brood
(brüd)

(n.) a family of young animals, especially birds; any group having the same nature and origin; *(v.)* to think over in a worried, unhappy way

The mother bird fed her _____ **brood** _____ .

The pioneers did not _____ **brood** _____ over the hardships they suffered on the long journey.

SYNONYMS: *(v.)* ponder, meditate, worry, agonize

3. culminate
(kəl' mə nāt)

(v.) to reach a high point of development; to end, climax

The President's military advisors hoped the overseas action would not _____ **culminate** _____ in disaster.

SYNONYMS: conclude, terminate
ANTONYMS: begin, initiate, kick off, commence

4. downright
(daùn' rīt)

(adv.) thoroughly; *(adj.)* absolute, complete; frank, blunt

Our neighbor, who chopped down our tree and destroyed our fence, is just _____ **downright** _____ mean.

The actor felt like a _____ **downright** _____ fool when he forgot his lines.

SYNONYMS: *(adj.)* total, out-and-out, unqualified

5. drone
(drōn)

(n.) a loafer, idler; a buzzing or humming sound; a remote-control device; a male bee; *(v.)* to make a buzzing sound; to speak in a dull tone of voice

The steady _____ **drone** _____ of the engine put us all to sleep.

The speaker _____ **droned** _____ on and on, ignoring the fact that much of the audience had left.

SYNONYMS: *(n.)* bum, do-nothing; *(v.)* hum, buzz, purr
ANTONYMS: *(n.)* hard worker, workaholic

6. goad
(gōd)

(v.) to drive or urge on; *(n.)* something used to drive or urge on

The sergeant had to _____ **goad** _____ the reluctant soldiers into action.

The cowhand used a **goad** to prod the sluggish cattle.

SYNONYMS: (v.) prod, spur on, incite
ANTONYMS: (v.) curb, check, restrain

7. indulge
(in dəlj′)

(v.) to give in to a wish or desire, give oneself up to

Sometimes the members of a losing team will **indulge** in self-pity.

SYNONYMS: oblige, humor, coddle, pamper
ANTONYMS: deny, refuse

8. ingredient
(in grē′ dē ənt)

(n.) one of the materials in a mixture, recipe, or formula

Before adding the **ingredient** to the mixture, I first had to put it through a food processor.

SYNONYMS: element, component, constituent, factor

9. literate
(lit′ ə rət)

(adj.) able to read and write; showing an excellent educational background; having knowledge or training

Compared with others in the colonial settlement, she was a highly **literate** young woman.

SYNONYMS: educated, trained
ANTONYMS: unlettered, unschooled, ignorant

10. loom
(lüm)

(v.) to come into view; to appear in exaggerated form; (n.) a machine for weaving

The climbers were awestruck to see the peak **loom** up before them.

The antique **loom**, once used to make cloth, was on display in the crafts museum.

SYNONYMS: (v.) emerge, surface, hover, tower

11. luster
(ləs′ tər)

(n.) the quality of giving off light, brightness, glitter, brilliance

The polished gold dome atop the state capitol shone with a starry **luster**.

SYNONYMS: gloss, sheen, shine
ANTONYMS: tarnish, dullness

12. miscellaneous
(mis ə lā′ nē əs)

(adj.) mixed, of different kinds

A collection of **miscellaneous** items was gathering dust in the attic.

SYNONYMS: varied, assorted, motley
ANTONYMS: identical, uniform, homogeneous

13. oration
(ô rā′ shən)

(n.) a public speech for a formal occasion

Cicero's **orations** in the Roman Senate are still studied by speakers today.

SYNONYMS: address, harangue

14. peevish
(pē′ vish)

(adj.) cross, complaining, irritable; contrary

Although the members of the tour group were usually in good humor, hunger made them _____ **peevish** _____ .

SYNONYMS: crabby, cranky, testy, stubborn
ANTONYMS: agreeable, amiable, even-tempered, pleasant

15. seethe
(sēth)

(v.) to boil or foam; to be excited or disturbed

Mother would _____ **seethe** _____ with rage each time she learned that a dog had been mistreated.

SYNONYMS: churn, simmer, stew

16. singe
(sinj)

(v.) to burn slightly; *(n.)* a burn at the ends or edges

Getting too close to the flame of the campfire caused the camper to _____ **singe** _____ his eyelashes.
A _____ **singe** _____ from a cigar ash had destroyed the last word in the document.

SYNONYMS: *(v.)* scorch, char, sear
ANTONYMS: *(v.)* incinerate

17. unique
(yü nēk′)

(adj.) one of a kind; unequaled; unusual; found only in a given class, place, or situation

Most people would agree that finding an elephant in one's bathtub would constitute a _____ **unique** _____ situation.

SYNONYMS: unparalleled, distinctive, singular
ANTONYMS: ordinary, commonplace, run-of-the-mill

18. upright
(əp′ rīt)

(adj.) vertical, straight; good, honest; *(adv.)* in a vertical position

The senator showed her _____ **upright** _____ character by voting for bills she believed to be morally right.
The patient was finally standing _____ **upright** _____ .

SYNONYMS: *(adj.)* perpendicular, virtuous
ANTONYMS: *(adj.)* horizontal, prone, dishonest, corrupt

19. verify
(ver′ ə fī)

(v.) to establish the truth or accuracy of, confirm

The reporter hurried to _____ **verify** _____ the source of the controversial statement.

SYNONYMS: prove, validate, substantiate
ANTONYMS: disprove, refute, discredit

20. yearn
(yərn)

(v.) to have a strong and earnest desire

Who wouldn't _____ **yearn** _____ to see old friends again?

SYNONYMS: crave, long for, want

Completing the Sentence

From the words for this unit, choose the one that best completes each of the following sentences. Write the word in the space provided.

1. The resentment of the American colonists against the harsh policies of the British government _____ **culminated** _____ in armed rebellion.

2. The Fourth of July _____ **oration** _____ will be delivered in City Square by the mayor.

3. Only one half of the population of that underdeveloped nation is _____ **literate** _____ .

4. The dull conversation became much more _____ **animated** _____ when it turned to a subject in which we were all interested.

5. The sunlight shining on her beautiful, copper-colored hair gave it an almost metallic _____ **luster** _____ .

6. The man was the prime suspect in the crime until two eyewitnesses came forward to _____ **verify** _____ his alibi.

7. Those books which do not fit logically under any of the subjects indicated will be placed in a group labeled "_____ **miscellaneous** _____ ."

8. When storm clouds _____ **loomed** _____ on the horizon, we hurried to find shelter.

9. We put supports around the tree that had been partially uprooted by the storm, and it was soon standing _____ **upright** _____ again.

10. Like some storm-tossed sea, her inventive brain _____ **seethes *or* seethed** _____ with all kinds of new and imaginative answers to old problems and questions.

11. Like the traffic guard at a school crossing, the mother hen directed her large _____ **brood** _____ across the yard toward a torn sack of feed.

12. Indian elephant keepers usually use a short wooden _____ **goad** _____ to control and direct the movements of their huge charges.

13. The first mark of a good cook is the ability to choose the best possible _____ **ingredients** _____ for the dishes he or she will prepare.

14. When I saw how handsome my father looked in his brand-new jacket, I _____ **yearned** _____ for one exactly like it.

15. I don't know which is worse—parents who are too strict with their children or parents who _____ **indulge** _____ them too much.

16. I believe in being careful, but Dan is _____ **downright** _____ miserly when it comes to spending money.

17. I'm normally fairly even-tempered, but I can become _____ **peevish** _____ and irritable when I'm tired or frustrated.

18. Larry has the _____unique_____ distinction of being the only student in our school ever to win varsity letters in four sports.

19. "You're just supposed to _____singe_____ the meat," I shouted at him in dismay, "not burn it to a crisp!"

20. How pleasant it is for us city dwellers to smell the new-mown hay and listen to the _____drone_____ of bees in the clover patch!

 **Synonyms**

*Choose the word from this unit that is **the same** or **most nearly the same** in meaning as the **boldface** word or expression in the given phrase. Write the word on the line provided.*

1. is the key **element** in the stew _____ingredient_____

2. despite the danger that seemed to **appear** ahead _____loom_____

3. started to **sear** the fringe of the tablecloth _____singe_____

4. found a mile-high **assorted** collection of magazines _____miscellaneous_____

5. will **pamper** her willful son _____indulge_____

6. **trained** in that computer language _____literate_____

7. was a **total** disaster from any perspective _____downright_____

8. had a **singular** opportunity to excel _____unique_____

9. caused the player's stomach to **churn** with excitement _____seethe_____

10. gave a wonderful **address** worthy of a standing ovation _____oration_____

11. began to **agonize** over her loss _____brood_____

12. became **crabby** when chores were assigned _____peevish_____

13. would **desire** to be in Paris in the spring _____yearn_____

14. lost some of its **brilliance** with each performance _____luster_____

15. attempted to **incite** the others into acting _____goad_____

 **Antonyms**

*Choose the word from this unit that is **most nearly opposite** in meaning to the **boldface** word or expression in the given phrase. Write the word on the line provided.*

16. would **begin** in his being elected senator _____culminate_____

17. had a deserved reputation as a **workaholic** _____drone_____

18. overheard a very **dull** discussion _____animated_____

19. unable to **refute** her story _____verify_____

20. was on stage in an almost **horizontal** position _____upright_____

1. Probably no (**oration,** luster) in American history is so well known and loved as Lincoln's address on the battlefield of Gettysburg.

2. In his many years in Congress, he has been (**animated,** culminated) mainly by a strong desire to help the underdogs in our society.

3. Though the colonies long (**seethed,** singed) with resentment at the British, the cauldron of their discontent did not boil over into rebellion until 1776.

4. Modern scientists often try to (loom, **verify**) their ideas and theories by conducting extensive experiments in their laboratories.

5. The last thing I heard before falling asleep was the (goad, **drone**) of their voices as they continued their endless discussion of politics.

6. Each year the professional football season (**culminates,** broods) in the Super Bowl.

7. An important (ingredient, **oration**) of what is commonly called luck is the willingness to take chances when an opportunity appears.

8. Even those who do not like New York must admit that it is a truly (**unique,** literate) city, quite unlike any other in the world.

9. The man was not just "a little careless" in handling the club's funds; he was (**downright,** upright) dishonest!

10. Instead of (droning, **brooding**) about the misfortunes that have befallen you, why don't you go out and do something to correct the situation?

11. It's all right for us to disagree, but let's argue about the facts only, without (**indulging,** yearning) in name-calling.

12. I have my doubts about people who spend too much time telling the world how noble and (**upright,** downright) they are.

13. This magazine is published not for a mass circulation but for a very small audience of highly (peevish, **literate**) people.

14. The (**luster,** loom) of her reputation as a friend of humanity has grown brighter with the years.

15. "If you choose to play with fire," I warned them, "you run the risk of (animating, **singeing**) your fingers."

16. Glenn has such a store of (**miscellaneous,** upright) information in his head that we have nicknamed him "The Encyclopedia"!

17. The American people must take action right now to deal with the problem of pollution that (**looms,** seethes) so large on our horizons.

18. Neither threats nor force will (indulge, **goad**) me into doing something that in my heart I know is wrong.

19. You may make friends very easily, but if you continue to be so (**peevish,** upright), you aren't going to keep them for long.

20. By Friday afternoon, all of us were (indulging, **yearning**) for the weekend.

Vocabulary in Context

*Read the following passage, in which some of the words you have studied in this unit appear in **boldface** type. Then complete each statement given below the passage by circling the letter of the item that is **the same** or **almost the same** in meaning as the highlighted word.*

The Art of Speaking Out

(Line)

In the period between the American Revolution and the Civil War, Americans—**literate** and unschooled alike—were fascinated with public speaking. People from all walks of life eagerly attended debates and lectures on the political and social issues of the day. Great speakers like Daniel Webster and Edward Everett
(5) engaged the passions of enthusiastic audiences, captivating listeners with their rhythmic and repetitive speech patterns.

The style of **oration** during that era was both personal and interactive. Prominent minister Henry Ward Beecher ignored his notes and spoke from the heart, as did the
(10) suffragist Lucretia Mott. Henry Clay stood close to his audience, while the abolitionist William Lloyd Garrison encouraged audience involvement.

The best-known debates of the period
(15) were probably the seven **animated** encounters between Abraham Lincoln and Stephen A. Douglas. At the time, Lincoln was not known outside of Illinois, while Douglas was a national political figure.
(20) Their debates drew thousands of listeners, who regularly interrupted the speakers with cheers, groans, and questions. Such

Lincoln speaking at a Lincoln-Douglas debate

audience participation proved to be a key **ingredient** of the debates, as reporters recorded everything said, including audience reactions and remarks.
(25) In the fashion of the time, the Lincoln-Douglas debates followed a preset format. One man spoke first, for an hour, attacking his opponent, who often **seethed** with anger while awaiting his turn. The second responded for an hour and a half, both defending himself and returning the fire. Then the first spoke again for another hour. The audience hung on every word as the two speakers applied their best
(30) arguments, for the stakes were enormous—no less than the future of slavery in the United States and the preservation of the Union.

---

1. The meaning of **literate** (line 2) is
  a. ignorant
  (c.) educated
  b. unlettered
  d. messy

2. Oration (line 7) is best defined as
  a. eating
  c. celebration
  b. listening
  (d.) speech

3. Animated (line 15) most nearly means
  (a.) lively
  c. zoological
  b. dull
  d. lifeless

4. The meaning of **ingredient** (line 23) is
  a. spice
  c. mixture
  (b.) component
  d. addition

5. Seethed (line 26) most nearly means
  a. warmed
  c. twitched
  (b.) boiled
  d. worried

Vocabulary for Comprehension

*Read the following passage, in which some of the words you have studied in Units 1–3 appear in **boldface** type. Then answer questions 1–12 on page 43 on the basis of what is <u>stated</u> or <u>implied</u> in the passage and in the introductory statement.*

The following passage discusses the llama, an amazing and extremely useful animal.

(Line)

For thousands of years, the llama has been a working animal. In fact, in the **barren**, rugged highlands of Peru, this **unique** animal has for
(5) centuries proved to be a reliable beast of burden, carrying heavy packs to lowland markets. Then, about one hundred years ago, the llama was brought to the United
(10) States. In this country, however, the llama has added to its **résumé** by gaining some unusual work experience, so strange in fact that here its "odd job" has all but
(15) replaced its **customary** use as a pack animal.

Because of its tendency to work hard, eat cheaply, go many miles without water, and get along well with
(20) people and other animals, the llama has proved to be a match for many other working animals. Yet it is not just in **trivial** matters, such as carrying golf bags (although llamas
(25) do serve as caddies) or in maintaining hiking trails (they do work for the National Park Service), that llamas have distinguished themselves in this country. In fact, in
(30) the United States the llama's true calling seems to be in "predator protection," acting as a kind of fantastic "sheepdog."

Interestingly, llamas make good
(35) "guard dogs" for the following reasons: They are quick studies, learning in a few days what it might take a dog a year to master. Also, llamas and sheep get along famously.
(40) Most important, llamas have a natural distaste for coyotes, the sheep's main predator, and they don't get frazzled in the face of danger. When brazen predators approach the herd,
(45) llamas aggressively chase away the intruders.

So serious is this problem that in the United States **vicious** predators have killed hundreds of millions of
(50) dollars worth of sheep in the past few years. Although efforts have been under way to destroy the coyotes, the thinking now is to focus on protecting the sheep. It would seem that the
(55) best way to do that is to "hire" a llama. In fact, when interviewed in an Iowa study, half the llama-owning sheep farmers reported sheep losses down to zero since getting a llama,
(60) which just goes to show that there's nothing like having a good guard dog, especially when it's a llama.

1. The main purpose of the passage is to
  a. persuade the reader of the benefits of raising llamas
  b. explain the difference between llamas and sheepdogs
  c. describe a typical day in the life of a llama
  d. describe the physical characteristics of a llama
  e. inform the reader about a nontraditional use of llamas

2. The meaning of **barren** (line 3) is
  a. fertile
  b. arid
  c. lush
  d. productive
  e. boring

3. Unique (line 4) most nearly means
  a. docile
  b. aggressive
  c. commonplace
  d. singular
  e. friendly

4. Résumé (line 11) is best defined as
  a. job history
  b. qualifications
  c. experience
  d. story
  e. regime

5. Customary (line 15) most nearly means
  a. untraditional
  b. legal
  c. reliable
  d. eccentric
  e. traditional

6. Trivial (line 23) is best defined as
  a. entertaining
  b. exceptional
  c. profitable
  d. important
  e. trifling

7. From the first two paragraphs (lines 1–33), you can infer that in most of the world, a llama's usual work is
  a. to carry golf bags
  b. to carry heavy burdens

  c. to maintain hiking trails
  d. to climb mountains
  e. to protect sheep

8. From the first sentence (lines 34–38) in paragraph 3, you know that this paragraph contains several
  a. explanations
  b. descriptions
  c. reasons
  d. comparisons
  e. contrasts

9. The meaning of **vicious** (line 48) is
  a. natural
  b. hungry
  c. savage
  d. dangerous
  e. rabid

10. The author refers to an Iowa study of sheep farmers (lines 56–62) in order to support the preceding sentence with
  a. a statistic
  b. an anecdote
  c. a theory
  d. an explanation
  e. a description

11. The tone of this passage can best be described as
  a. informal
  b. philosophical
  c. biased
  d. frivolous
  e. ironic

12. Which of the following generalizations is the author likely to agree with?
  a. Government efforts to destroy coyotes have proved useless.
  b. Coyotes and sheep are part of a natural plan and need no intervention.
  c. Coyotes are an endangered species and should be protected.
  d. Llamas protect sheep more efficiently than sheepdogs.
  e. Sheepdogs are the most experienced and best protectors of sheep.

Grammar in Context

There is nothing wrong with these two sentences: "They are quick studies, learning in a few days what it takes a dog a year to master. Also, llamas and sheep get along famously" (lines 36–39 on page 42). But suppose that the author had written the same ideas this way: "They are quick studies, learning in a few days what it might take a dog a year to master, also, llamas and sheep get along famously." It would not work because the group of words is now a run-on sentence.

A **sentence** is a group of words that expresses a complete thought. It has two main parts: a complete subject (a noun or pronoun plus any modifiers) and a complete predicate (a verb or verb phrase plus any modifiers). When you write, be sure to write complete sentences.

A **run-on sentence** is really two or more sentences masquerading as a single sentence. This error is due to incorrect punctuation. To avoid run-ons, there are four things you can do: (1) Use capitalization and punctuation to separate the sentence into two short sentences. (2) Use a conjunction preceded by a comma. (3) Insert a semicolon or a semicolon with a transitional word or phrase followed by a comma. (4) Use a subordinating conjunction to make one of the two sentences a subordinate clause.

On the lines provided, rewrite each of the groups of words to eliminate the run-ons and fragments. Write "correct" if the sentence is correct.

Answers may vary; sample answers given.

1. Used llamas to carry heavy packs.
   People have long used llamas to carry heavy packs.

2. When you compare the sheep-protection skills of llamas and dogs.
   When you compare the sheep-protection skills of llamas and dogs, you see that llamas do it better.

3. Llamas are easygoing, hard workers, they get along with people and other animals, too.
   Llamas are easygoing, hard workers. They get along with people and other animals, too.

4. Because they are unafraid of coyotes, llamas can become quite fierce in their presence.
   correct

5. I used a caddy when I played golf with my friend Ernesto, he used a llama to carry his bags.
   I used a caddy when I played golf with my friend Ernesto, but he used a llama to carry his bags.

6. The only thing for which dogs are better suited than llamas.
   Barking is the only thing for which dogs are better suited than llamas.

Two-Word Completions

Circle the pair of words that best complete the meaning of each of the following passages.

See pages T38–T48 for explanations of answers.

1. When I was very young, I truly _____ a life of excitement, adventure, and danger. But now that I'm a good deal older, I'm perfectly content with my rather _____ existence.
a. brooded about . . . interminable
b. yearned for . . . humdrum
c. alighted on . . . trivial
d. indulged in . . . hazardous

2. At one point in last night's hockey game, home-team fans became so angry with the referee that they began to _____ him with refuse. Programs, paper cups, and even a dead fish _____ through the air and landed at his feet.
a. pelt . . . hurtled
b. disrupt . . . droned
c. indulge . . . loomed
d. singe . . . trickled

3. Running our country is full of all kinds of hidden _____ and traps for the unwary. For that reason, no President, no matter how alert or cautious he may be, ever leaves office entirely _____ by the experience.
a. regimes . . . lubricated
b. firebrands . . . poised
c. ingredients . . . animated
d. hazards . . . unscathed

4. When the new _____ took office, its first order of business was to pacify the country by arranging a _____ with the rebel forces that had been waging all-out war against the previous administration.
a. dynasty . . . plague
b. drone . . . homicide
c. firebrand . . . loom
d. regime . . . truce

5. Though crabmeat is one of the _____ mentioned in the classic recipe for a New Orleans fish stew, it isn't always "in season." Accordingly, professional chefs often replace it with whatever shellfish is _____ at the time without any noticeable damage to the dish.
a. résumés . . . adjacent
b. broods . . . indispensable
c. ingredients . . . available
d. orations . . . customary

6. Strong winds fanned the flames, and the fire in the factory quickly spread to _____ buildings. Though the firefighters worked very hard to _____ its progress, the blaze soon engulfed the entire block.
a. available . . . goad
b. adjacent . . . retard
c. miscellaneous . . . animate
d. upright . . . germinate

Choosing the Right Meaning

Read each sentence carefully. Then circle the item that best completes the statement below the sentence.

See pages T38–T48 for explanations of answers.

At the height of the Cuban missile crisis, in October 1962, the world seemed poised on the brink of full-scale nuclear war. (2)

1. The word **poised** in line 1 is best defined as

a. calm   (b. suspended)   c. controlled   d. collected

The boss's downright manner does not sit well with some; but I, for one, find his frankness downright refreshing. (2)

2. In line 1 the word **downright** is used to mean

(a. blunt)   b. absolute   c. complete   d. unqualified

Although the vicious headaches called *migraines* have been known to medicine for centuries, their cause is still unknown. (2)

3. The word **vicious** in line 1 most nearly means

a. spiteful   b. malicious   c. evil   (d. severe)

The fact that many species, including the kangaroo and platypus, are unique to Australia is due to its isolation from other continents. (2)

4. In line 1 the phrase **unique to** most nearly means

a. unparalleled in   b unequaled in   (c. found only in)   d. distinctive in

Though in looks the twins cannot be told apart, in temperament they could not be more different—one as meek as a lamb, the other as peevish as a mule. (2)

5. In line 2 the word **peevish** is used to mean

(a. obstinate)   b. irritable   c. complaining   d. cross

Antonyms

*In each of the following groups, circle the word or expression that is most nearly the **opposite** of the word in **boldface** type.*

1. adjacent
a. nearby
b. well-lit
(c. remote)
d. stuffy

2. transparent
(a. muddy)
b. clear
c. drinkable
d. dangerous

3. miscellaneous
a. valuable
(b. similar)
c. colorful
d. used

4. verify
a. read
b. confirm
(c. disprove)
d. type

5. indignant
(a. delighted)
b. long
c. offended
d. sleepy

6. trivial
a. new
b. puzzling
(c. important)
d. minor

7. animated
a. lively
(b. dull)
c. well-informed
d. unpleasant

8. culminated
a. displaced
(b. began)
c. announced
d. ended

9. unique
(a. commonplace)
b. matchless
c. modern
d. popular

11. vicious
a. bitter
b. inaccurate
c. nasty
(d. kind)

13. retard
a. hold back
(b. speed up)
c. account for
d. observe

15. interminable
a. pleasant
b. unimportant
c. difficult
(d. brief)

10. peevish
a. irritable
(b. agreeable)
c. snobbish
d. puzzling

12. luster
a. value
(b. dullness)
c. appeal
d. glow

14. sullen
a. strange
b. ugly
c. thoughtful
(d. sociable)

16. disrupt
a. upset
b. dismount
(c. organize)
d. disorder

Word Families

A. *On the line provided, write the word you have learned in Units 1–3 that is related to each of the following nouns.*
EXAMPLE: culmination—**culminate**

1. catering, caterer — cater
2. trivia, triviality — trivial
3. yearning, yearner — yearn
4. uniqueness — unique
5. viciousness, vice — vicious
6. lubricant, lubricator, lubrication — lubricate
7. transparentness, transparency — transparent
8. verification, verifier, verifiableness, verifiability — verify
9. custom, customariness — customary
10. insinuation, insinuator — insinuate
11. renovation, renovator — renovate
12. indignation — indignant
13. literacy, literati, literature — literate
14. indulgence, indulger — indulge
15. germination, germinability, germ — germinate

B. *On the line provided, write the word you have learned in Units 1–3 that is related to each of the following verbs.*
EXAMPLE: interrogate—**interrogation**

16. avail — available
17. animate — animated
18. dispense — indispensable
19. poise — poised
20. orate — oration

Word Associations

In each of the following groups, circle the word that is best defined or suggested by the given phrase.

1. to discourage from doing something
a. disrupt   b. germinate   c. recompense   (d. dissuade)

2. a basic element in a recipe
a. drone   b. foretaste   (c. ingredient)   d. indifference

3. a totally desolate wasteland
a. unique   (b. barren)   c. sullen   d. transparent

4. to bombard with snowballs
a. retard   b. goad   (c. pelt)   d. alight

5. to drive someone into a rage
(a. goad)   b. indulge   c. hurtle   d. plague

6. charged with the crime of murder
a. indifference   (b. homicide)   c. hazard   d. regime

7. to restore the building to its original condition
a. disrupt   (b. renovate)   c. culminate   d. cater

8. one who assumes the risk of a business
a. regime   b. dynasty   (c. entrepreneur)   d. firebrand

9. to burn one's eyebrows slightly
a. pelt   b. alight   c. seethe   (d. singe)

10. a routine procedure
a. indispensable   (b. customary)   c. available   d. mutual

11. tasks that are monotonous and dull
a. indignant   b. sullen   c. barren   (d. humdrum)

12. to declare a binding cease-fire
a. foretaste   b. firebrand   (c. truce)   d. oration

13. to worry over a loss or an illness
a. insinuate   (b. brood)   c. germinate   d. indulge

14. essential equipment
a. interminable   (b. indispensable)   c. trivial   d. customary

15. the honest citizens of the community
(a. upright)   b. downright   c. animated   d. literate

16. hurt by their unconcern
a. homicide   b. regime   c. hazard   (d. indifference)

17. to grease the axle of a car
a. retard   b. indulge   c. seethe   (d. lubricate)

18. to question a witness thoroughly
(a. interrogate)   b. insinuate   c. verify   d. yearn

19. to dismount from a horse
a. disrupt   (b. alight)   c. hurtle   d. dissuade

20. a sample of what is to come
(a. foretaste)   b. brood   c. dynasty   d. loom

pend, pens—to hang, weigh; to pay; to set aside

Building with Classical Roots

This root appears in **indispensable** (page 29), literally "not able to be set aside or done away with." The word now has the meaning "essential or necessary." Some other words based on the same root are listed below.

dependent	dispense	expenditure	perpendicular
dispensary	expendable	pension	suspense

From the list of words above, choose the one that corresponds to each of the brief definitions below. Write the word in the blank space in the illustrative sentence below the definition.

1. relying on another for help or support; determined or conditioned by something else; a person who is supported by another

A lion cub is _____**dependent**_____ on its mother for nourishment and protection.

2. to give out, distribute

It is a judge's duty to _____**dispense**_____ justice with an even hand.

3. replaceable, nonessential

It is difficult for some employees to realize that they are _____**expendable**_____ and can be let go at any time.

4. at right angles; exactly upright, vertical

The wall is _____**perpendicular**_____ to the floor.

5. the state of being uncertain or undecided; anxiety, nervous uncertainty

The audience was kept in _____**suspense**_____ until the winner was announced.

6. the amount of money spent; spending, using up (*"paying out"*)

Worrying is a needless _____**expenditure**_____ of energy.

7. a place where medicines are made or given out (*"place from which things are weighed out"*)

The nurse obtained the medicine she needed in the hospital _____**dispensary**_____.

8. a fixed amount paid to retired employees or their families

At age 65 he will receive a small _____**pension**_____ from his company.

From the list of words above, choose the one that best completes each of the following sentences. Write the word in the blank space provided.

1. Rescue workers set up a makeshift _____**dispensary**_____, where medical supplies were provided to the survivors of the disaster.

2. As the value of the dollar shrinks, my grandmother finds it harder and harder to live on the small _____**pension**_____ she receives from the government.

3. A section of the bookstore in my neighborhood is devoted to novels of mystery and _____**suspense**_____ .

4. Because drugs can be dangerous, only trained pharmacists are licensed to _____**dispense**_____ prescription medicines.

5. This tremendous project will represent an enormous _____**expenditure**_____ of public money.

6. "Unlike human beings," said the captain, "supplies and equipment are _____**expendable**_____, since they can be replaced."

7. Whether or not we have our picnic tomorrow is _____**dependent**_____ on the weather.

8. In italic type the letters are slanted to the right, but in roman type they are _____**perpendicular**_____ .

---

*Circle the **boldface** word that more satisfactorily completes each of the following sentences.*

1. Last year, our school's (**expenditure**, dispensary) on software was five times greater than it was the year before.

2. A retiree's (dependent, **pension**) may not provide enough money to cover all living expenses.

3. Certain fish are (perpendicular, **dependent**) on the sea anemone for protection.

4. As automation becomes widespread, unskilled laborers become (**expendable,** expenditure).

5. You can have this prescription filled at the (pension, **dispensary**) in the clinic.

6. The traffic light should be (**perpendicular,** expendable) to the sidewalk.

7. Many doctors (**dispense,** suspense) both good advice and expert medical care.

8. Theatergoers were kept in (dispensary, **suspense**) by the well-constructed plot of the thrilling play.

Definitions

Note carefully the spelling, pronunciation, part(s) of speech, and definition(s) of each of the following words. Then write the word in the blank space(s) in the illustrative sentence(s) following. Finally, study the lists of synonyms and antonyms given at the end of each entry.

1. alliance
(ə lī′ əns)

(*n.*) a joining together for some common purpose

The two nations formed an _____**alliance**_____ to defend each other in case of attack.

SYNONYMS: pact, league, coalition
ANTONYMS: rift, split

2. bewilder
(bi wil′ dər)

(*v.*) to puzzle completely, confuse

The captain continues to _____**bewilder**_____ his troops by giving contradictory orders.

SYNONYMS: baffle, perplex
ANTONYMS: set straight, enlighten

3. buffoon
(bə fün′)

(*n.*) a clown; a coarse, stupid person

Some students think that they need to play the _____**buffoon**_____ in order to entertain their classmates.

SYNONYMS: jester, fool

4. controversial
(kän trə vər′ shəl)

(*adj.*) arousing argument, dispute, or disagreement

The school board waited until all members were present before issuing the _____**controversial**_____ proposal to ban after-school programs.

SYNONYMS: arguable, debatable

5. dishearten
(dis härt′ ən)

(*v.*) to discourage

Do not let your low score on the math test _____**dishearten**_____ you.

SYNONYMS: dismay, demoralize, dispirit
ANTONYMS: encourage, hearten

6. fruitless
(früt′ ləs)

(*adj.*) not producing the desired results, unsuccessful

When their efforts to fight the infection with penicillin proved _____**fruitless**_____, the doctors tried a different antibiotic.

SYNONYMS: useless, vain, unproductive, futile
ANTONYMS: productive, effective

7. hostile
(häs′ təl)

(*adj.*) unfriendly; unfavorable; warlike, aggressive

Relations between the two nations have been _____ **hostile** _____ for decades.

ANTONYMS: friendly, cordial, peaceful

8. inflammable
(in flam′ ə bəl)

(*adj.*) easily set on fire; easily angered or aroused

Always be cautious when using _____ **inflammable** _____ cleaning solvents.

SYNONYMS: combustible, flammable, excitable
ANTONYMS: fireproof, fire-resistant, calm

9. inflict
(in flikt′)

(*v.*) to give or cause something unpleasant, impose

Despite all the jokes, doctors do not like to _____ **inflict** _____ pain on their patients.

SYNONYMS: deal out, visit upon
ANTONYMS: suffer, undergo, sustain

10. malignant
(mə lig′ nənt)

(*adj.*) deadly, extremely harmful, evil; spiteful, malicious

Much to the patient's relief, the X ray revealed no _____ **malignant** _____ growth.

SYNONYMS: lethal, wicked
ANTONYMS: wholesome, beneficial, benign

11. mortify
(môrt′ ə fī)

(*v.*) to hurt someone's feelings deeply; to cause embarrassment or humiliation; to subdue or discipline by self-denial or suffering

The teacher was _____ **mortified** _____ by the students' childish behavior on the field trip.

SYNONYMS: humiliate, embarrass, abash

12. orthodox
(ôr′ thə däks)

(*adj.*) in agreement with established or generally accepted beliefs or ways of doing things

Our principal, who believes in proven teaching methods, takes an _____ **orthodox** _____ approach to education.

SYNONYMS: traditional, standard, customary
ANTONYMS: unusual, unconventional, heretical

13. procure
(prə kyür′)

(*v.*) to obtain through special effort; to bring about

The hospital held a raffle to _____ **procure** _____ the necessary funds for the new children's wing.

SYNONYMS: gain, acquire, achieve

14. scurry
(skər′ ē)

(*v.*) to run quickly, scamper, hurry

The reappearance of the teacher caused the students in the class to _____ **scurry** _____ back to their seats.

SYNONYMS: rush, dash, scramble
ANTONYMS: trudge, plod, creep, crawl

15. sodden
(säd' ən)

(*adj.*) soaked with liquid or moisture; expressionless, dull; spiritless, listless

All at once, and with much loud honking, the flock of geese rose from the _____ **sodden** _____ marshlands.

SYNONYMS: drenched, waterlogged, saturated
ANTONYMS: parched, arid

16. spirited
(spir' ə tid)

(*adj.*) full of life and vigor; courageous

The royal soldiers put up a _____ **spirited** _____ defense against the invading army.

SYNONYMS: lively, animated, gallant
ANTONYMS: lifeless, dull, lackluster

17. virtual
(vər' chü əl)

(*adj.*) having a certain force or effect in fact but not in name; so close as to be equivalent to the real thing

To those who worked in the office, the bossy new manager was a _____ **virtual** _____ dictator.

SYNONYMS: functioning as, equivalent to

18. void
(void)

(*adj.*) completely empty; having no legal force or effect; (*n.*) empty or unfilled space; (*v.*) to cancel or nullify

I thought that poem was completely _____ **void** _____ of sense.

Grandmother's death left a great _____ **void** _____ in my grandfather's life.

Do you know how to _____ **void** _____ a check?

SYNONYMS: (*adj.*) invalid, vacant, bare
ANTONYMS: (*adj.*) in effect, teeming with; (*v.*) confirm

19. wayward
(wā' wərd)

(*adj.*) disobedient, willful; unpredictable, capricious

Tracking the _____ **wayward** _____ path of a comet is no easy matter.

SYNONYM: perverse
ANTONYMS: docile, well-behaved, predictable

20. wince
(wins)

(*v.*) to draw back suddenly, as though in pain or fear; (*n.*) the act of drawing back in this way

The dog's bite made the child _____ **wince** _____ in pain.

The patient's _____ **wince** _____ told the doctor to press more gently.

SYNONYMS: (*v.*) flinch, shudder, recoil

Completing the Sentence

From the words for this unit, choose the one that best completes each of the following sentences. Write the word in the space provided.

1. The frozen wastes of the Arctic may seem _____ **hostile** _____ to human life, but in fact thousands of people are able to survive there.

2. After four days of steady rainfall, the _____ **sodden** _____ ground actually gurgled as we trudged wearily over it.

3. Before we set out on the camping trip, I was given sole responsibility for _____ **procuring** _____ all the necessary equipment and supplies.

4. Would it be a bad pun if I were to say that our attempts to set up an apple orchard have proved to be _____ **fruitless** _____?

5. In 1949, the United States formed a(n) _____ **alliance** _____ with eleven other nations, organized into the North Atlantic Treaty Organization.

6. When the Supreme Court finds a law unconstitutional, that law is said to be null and _____ **void** _____.

7. Some parts of the President's proposal were agreeable to everyone; others proved highly _____ **controversial** _____.

8. We _____ **inflicted** _____ such heavy casualties on the enemy that they were forced to break off the engagement and retreat.

9. Though the gallant defenders of the fort were hopelessly outnumbered, they put up a truly _____ **spirited** _____ fight.

10. Their behavior is so _____ **wayward** _____ and unpredictable that I never know what they are going to do next.

11. Since the gas did not burn when we brought a flame to it, the experiment showed that carbon dioxide is not _____ **inflammable** _____.

12. The directions he gave us for driving to the beach were so complicated that I was completely _____ **bewildered** _____ by them.

13. Even though you like to do things in your own way, I suggest that you first learn the _____ **orthodox** _____ method of batting.

14. Despite the fact that she has no official title of any kind, she has become the _____ **virtual** _____ director of the company.

15. Even though I'm an adult, I still _____ **wince** _____ in discomfort at the thought of a trip to the dentist.

16. I was thoroughly _____ **mortified** _____ when I suddenly stumbled and spilled punch all over the host's tuxedo.

17. If it is allowed to spread unchecked, the poison of racial prejudice will have a decidedly _____ **malignant** _____ effect on our community.

18. When the naughty children heard their mother's footsteps approaching, they quickly _____**scurried**_____ back to bed.

19. The court of many a medieval king or prince was enlivened by the pranks and antics of jesters and other _____**buffoons**_____ .

20. Refusing to be _____**disheartened**_____ by her early failures to find a summer job, Lucy made up her mind to try again.

Synonyms

Choose the word from this unit that is **the same** or **most nearly the same** in meaning as the **boldface** word or expression in the given phrase. Write the word on the line provided.

1. to **recoil** at the idea of getting up so early _____wince_____

2. showed a **perverse** unwillingness to study _____wayward_____

3. made a **futile** effort to defeat the enemy _____fruitless_____

4. persuaded the partners to **cancel** the contract _____void_____

5. **baffle** friends with their odd reaction _____bewilder_____

6. sank into the grass **drenched** with rain _____sodden_____

7. would **humiliate** her parents with her crude behavior _____mortify_____

8. used a highly **combustible** cleaning fluid _____inflammable_____

9. did not become **discouraged** by the lack of money needed _____disheartened_____

10. was **equivalent to** freedom to the inmates _____virtual_____

11. was suffering from a **deadly** brain tumor _____malignant_____

12. formed a strong **coalition** with that political party _____alliance_____

13. tries to **acquire** the freshest produce _____procure_____

14. acts like a **clown** in front of his friends _____buffoon_____

15. made the **debatable** call that ended the game _____controversial_____

Antonyms

Choose the word from this unit that is **most nearly opposite** in meaning to the **boldface** word or expression in the given phrase. Write the word on the line provided.

16. would **trudge** up the hill once a day _____scurry_____

17. gave a **lackluster** performance for the audience _____spirited_____

18. was introduced to the **friendly** crowd _____hostile_____

19. held **unconventional** political beliefs _____orthodox_____

20. to **suffer** serious wounds in battle _____inflict_____

Choosing the Right Word

*Circle the **boldface** word that more satisfactorily completes each of the following sentences.*

1. In high school, students should (**procure,** void) training in basic skills that they will need to qualify for good jobs in later life.

2. The scrappy coach's (**fruitless, spirited**) pep talk lifted the team out of its "losing-season blues" almost overnight.

3. "It's hard not to be a little (**procured, disheartened**) when your favorite team is in the cellar two weeks before the playoffs," I replied.

4. I can understand that you want to be witty and amusing, but take care not to give everyone the impression that you're a mere (**alliance, buffoon**).

5. I could see from the (**inflicted, bewildered**) expression on the child's face that he was quite lost.

6. Because I no longer go to high school, my student bus pass has been (**voided,** disheartened).

7. Instead of being so (**mortified, hostile**), why don't you try to show some friendliness to those newcomers?

8. Our supervisor gives the impression of being an easygoing man, but we have learned that he has a very (**orthodox, inflammable**) temper.

9. A severe cold spell in December (**inflicted,** bewildered) heavy losses on the Florida citrus crop.

10. When his army seemed (**virtually,** soddenly) defeated by the British, George Washington crossed the Delaware and won a major victory.

11. (**Fruitless, Controversial**) political figures are likely to have as many critics as they have supporters.

12. On the hottest night of the entire summer, the sheets on my bed became so (**sodden,** malignant) with perspiration that I had to change them.

13. Though her views about the role of women in society are far from (**hostile, orthodox**), even conservatives and traditionalists listen to them.

14. Walking through the meadow at night, we could hear mice and other small animals (**scurrying,** wincing) about in the grass.

15. "Whenever you find (**wayward,** controversial) children," the speaker said, "you also find ineffective parents."

16. All our efforts to control pollution will be (**fruitless,** inflammable) unless we work out a careful, detailed plan in advance.

17. Being scolded for my shortcomings in front of the entire basketball squad was a truly (**mortifying,** wayward) experience for me.

18. (**Malignant,** Virtual) gossip has unjustly damaged their reputation.

19. I still (scurry, **wince**) when I think of the two bad errors that cost us the championship game.

20. We are going to form a broad (void, **alliance**) among all the groups that are working to improve life in our community.

Vocabulary in Context

*Read the following passage, in which some of the words you have studied in this unit appear in **boldface** type. Then complete each statement given below the passage by circling the letter of the item that is **the same** or **almost the same** in meaning as the highlighted word.*

(Line)

The Lewis and Clark Expedition

In 1803 President Thomas Jefferson sent his friend James Monroe to Paris to try to buy the port of New Orleans in the French-owned Louisiana Territory. Yet when the French response came, it would **bewilder** both men.

(5) Shortly after negotiations had begun, an impatient French official asked Monroe, "How much will you give for the whole of Louisiana?" France needed money for its war with Great Britain. An agreement between France and the United States was soon reached. For just $15 million, about three cents an acre, the United States

(10) would **procure** this huge piece of land.

Once the Louisiana Purchase had been made, Jefferson asked Meriwether Lewis to lead an expedition to explore the territory. The President also hoped that

(15) Lewis would find a safe water route to the Pacific. To ready himself for the journey, Lewis engaged in a **spirited** study of scientific techniques. He also asked his friend William Clark to join him on the trip.

Sacajawea Leading Lewis and Clark by Alfred Russell

(20) On May 14, 1804, Lewis and Clark and a group of 42 men, calling itself the "Corps of Discovery," left from St. Louis.

As the men followed the Missouri River and struggled to cross the Rockies, much happened to **dishearten** them. They suffered from all the hazards associated with crossing a rugged and often **hostile** wilderness. For all their troubles, however, they

(25) never found a fully navigable water route to the Pacific Ocean.

Yet the strenuous journey was far from **fruitless**. After eighteen months, Lewis and Clark reached the Pacific Ocean. Along the way, they had mapped more than 3,000 miles. They had learned about new plants and animals. With the help of Sacajawea, a Shoshone woman, they had met many Native American groups. In

(30) the words of Thomas Jefferson, the Lewis and Clark expedition had shown that the United States was "a rising nation, spread over a wide and fruitful land."

---

1. The meaning of **bewilder** (line 3) is
a. scramble
b. puzzle
c. enlighten
d. flinch

2. Procure (line 10) most nearly means
a. give
b. confirm
c. gain
d. provide

3. Spirited (line 17) is best defined as
a. lively
b. lackluster
c. wicked
d. gallant

4. Dishearten (line 23) most nearly means
a. fool
b. cheer
c. discourage
d. inform

5. The meaning of **hostile** (line 24) is
a. hospitable
b. arguable
c. cordial
d. unfriendly

6. Fruitless (line 26) most nearly means
a. effective
b. unproductive
c. useful
d. productive

Definitions

Note carefully the spelling, pronunciation, part(s) of speech, and definition(s) of each of the following words. Then write the word in the blank space(s) in the illustrative sentence(s) following. Finally, study the lists of synonyms and antonyms given at the end of each entry.

1. anecdote
(an' ek dōt)

(*n.*) a short account of an incident in someone's life

The governor told a humorous ___**anecdote**___ about her first day in office.

SYNONYMS: tale, story, sketch, vignette, yarn

2. consolidate
(kən säl' ə dāt)

(*v.*) to combine, unite; to make solid or firm

The generals agreed to ___**consolidate**___ their forces for the invasion.

SYNONYMS: strengthen, firm up, merge
ANTONYMS: scatter, disperse, dissipate, separate

3. counterfeit
(kaùn' tər fit)

(*n.*) an imitation designed to deceive; (*adj.*) not genuine, fake; (*v.*) to make an illegal copy

The painting was a ___**counterfeit**___ of Gainsborough's *Blue Boy*.

The forger was selling ___**counterfeit**___ postage stamps.

It is a crime to ___**counterfeit**___ money.

SYNONYMS: (*adj.*) false, phony, bogus
ANTONYMS: (*adj.*) genuine, real, authentic

4. docile
(däs' əl)

(*adj.*) easily taught, led, or managed; obedient

She was a ___**docile**___ child, eager to learn and to please.

SYNONYMS: manageable, teachable, pliant
ANTONYMS: unruly, wayward, intractable, disobedient

5. dominate
(däm' ə nāt)

(*v.*) to rule over by strength or power, control; to tower over, command due to height

History shows us that powerful nations tend to ___**dominate**___ weaker ones.

SYNONYMS: control, govern, overlook

6. entreat
(en trēt')

(*v.*) to beg, implore, ask earnestly

The dog's eyes seemed to ___**entreat**___ me for an extra helping of dinner.

SYNONYMS: plead, beseech
ANTONYM: clamor for

7. fallible
(fal′ ə bəl)

(*adj.*) capable of being wrong, mistaken, or inaccurate

The researcher's _____fallible_____ methods led to faulty conclusions.

SYNONYMS: imperfect, errant
ANTONYMS: foolproof, unfailing, flawless

8. fickle
(fik′ əl)

(*adj.*) liable to change very rapidly, erratic; marked by a lack of constancy or steadiness, inconsistent

My aunt's interests change with the weather, showing she is a truly _____fickle_____ person.

SYNONYMS: capricious, inconstant, faithless
ANTONYMS: constant, steady, invariable

9. fugitive
(fyü′ jə tiv)

(*n.*) one who flees or runs away; (*adj.*) fleeting, lasting a very short time; wandering; difficult to grasp

That thief is a _____fugitive_____ from justice, wanted in several states.

The couple had a few _____fugitive_____ moments together before the wife boarded the train.

SYNONYMS: (*n.*) runaway, deserter; (*adj.*) elusive
ANTONYMS: (*adj.*) lasting, enduring, permanent

10. grimy
(grī′ mē)

(*adj.*) very dirty, covered with dirt or soot

The miners emerged from the pits with _____grimy_____ hands and faces.

SYNONYMS: filthy, sooty, soiled, dirt-encrusted
ANTONYMS: spotless, spick-and-span, immaculate

11. iota
(ī ō′ tə)

(*n.*) a very small part or quantity

The employer had not an _____iota_____ of proof, but he blamed the new clerk for the theft anyway.

SYNONYMS: speck, dab, jot, bit, smidgen
ANTONYMS: flood, deluge, avalanche, glut

12. maul
(môl)

(*v.*) to beat or knock about, handle roughly; to mangle; (*n.*) a heavy hammer

The tiger was about to _____maul_____ its victim when the zookeeper intervened.

SYNONYMS: (*v.*) rough up, manhandle, batter

13. potential
(pə ten′ chəl)

(*adj.*) possible, able to happen; (*n.*) something that can develop or become a reality

Hurricanes are a _____potential_____ threat to this area in the late summer and early fall.

They were a football team with _____potential_____.

SYNONYMS: (*n.*) possibility, capability
ANTONYMS: (*adj.*) actual, real, unlikely, impossible

14. radiant
(rā′ dē ənt)

(*adj.*) shining, bright; giving forth light or energy

A model needs to have a _____radiant_____ smile in order to advertise toothpaste.

SYNONYMS: glowing, brilliant, dazzling, resplendent
ANTONYMS: dull, tarnished, lackluster

15. rural
(rür′ əl)

(*adj.*) relating to farm areas and life in the country

They settled in a _____rural_____ community that was miles from the nearest large city.

SYNONYMS: countrified, rustic
ANTONYMS: urban, metropolitan, citified

16. substantial
(səb stan′ shəl)

(*adj.*) large, important; major, significant; prosperous; not imaginary, material

Expecting a _____substantial_____ raise in salary, the employee put a down payment on a new car.

SYNONYMS: considerable, tangible, big
ANTONYMS: minor, insignificant, negligible

17. tactful
(takt′ fəl)

(*adj.*) skilled in handling difficult situations or people, polite

A _____tactful_____ approach is usually the wisest one to take with coworkers.

SYNONYMS: skillful, diplomatic, discreet
ANTONYMS: clumsy, gauche, boorish, indiscreet

18. tamper
(tam′ pər)

(*v.*) to interfere with; to meddle rashly or foolishly with; to handle in a secret and improper way

Please don't _____tamper_____ with our baggage.

SYNONYMS: monkey with, fool with, mess with

19. ultimate
(əl′ tə mət)

(*adj.*) last, final; most important or extreme; eventual; basic, fundamental

California is the _____ultimate_____ destination on our cross-country trip.

SYNONYMS: farthest, furthest, terminal
ANTONYMS: first, initial, most immediate, nearest

20. uncertainty
(ən sər′ tən tē)

(*n.*) doubt, the state of being unsure

It was the _____uncertainty_____ about the future that was of the greatest concern to the immigrants.

SYNONYMS: doubtfulness, unsureness, hesitation
ANTONYMS: sureness, certainty, confidence

Completing the Sentence

From the words for this unit, choose the one that best completes each of the following sentences. Write the word in the space provided.

1. The new book of presidential _____**anecdotes**_____ contains many amusing stories involving our Chief Executives, both past and present.

2. Though the UN has many lesser objectives, its _____**ultimate**_____ goal is to achieve lasting world peace.

3. The wily old senator had such a forceful and aggressive personality that he soon came to _____**dominate**_____ his entire party.

4. Since I had expected the children to be hard to handle, I was pleasantly surprised by their _____**docile**_____ behavior.

5. To be _____**tactful**_____ in everyday life means doing whatever you can to avoid hurting the feelings of other people.

6. As she told us the good news, her face was _____**radiant**_____ with joy.

7. Trying desperately to avoid the police, the _____**fugitive**_____ hid in the cellar of the abandoned house.

8. The boat has been so badly _____**mauled**_____ by the storm that it will have to be overhauled before it can be used again.

9. Despite the doctor's best efforts, there has been no _____**substantial**_____ change in the patient's condition for weeks.

10. The windows had become so _____**grimy**_____ and spotted that it took me some time to get them clean.

11. Since all our cashiers handle large sums of money, we have given them special training in recognizing _____**counterfeit**_____ bills.

12. "As a mother," the woman said to the judge, "I _____**entreat**_____ you to show leniency toward my son."

13. There is an old saying that pencils are made with erasers because human beings are _____**fallible**_____ .

14. Unwilling to bear the _____**uncertainty**_____ any longer, I called the Dean of Admissions to find out if I had been accepted.

15. We discovered that there was not a(n) _____**iota**_____ of truth in the rumors that they had spread so eagerly.

16. Though Company A has very little chance of expanding in the near future, the _____**potential**_____ growth rate of Company B is staggering.

17. I took my broken TV set to a qualified repair service, rather than run the risk of damaging it further by _____**tampering**_____ with it myself.

18. The taste of the public is so _____ fickle _____ that a TV performer who is a big hit one season may be out of a job the next.

19. The Board of Education believes it would save considerable money to _____ consolidate _____ three small schools into one big school.

20. After having lived for so long in a large city, I was happy to spend a few weeks in those beautiful _____ rural _____ surroundings.

Synonyms

*Choose the word from this unit that is **the same** or **most nearly the same** in meaning as the **boldface** word or expression in the given phrase. Write the word on the line provided.*

1. saw a **dazzling** sunrise _____ radiant _____

2. avoid a **possible** source of trouble _____ potential _____

3. to **meddle** with the truth _____ tamper _____

4. made **significant** progress last week _____ substantial _____

5. watched the lion **rough up** its prey _____ maul _____

6. made a **diplomatic** remark _____ tactful _____

7. is **capricious** in her affections _____ fickle _____

8. found the plan to be **imperfect** _____ fallible _____

9. paid with a **bogus** $50 bill _____ counterfeit _____

10. will **control** the game with their speed _____ dominate _____

11. found a way to **combine** several companies _____ consolidate _____

12. would **implore** me to contribute money _____ entreat _____

13. moved forward with no **hesitation** _____ uncertainty _____

14. was a **runaway** from oppression _____ fugitive _____

15. shared a charming **story** from her childhood _____ anecdote _____

Antonyms

*Choose the word from this unit that is **most nearly opposite** in meaning to the **boldface** word or expression in the given phrase. Write the word on the line provided.*

16. held a **spotless** handkerchief _____ grimy _____

17. owned a **disobedient** pet _____ docile _____

18. lives in a **metropolitan** area _____ rural _____

19. does not have an **avalanche** of evidence against her _____ iota _____

20. reached the **initial** stop on the journey _____ ultimate _____

Choosing the Right Word

*Circle the **boldface** word that more satisfactorily completes each of the following sentences.*

1. Throughout the course of its history, the United States has opened its gates to (**fugitives,** counterfeits) from tyranny in other lands.

2. Although the ideals of my youth have been (**entreated, mauled**) by hard experience, they have not been totally destroyed.

3. The (**ultimate, rural**) population of the United States is growing smaller, but the people living on farms are as important as ever to the nation.

4. The mayor has no chance for reelection unless she can (**consolidate,** maul) the different groups and forces supporting her.

5. There, in the very heart of the noisy and (**grimy,** fallible) city was a truly beautiful little park with green lawns, flowers, and a fountain.

6. Rarely in our history has a single man so (**dominated,** entreated) the federal government as Franklin D. Roosevelt did during his four terms.

7. The only certain thing in life is that there will always be many (**fugitives, uncertainties**).

8. It wasn't very (**docile, tactful**) of you to tell her that she seemed to have gained weight.

9. I found his (**anecdotes,** entreaties) amusing, but I fail to see what they had to do with the central idea of his talk.

10. The young man who seemed so quiet and (**docile,** substantial) turned out to be very well informed and to have strong opinions of his own.

11. I suspected that his expression of happiness was (potential, **counterfeit**) and that he was really jealous of our success.

12. Evidence showed that the lawyer had tried to (consolidate, **tamper**) with the witnesses by offering them bribes to change their testimony.

13. Imagine someone as changeable as George having the nerve to say that I'm (radiant, **fickle**)!

14. Larry got good grades on the midterm tests, but he is headed for trouble because he hasn't done an (anecdote, **iota**) of work since then.

15. I know from personal experience how much harm smoking can do, and I (dominate, **entreat**) you not to get started on that miserable habit.

16. As soon as 300-pound Horace settled down in that delicate little chair, we realized he should have something more (grimy, **substantial**) to sit on.

17. If you want to see the (iota, **ultimate**) in shoe styles, ask Beth to show you the new sandals she bought for the spring dance.

18. How can we properly direct the (uncertainties, **potential**) for good and evil in each of us into useful channels?

19. In modern hospitals, everything possible is done to prevent and control mistakes resulting from human (**fallibility,** fickleness).

20. One of our best hopes of solving the energy problem lies in making direct use of (**radiant,** fugitive) energy from the sun.

*Read the following passage, in which some of the words you have studied in this unit appear in **boldface** type. Then complete each statement given below the passage by circling the letter of the item that is **the same** or **almost the same** in meaning as the highlighted word.*

A Giant Find

(Line)

In 1869, near the town of Cardiff, in a **rural** area of New York State, workers digging a well unearthed a giant humanlike figure. The Cardiff Giant, as it came to be known, was more than 10 feet tall and appeared to be of ancient origin. The discovery created a national sensation. Was the Cardiff Giant one of the greatest scientific discoveries of the century? (5)

A number of people thought that it was. Newspaper reporters called it the "eighth wonder of the world." William Newell, who owned the farm on which the discovery was made, erected a tent around the Giant and charged admission to view it. Thousands came. Then a group of prominent Syracuse, New York, businesspeople saw the **potential** for making even greater profits. They purchased (10) a three-fourths interest in the Cardiff Giant for $30,000 and moved it to Syracuse, where it could attract even larger crowds.

Cardiff Giant on display

At this point, some anthropologists began to express **uncertainty** about the authenticity (15) of the Giant. Shortly thereafter, it was exposed as a **counterfeit**, a hoax engineered by George Hull, a tobacco farmer and cigar manufacturer. Hull had bought a large block of gypsum, a white (20) mineral, and had had two sculptors carve from it the likeness of a human being. He then attended to every detail to give the statue an aged look. When the Giant was complete, Hull and Newell had buried it.

Hull's Cardiff Giant was the **ultimate** American anthropological hoax. Ironically, (25) people still wanted to see the fake. It was moved to Albany and then to New York City. Thwarted in his attempt to buy the giant, the great promoter P.T. Barnum had an imitation made. Barnum's fake was soon drawing larger crowds than the original!

Over the years, the Cardiff Giant has been displayed by its many owners. In 1948 the Giant was moved to the Farmers' Museum in Cooperstown, New York, (30) where you can still see it today.

---

1. The meaning of **rural** (line 1) is
a. urban
c. rustic
b. majestic
d. metropolitan

2. Potential (line 10) most nearly means
a. danger
c. strength
b. possibility
d. uncertainty

3. Uncertainty (line 15) is best defined as
a. confidence
c. doubt
b. importance
d. sureness

4. The meaning of **counterfeit** (line 17) is
a. fake
c. discovery
b. coin
d. game

5. Ultimate (line 25) most nearly means
a. imperfect
c. first
b. lasting
d. most extreme

Definitions

Note carefully the spelling, pronunciation, part(s) of speech, and definition(s) of each of the following words. Then write the word in the blank space(s) in the illustrative sentence(s) following. Finally, study the lists of synonyms and antonyms given at the end of each entry.

1. anonymous
(ə nän′ ə məs)

(*adj.*) unnamed, without the name of the person involved (writer, composer, etc.); unknown; lacking individuality or character

The detective received an _____**anonymous**_____ tip that helped to narrow the search for the thief.

SYNONYM: nameless

2. browse
(braüz)

(*v.*) to nibble, graze; to read casually; to window-shop

I like to _____**browse**_____ through a book before I buy it.

SYNONYMS: skim, scan, dip into, graze
ANTONYMS: pore over, scrutinize

3. dupe
(düp)

(*n.*) a person easily tricked or deceived; (*v.*) to deceive

He played the _____**dupe**_____ in one of Shakespeare's comedies.

The villain in the play tried to _____**dupe**_____ the hero out of his money.

SYNONYMS: (*v.*) fool, mislead, hoodwink, delude
ANTONYMS: (*v.*) undeceive, disabuse

4. dynamic
(dī nam′ ik)

(*adj.*) active, energetic, forceful

The advertising agency was looking to hire a creative person with a _____**dynamic**_____ personality.

SYNONYMS: vigorous, high-powered
ANTONYMS: lazy, lackadaisical, lethargic, sluggish

5. eradicate
(i rad′ ə kāt)

(*v.*) to root out, get rid of, destroy completely

The team of doctors and researchers worked tirelessly to _____**eradicate**_____ the disease.

SYNONYMS: wipe out, uproot
ANTONYMS: implant, instill, foster, promote

6. frustrate
(frəs′ trāt)

(*v.*) to prevent from accomplishing a purpose or fulfilling a desire; to cause feelings of discouragement

Nothing could _____**frustrate**_____ our plans to storm the fort.

SYNONYMS: thwart, foil, baffle, disappoint
ANTONYMS: help, assist, abet

7. grim
(grim)

(*adj.*) stern, merciless; fierce, savage, cruel

Many Third World nations face the
_____ grim _____ prospect of famine.

SYNONYMS: dreadful, frightful, ferocious
ANTONYMS: mild, merciful, delightful

8. inimitable
(in im' ə tə bəl)

(*adj.*) not capable of being copied or imitated

The young performer stole the show with her
_____ inimitable _____ charm.

SYNONYMS: matchless, incomparable, unique

9. makeshift
(māk' shift)

(*n.*) a temporary substitute for something else; (*adj.*) crude, flimsy, or temporary

The boards and cinder blocks are only a
_____ makeshift _____ until the bookcase arrives.

That army cot serves as a _____ makeshift _____ bed for guests.

SYNONYMS: (*n.*) stopgap, substitute
ANTONYMS: (*adj.*) permanent, durable, solid, sturdy

10. marginal
(märj' ən əl)

(*adj.*) in, at, or near the edge or margin; only barely good, large, or important enough for the purpose

During times of economic hardship, many people have
only a _____ marginal _____ standard of living.

SYNONYMS: borderline, minimal, peripheral
ANTONYMS: central, pivotal, focal

11. pending
(pen' diŋ)

(*adj.*) waiting to be settled; (*prep.*) until

Curiosity about the _____ pending _____ trial builds with each day.

Sentencing of the convicted criminal was postponed
_____ pending _____ the judge's decision.

SYNONYMS: (*adj.*) undecided, unsettled
ANTONYMS: (*adj.*) settled, decided, resolved

12. prescribe
(pri skrīb')

(*v.*) to order as a rule or course to be followed; to order for medical purposes

The doctor was quick to _____ prescribe _____ complete bed rest.

SYNONYMS: specify, appoint, recommend

13. preview
(prē' vyü)

(*n.*) something seen in advance; (*v.*) to view beforehand

The critics saw a _____ preview _____ of the new movie.

The teacher wished to _____ preview _____ the video before showing it to the class.

SYNONYM: (*n.*) foretaste

14. prominent
(präm′ ə nənt)

(*adj.*) standing out so as to be easily seen; important, well-known

Some famous authors are _____**prominent**_____ figures in society.

SYNONYMS: conspicuous, noticeable
ANTONYMS: inconspicuous, unnoticeable, obscure

15. quaint
(kwānt)

(*adj.*) odd or old-fashioned in a pleasing way; clever, ingenious; skillfully made

My parents stayed at a _____**quaint**_____ old inn in Vermont.

SYNONYMS: picturesque, peculiar, strange, curious
ANTONYMS: familiar, commonplace, modern, contemporary

16. reluctant
(ri lək′ tənt)

(*adj.*) unwilling, holding back

The attorney called the _____**reluctant**_____ witness to the stand.

SYNONYMS: hesitant, loath, disinclined
ANTONYMS: willing, eager, inclined

17. scrimp
(skrimp)

(*v.*) to handle very economically or stingily; to supply in a way that is small, short, or scanty

When the factory closed and other work was scarce, many people were forced to _____**scrimp**_____.

SYNONYM: economize
ANTONYM: splurge

18. snare
(snâr)

(*v.*) to trap, catch; (*n.*) a trap or entanglement

They set a trap to _____**snare**_____ the rodents that were getting into the garden.

The unsuspecting spy was caught in a _____**snare**_____ set by the other side.

SYNONYMS: (*n.*) pitfall; (*v.*) entrap
ANTONYM: liberate

19. utmost
(ət′ most)

(*adj.*) greatest, highest, farthest; (*n.*) the extreme limit

The voters had the _____**utmost**_____ regard for her ability as a leader.

SYNONYMS: (*adj., n.*) maximum, supreme, best
ANTONYM: least

20. vengeance
(ven′ jəns)

(*n.*) punishment in return for an injury or a wrong; unusual force or violence

History is filled with examples of wronged rulers seeking _____**vengeance**_____ against their enemies.

SYNONYMS: revenge, retaliation, reprisal
ANTONYMS: forgiveness, pardon

From the words for this unit, choose the one that best completes each of the following sentences. Write the word in the space provided.

1. The most _____ **prominent** _____ feature of the skyline of that little town in Iowa is the four-story grain elevator.

2. When we visited Salem, Massachusetts, last year, we were charmed by the _____ **quaint** _____ 18th-century houses in the town.

3. After the angler _____ **snared** _____ the fish, he unhooked it from his line and threw it back into the stream.

4. We may not be able to _____ **eradicate** _____ crime in our community, but if we go about it in the right way, I am sure we can reduce it greatly.

5. Instead of seeking personal _____ **vengence** _____ for the wrong that has been done to you, why don't you look for justice under the law?

6. When unexpected guests turned up on the doorstep, I hurriedly made a few _____ **makeshift** _____ arrangements to accommodate them.

7. After several unsuccessful attempts to catch the waiter's eye, I began to become a little _____ **frustrated** _____ .

8. When we saw the _____ **grim** _____ expression on the poor man's face, we realized that the situation was indeed serious.

9. Safety measures are of the _____ **utmost** _____ importance when you are planning a canoe trip over rivers filled with dangerous rapids.

10. For weeks I _____ **scrimped** _____ on everything to save enough money to buy the replacement tires for my bicycle.

11. There is quite a contrast between the _____ **dynamic** _____ administration that now runs that country and the "do-nothing" regime that preceded it.

12. Many books have been written about boys, but none of them can match the _____ **inimitable** _____ qualities of *Tom Sawyer* and *Huckleberry Finn*.

13. Although we know who wrote such famous epics as the *Aeneid* and the *Iliad*, the author of *Beowulf* remains _____ **anonymous** _____ .

14. The suspect was held in the local police station _____ **pending** _____ the outcome of the investigation.

15. The eyewitness was _____ **reluctant** _____ to tell the police all that she had seen, but we convinced her that it was the only right thing to do.

16. I was _____ **duped** _____ into trusting him, and I have paid a heavy price for being misled so easily.

17. I like to write _____ **marginal** _____ notes in a book alongside important material, but I never do so unless the book belongs to me.

18. Each unit in the textbook opens with a section that _____**previews**_____ and highlights the material in the chapters that follow.

19. It took the pharmacist about an hour to prepare the medicine that the doctor had _____**prescribed**_____ for my cold.

20. Is there any sight in the world more restful than cows _____**browsing**_____ in a meadow alongside a little brook?

Synonyms

*Choose the word from this unit that is **the same** or **most nearly the same** in meaning as the **boldface** word or expression in the given phrase. Write the word on the line provided.*

1. has an **incomparable** sense of humor	inimitable
2. had a **foretaste** of the new spring clothing	preview
3. wanted to **wipe out** poverty	eradicate
4. was of **minimal** help to the team	marginal
5. is an issue that is still **undecided**	pending
6. tried to **economize** on nonessential items	scrimp
7. set a **trap** for the gophers	snare
8. waited to hear what the doctor would **order**	prescribe
9. gave a very **vigorous** effort	dynamic
10. will demand swift **revenge**	vengeance
11. likes to **skim** through the books on the shelves	browse
12. attempted to **thwart** his opponent	frustrate
13. received a card from an **unknown** admirer	anonymous
14. is of the **highest** priority	utmost
15. was unable to **fool** the audience	dupe

Antonyms

*Choose the word from this unit that is **most nearly opposite** in meaning to the **boldface** word or expression in the given phrase. Write the word on the line provided.*

16. was **eager** to join the others	reluctant
17. remained a very **obscure** playwright	prominent
18. amused by the guest's **modern** notions	quaint
19. built a **permanent** shelter	makeshift
20. heard the **delightful** news on the radio	grim

Choosing the Right Word

*Circle the **boldface** word that more satisfactorily completes each of the following sentences.*

1. As I was (**previewing**, **browsing**) my way lazily through the newspaper, I was shocked to see my own name in a headline!

2. He still doesn't realize that he has been used as a (**dupe**, **snare**) by our opponents to do their dirty work for them.

3. The mistaken idea that the most important thing in life is to "have fun" is a (**snare**, **vengeance**) that leads to serious trouble for many young people.

4. We have many good musicians in our school orchestra, but they need a (**makeshift**, **dynamic**) conductor to make them play as a unit.

5. Although the announcement had promised us "a (**prominent**, **reluctant**) speaker," the person turned out to be a very minor public official.

6. Although we cannot mention her by name, we want to express our heartfelt gratitude to the (**quaint**, **anonymous**) donor who gave us this generous gift.

7. I understand your (**reluctance**, **vengeance**) to be our candidate in the next election, but I think it is your duty to accept the nomination.

8. (**Pending**, **Eradicating**) the outcome of our national election, none of the foreign governments is willing to take any definite action.

9. His reference to a "historic downfall" after I had failed the history test struck me as a rather (**dynamic**, **grim**) joke.

10. For months the winter was unusually mild, but when the cold weather did come, it struck with a (**vengeance**, **prominence**).

11. The new parking regulations are only a (**snare**, **makeshift**) that will have to be replaced by a better plan within a few years.

12. The exhibition at the fair is intended to give people a (**preview**, **dupe**) of what life may be like fifty years from now.

13. To improve your unsatisfactory school record, I would (**browse**, **prescribe**) regular doses of study, to be taken every day for as long as is necessary.

14. It is very easy to say that our city government should (**scrimp**, **snare**) to balance its budget, but which departments should spend less?

15. You must realize that, although we may find the customs of other lands (**anonymous**, **quaint**), they are just part of everyday life in those areas.

16. The wily champion used every tennis trick she knew to (**frustrate**, **scrimp**) her opponent's attempts to come to the net and hit a winner.

17. Landing a man on the moon was a great achievement, but it is far from being the (**utmost**, **pending**) limit of our space program.

18. Since my job is only (**marginal**, **inimitable**), I'm afraid that if business falls off a little, my employer may let me go.

19. Even before we saw Alice, we heard her (**inimitable**, **grim**) high-pitched giggle and knew she was at the party.

20. Nothing can (**eradicate**, **scrimp**) the love of liberty from the hearts of a free people!

*Read the following passage, in which some of the words you have studied in this unit appear in **boldface** type. Then complete each statement given below the passage by circling the letter of the item that is **the same** or **almost the same** in meaning as the highlighted word.*

More Than an Explorer

(Line)

The **dynamic** John Wesley Powell was perhaps the greatest example of the fearless American explorer of the nineteenth century. Powell maintained that he was neither an adventurer nor just an explorer. To Powell, it was the pursuit of science that was of the **utmost** importance. Indeed, his exploration of the Colorado River
(5) and the Grand Canyon actually led to the development of some of the principles of geology. It also prompted the settlement of the American Southwest.

In 1869, Powell, who had lost an arm during the Civil War, and nine companions set out to explore and map the largely
(10) uncharted canyons of the Green and Colorado rivers. The party had just four flimsy wooden boats and a meager supply of rations. The hazards of the **grim** journey challenged the group at every turn. In fact,
(15) Powell and his party surprised even the local Native Americans, who were themselves **reluctant** to navigate the dangerous Grand Canyon River Gorge. Yet Powell would not let anything **frustrate** his
(20) plans for exploration—not even the three reports of his death!

Majestic Grand Canyon in Arizona

Fortunately, Powell did not die on the river, and the one-thousand-mile journey was a success, as was a second trip he led two years later. Powell's book about the Grand Canyon region, as well as the photographs, topographic map, diaries,
(25) and field notes prepared by several other members of his party, provided valuable information about the area.

Soon after his second expedition, Powell became a **prominent** government official, involved in the management of arid western lands. He went on to become the Director of the Bureau of Ethnology, which collected data about fast
(30) disappearing North American Indian groups, and later, the Director of the U.S. Geological Survey.

---

1. The meaning of **dynamic** (line 1) is
   a. explosive   c. lethargic
   b. energetic   d. sturdy

2. Utmost (line 4) is best defined as
   a. strangest   c. greatest
   b. high-powered d. least

3. Grim (line 13) most nearly means
   a. merciful   c. dirty
   b. short   d. frightful

4. Reluctant (line 17) is best defined as
   a. hesitant   c. undecided
   b. willing   d. delighted

5. Frustrate (line 19) most nearly means
   a. assist   c. settle
   b. foil   d. mislead

6. The meaning of **prominent** (line 27) is
   a. inconspicuous c. central
   b. curious   d. well-known

REVIEW UNITS 4–6

Visit us at www.sadlier-oxford.com
for interactive puzzles and games.

Read the following passage, in which some of the
words you have studied in Units 4–6 appear in
boldface type. Then answer questions 1–11 on
page 73 on the basis of what is <u>stated</u> or <u>implied</u>
in the passage and in the introductory statement.

*Nellie Bly (1864–1922), the subject of this
passage, was a groundbreaking American
journalist whose stories shocked her readers.*

(Line)

Nellie Bly wasn't her real name;
but when 18-year-old Elizabeth
Cochrane, a **spirited** young woman
from a small town in Pennsylvania,
(5) moved to Pittsburgh in 1885 to
become a writer, the aspiring reporter
knew she would need a catchy new
name. She chose Nellie Bly, from the
title of a popular Stephen Foster tune,
(10) and turned out stories on
controversial subjects that would
sell record numbers of newspapers.

Under the byline "Nellie Bly," the
young woman wrote articles for the
(15) *Pittsburgh Dispatch* that were spiced
with shocking **anecdotes** she heard
from the older women living in her
boardinghouse. Nellie's writing rang
true; and soon she was exposing the
(20) **grim** conditions in Pittsburgh's slums,
jails, and factories. When her stories
became too sensational for her
editors, Nellie left Pittsburgh for New
York City. There she joined the staff of
(25) Joseph Pulitzer's *New York World*.

Once again, there was nothing
typical about the topics Nellie chose
to write about and nothing **orthodox**
about the way she researched them.
(30) To expose the dreadful conditions in
New York's insane asylum, Bellevue,
she threw a fit and got admitted to
the hospital. To test the capabilities of

a ferry rescue crew, she jumped
(35) overboard into the Hudson River. To
expose shameful prison conditions,
Nellie framed herself on a robbery
charge and landed in jail. Her stories
both thrilled and embarrassed
(40) readers. Some of her work led to
social reform. It also made her
famous.

In the name of grabbing headlines,
Nellie had her share of adventures.
(45) Yet a stunt she pulled in 1889 would
be the greatest adventure of her
career. Responding to the fame of
Jules Verne's novel *Around the World
in Eighty Days*, Nellie proposed to
(50) outdo the book's fictional character,
Phileas Fogg, and circle the globe in
less time. Pulitzer accepted her idea;
and as readers breathlessly followed
her course, Nellie made her way
(55) around the world. In the end, she
bested Fogg. Her time: 72 days.
People had said that it couldn't be
done, but then Nellie Bly, still only 21,
was used to beating the odds.

1. Which of the following would make the best title for this passage?
  a. Nellie Bly: Investigative Reporter
  b. Elizabeth Cochrane vs. Nellie Bly
  c. Around the World in Eighty Days
  d. A Success Story
  e. Nineteenth-Century Women Reporters

2. The meaning of **spirited** (line 3) is
  a. good-natured
  b. ambitious
  c. atypical
  d. psychic
  e. lively

3. **Controversial** (line 11) most nearly means
  a. patriotic
  b. debatable
  c. agreeable
  d. strange
  e. depressing

4. The last sentence in paragraph 1 (lines 7–12)
  a. restates the main idea of paragraph 1
  b. summarizes the main idea of paragraph 4
  c. provides a focus for the entire passage
  d. describes Nelly Bly's relationship with Joseph Pulitzer
  e. foreshadows Nellie Bly's trip around the world

5. **Anecdotes** (line 16) is best defined as
  a. statistics
  b. stories
  c. prescriptions
  d. secrets
  e. disappointments

6. **Grim** (line 20) most nearly means
  a. dirty
  b. dreadful
  c. humorless
  d. benign
  e. predictable

7. **Orthodox** (line 28) is best defined as
  a. unusual
  b. subtle

  c. timid
  d. traditional
  e. illegal

8. From paragraph 3 (lines 26–41), you learn that an important consequence of Nellie Bly's reporting was
  a. the development of the editorial page
  b. an increased interest in the novels of Jules Verne
  c. social reforms related to her stories
  d. equal pay for women reporters
  e. her successful movie career

9. From paragraph 3, you can conclude that Nellie Bly's method of reporting relied primarily on
  a. interviewing older women in her boarding house
  b. experiencing first-hand the situations she wrote about
  c. imagining the details she included in her stories
  d. depending on others to supply her with information
  e. researching facts and details in library reference books

10. Which of the following best describes the writer's attitude toward Nellie Bly?
  a. critical
  b. outraged
  c. admiring
  d. skeptical
  e. pitying

11. Which of the following generalizations is author most likely agree with?
  a. Men reporters are more imaginative than women reporters.
  b. Women reporters are more reliable than men reporters.
  c. Nellie Bly was a second-rate reporter who accomplished little.
  d. Nellie Bly was a colorful reporter who wrote sensational stories.
  e. Nellie Bly was more interested in writing fiction than in reporting facts.

Grammar in Context

Read the opening sentence of the passage: "Nellie Bly wasn't her real name; but when 18-year-old Elizabeth Cochrane, a spirited young woman from a small town in Pennsylvania, moved to Pittsburgh in 1885 to become a writer, the aspiring reporter knew she would need a catchy new name" (lines 1–7 on page 72).

Notice that the author uses several adjectives to describe the woman's real name and her made-up name, her age, her town, and her career as a reporter. An **adjective** is a word that modifies a noun or a pronoun. Adjectives can appear either before or after the noun or pronoun. They answer questions such as *What kind? How many? How much? or Which one?* The name "Stephen Foster" (line 9) serves as a *proper* adjective. The indefinite articles *a* and *an* are also adjectives; so is the definite article *the*. An adjective may appear after a linking verb, too, as in the sentence "Nellie was <u>bold</u>."

Do not confuse adjectives with **adverbs**, which modify verbs, adjectives, other adverbs, and prepositional phrases (as in "<u>almost</u> to the end"). Adverbs can also modify complete sentences and subordinate clauses. They tell *how, when, where, to what extent, in what manner,* and *how much.* Negatives, such as *not, never,* and *hardly* are adverbs, too, as in the sentence "Nellie was <u>hardly</u> what we would call a shy young woman."

When you need to decide whether to use an adjective or an adverb, use what you have learned so far plus the following ideas and rules: (1) Don't count on the –*ly* ending to identify a modifier as an adverb. Words such as *friendly* and *elderly* are adjectives. (2) *Good* and *bad* are always adjectives. (3) *Badly* and *well* are adverbs, although *well* can be used as an adjective to describe a person's health.

Choose the modifier in parentheses that correctly completes each sentence, and write it on the line provided.

1. Nellie Bly was a (**particular, particularly**) adventurous reporter.
   <u>particularly</u>

2. Nellie experienced (**near, nearly**) instant success in her career.
   <u>nearly</u>

3. Nellie told her sensational stories (**well, good**).
   <u>well</u>

4. She must have felt (**fearful, fearfully**) when she jumped into the Hudson River.
   <u>fearful</u>

5. Compared with how other reporters got their stories, there was nothing (**typical, typically**) about Nellie's efforts and methods.
   <u>typical</u>

6. Some have said that Nellie was not a (**good, well**) reporter; they claimed that she was more of a publicity seeker than a true journalist.
   <u>good</u>

7. Nellie (**sure, surely**) made a splash in the newspaper world of her day.
   <u>surely</u>

Two-Word Completions

Circle the pair of words that best complete the meaning of each of the following passages.

See pages T38–T48 for explanations of answers.

1. The book is full of highly amusing stories involving many people who were _____ at the time. One of these witty little _____ tells how a famous director once used glue to get an actor to stand on his mark.

a. utmost . . . previews
b. inimitable . . . iotas
c. dominant . . . snares
d. prominent . . . anecdotes ⟵

2. "His methods are hardly what I'd call _____, but they do get results," the sales manager remarked about her star salesperson. "If he took a more traditional approach to his job, the company's profits might not be so _____."

a. dynamic . . . disheartening
b. quaint . . . marginal
c. orthodox . . . substantial ⟵
d. controversial . . . fruitless

3. I know that an injection of novocaine doesn't normally _____ a great deal of pain. Still, the mere thought of the dentist's sharp needle is enough to make me _____ in imaginary discomfort.

a. inflict . . . wince ⟵
b. consolidate . . . scurry
c. eradicate . . . maul
d. procure . . . scrimp

4. "The President's new economic program has stirred up a good deal of _____ on Capitol Hill," the reporter observed. "Some of the members of Congress are clearly in favor of the plan; others are definitely _____ to it."

a. vengeance . . . anonymous
b. controversy . . . hostile ⟵
c. bewilderment . . . malignant
d. uncertainty . . . reluctant

5. Despite setbacks that would have _____ a less determined person, she continued to do her _____ to become the top tennis player in the world. As she herself admitted, she knew that she wouldn't succeed unless she gave the task her "very best shot."

a. mortified . . . potential
b. entreated . . . ultimate
c. frustrated . . . virtual
d. disheartened . . . utmost ⟵

6. Two convicts escaped from the state prison last week. The police managed to recapture one of the _____ in a matter of hours. Yet their efforts to catch the other have so far proved _____.

a. buffoons . . . fallible
b. counterfeits . . . void
c. fugitives . . . fruitless ⟵
d. dupes . . . wayward

Choosing the Right Meaning

Read each sentence carefully. Then circle the item that best completes the statement below the sentence.

See pages T38–T48 for explanations of answers.

Perhaps the hectic touring schedule had taken its toll on the cast; at any rate I found last night's performance of the play decidedly sodden. (2)

1. The word **sodden** in line 2 is used to mean
a. drenched   b. brilliant   (c. listless)   d. soaked

In some early religious orders, members mortified their bodies by fasting and even, in some cases, by voluntarily suffering physical pain. (2)

2. In line 1 the word **mortified** is best defined as
a. embarrassed   (b. disciplined)   c. humiliated   d. strengthened

The suburban building boom of the 1950s saw entire developments of anonymous tract houses spring up practically overnight. (2)

3. The word **anonymous** in line 1 most nearly means
a. nameless   (b. indistinguishable)   c. unknown   d. inexpensive

Physicists use huge devices called *particle accelerators* to explore the ultimate building blocks of matter. (2)

4. In line 1 the word **ultimate** most nearly means
(a. basic)   b. final   c. eventual   d. most important

With three straight primary victories, the candidate consolidated her position as front-runner for the nomination of her party. (2)

5. The best definition for **consolidated** in line 1 is
(a. strengthened)   b. united   c. merged   d. combined

Antonyms

*In each of the following groups, circle the word or expression that is most nearly the **opposite** of the word in **boldface** type.*

1. grim
(a. happy)
b. sad
c. horrified
d. stern

2. substantial
a. large
(b. small)
c. generous
d. personal

3. spirited
a. amusing
(b. lackluster)
c. bitter
d. firm

4. grimy
a. mild
b. soiled
(c. immaculate)
d. matchless

5. scurry
a. scamper
b. fly
c. run
(d. trudge)

6. orthodox
a. familiar
(b. heretical)
c. interesting
d. puzzling

7. fruitless
(a. successful)
b. well-planned
c. exhausted
d. failing

8. uncertainty
a. doubtfulness
b. newness
c. strangeness
(d. sureness)

9. iota
(a. glut)
b. result
c. smidgen
d. failure

11. prominent
a. wealthy
b. unselfish
c. famous
(d. obscure)

13. malignant
(a. harmless)
b. dangerous
c. ugly
d. unexplained

15. snare
a. capture
b. kill
(c. release)
d. feed

10. potential
a. possible
(b. real)
c. new
d. minor

12. rural
(a. urban)
b. foreign
c. sizable
d. new

14. makeshift
a. temporary
(b. durable)
c. worthless
d. complicated

16. marginal
(a. central)
b. laughable
c. secondary
d. unworthy

Word Families

A. *On the line provided, write the word you have learned in Units 4–6 that is related to each of the following nouns.*
EXAMPLE: reluctance—**reluctant**

1. quaintness — quaint
2. entreaty, entreatment — entreat
3. domination, dominator, dominance — dominate
4. tact, tactfulness — tactful
5. malignancy, malignance — malignant
6. hostility — hostile
7. consolidation, consolidator — consolidate
8. spirit, spiritedness — spirited
9. bewilderment — bewilder
10. orthodoxy — orthodox
11. mortification — mortify
12. prescription, prescriber, prescript — prescribe
13. waywardness — wayward
14. fallibility — fallible
15. controversy, controversialist, controversialism, controverter — controversial

B. *On the line provided, write the word you have learned in Units 4–6 that is related to each of the following verbs.*
EXAMPLE: begrime—**grimy**

16. controvert — controversial
17. inflame — inflammable
18. avenge — vengeance
19. radiate — radiant
20. ally — alliance

 **Word Associations**

In each of the following groups, circle the word that is best defined or suggested by the given phrase.

1. something that the doctor does
   (a. prescribe)   b. preview   c. bewilder   d. wince

2. taking pains not to hurt someone's feelings
   a. wayward   (b. tactful)   c. reluctant   d. virtual

3. "Ouch!"
   (a. wince)   b. tamper   c. void   d. dupe

4. a court jester
   a. dupe   b. vengeance   c. fugitive   (d. buffoon)

5. a whole lot of nothing
   (a. void)   b. anecdote   c. vengeance   d. snare

6. "I'm afraid that I won't to able to find a job this summer."
   a. substantial   b. malignant   c. grimy   (d. disheartened)

7. like a sheep
   a. fallible   (b. docile)   c. dynamic   d. reluctant

8. "I haven't got a clue."
   a. inflict   b. dominate   c. preview   (d. bewilder)

9. rather badly chewed up by a tiger
   a. consolidate   (b. maul)   c. frustrate   d. eradicate

10. the North Atlantic Treaty Organization (NATO)
   a. iota   b. snare   (c. alliance)   d. uncertainty

11. "Have you heard the story about _____?"
   a. snare   b. void   (c. anecdote)   d. counterfeit

12. not at all foolproof
   a. marginal   b. inimitable   (c. fallible)   d. utmost

13. to pull something out by the roots
   a. browse   b. scrimp   c. entreat   (d. eradicate)

14. stray from the straight and narrow
   a. rural   b. marginal   (c. wayward)   d. orthodox

15. acquire the equipment we need for the trip
   (a. procure)   b. mortify   c. scurry   d. dominate

16. given to sudden and unexpected changes of mood
   (a. fickle)   b. docile   c. dynamic   d. radiant

17. not the real thing
   a. inimitable   b. orthodox   c. marginal   (d. counterfeit)

18. not yet decided
   a. sodden   (b. pending)   c. potential   d. virtual

19. to interfere with, as evidence or a witness
   a. consolidate   b. inflict   (c. tamper)   d. dominate

20. like greasy, dirty overalls
   (a. grimy)   b. fruitless   c. fickle   d. grim

Building with Classical Roots

scrib, scribe, script—to write

This root appears in **prescribe** (page 66). Literally "to write before," this word means "to set down as a rule, order for medical treatment, or give medical advice." Some other words based on the same root are listed below.

circumscribe	inscription	proscribe	subscribe
indescribable	postscript	script	transcribe

From the list of words above, choose the one that corresponds to each of the brief definitions below. Write the word in the blank space in the illustrative sentence below the definition.

1. handwriting; a manuscript of a play or movie

The actor read the _____ script _____ before he agreed to star in the new movie.

2. to draw a line around, encircle; to confine within limits, restrict

After major surgery, patients may need to _____ circumscribe _____ their physical activities for a while.

3. to write out or make a typewritten copy of; to write in another alphabet

The assistant will need to _____ transcribe _____ her shorthand notes before inputting the information.

4. that which is written on a monument, coin, building; a dedication in a book

The _____ inscription _____ on the monument is short and to the point.

5. to sign one's name; to express agreement or approval; to promise to take or to pay for

My parents _____ subscribe _____ to several newsmagazines.

6. beyond description

The joy the winning team felt was _____ indescribable _____.

7. to outlaw, forbid, prohibit; to banish

Building codes _____ proscribe _____ that type of flimsy construction.

8. an addition to a letter written after the writer's name has been signed

The _____ postscript _____ that she added to her letter was so long that it took up an entire page.

From the list of words above, choose the one that best completes each of the following sentences. Write the word in the space provided.

1. The _____ inscription _____ in the book identifies it as a birthday gift my father gave to his father 40 years ago!

2. We cannot _____ subscribe _____ to a plan that would be unfair to so many teenagers.

3. Because I had forgotten to ask a key question in the letter, I added it as a(n) _____postscript_____ at the bottom.

4. Using red pushpins, the police inspector _____circumscribed_____ an area on the street map in which the suspect most likely would be found.

5. The director made several changes in the _____script_____ to adapt the play to a smaller cast.

6. The foreign language specialist will _____transcribe_____ the Russian names into our roman alphabet.

7. The dictator _____proscribed_____ all public meetings other than the ones he himself ordered.

8. It is impossible to portray in words the way that the sunset filled the sky with those _____indescribable_____ colors!

---

*Circle the **boldface** word that more satisfactorily completes each of the following sentences.*

1. Our coach used chalk to (**subscribe**, **circumscribe**) the boundaries of the playing field.

2. Interviewers know that it is important to (**proscribe**, **transcribe**) their notes soon after an interview is completed.

3. The duke was exiled from his country and (**proscribed**, **circumscribed**) from ever returning.

4. It is the job of the poet to put the (**indescribable**, **postscript**) into words.

5. The (**postscript**, **inscription**) on the pharaoh's tomb was written in hieroglyphics.

6. The information in the (**inscription**, **postscript**) is so important that it should have been included in the actual body of the letter.

7. My parents heartily (**subscribe**, **proscribe**) to the idea of strict discipline.

8. It was difficult for the performer to recite her lines without glancing at the (**script**, **postscript**).

Analogies

In each of the following, circle the item that best completes the comparison.

See pages T38–48 for explanations of answers.

1. quaint is to **charm** as
a. marginal is to bulk
b. anonymous is to interest
c. malignant is to use
d. animated is to liveliness

2. inimitable is to **unique** as
a. makeshift is to potential
b. customary is to strange
c. interminable is to endless
d. miscellaneous is to indignant

3. lead is to **docile** as
a. separate is to mutual
b. preview is to orthodox
c. overlook is to prominent
d. dupe is to gullible

4. fruitless is to **barren** as
a. substantial is to trivial
b. grimy is to immaculate
c. adjacent is to distant
d. transparent is to clear

5. missile is to **pelt** as
a. feather is to maul
b. net is to snare
c. firebrand is to douse
d. hose is to singe

6. anecdote is to **biography** as
a. homicide is to forgery
b. epic is to lyric
c. alliance is to treaty
d. toast is to oration

7. dissuade is to **stubborn** as
a. dishearten is to confident
b. retard is to slow
c. indulge is to selfish
d. dupe is to shallow

8. bewilder is to **uncertain** as
a. irritate is to peevish
b. control is to wayward
c. procure is to reluctant
d. dominate is to hostile

9. humdrum is to **stimulation** as
a. spirited is to energy
b. literate is to intelligence
c. grim is to charm
d. sullen is to anger

10. poised is to **mortify** as
a. determined is to frustrate
b. certain is to verify
c. fallible is to recompense
d. controversial is to counterfeit

Choosing the Right Meaning

Read each sentence carefully. Then circle the item that best completes the statement below the sentence.

See pages T38–48 for explanations of answers.

When we open *Alice in Wonderland*, we leave behind the trivial world to which we are accustomed and inhabit for a time the fantastical, topsy-turvy universe of the author's (2) imagination.

1. In line 1 the word **trivial** most nearly means
a. minor   b. petty   c. ordinary   d. real

Alice's adventures in Wonderland begin when she chases after a white rabbit, dressed in a waistcoat, that has come pelting by. (2)

2. The phrase **pelting by** in line 2 is used to mean
a. shedding its fur   b. throwing things   c. nibbling   d. hurrying by

No matter how vivid and lifelike it may seem, "virtual reality" is no more substantial than a dream. (2)

3. The word **substantial** in line 1 is best defined as

a. important   b. prosperous   (c. tangible)   d. affordable

Of all the notions that humankind has ever pondered, is there any so fugitive as time?

4. The word **fugitive** in line 1 is best defined as

a. wandering   (b. elusive)   c. fleeting   d. puzzling

The quaint machines that Leonardo da Vinci sketched in his notebooks show him to have been as accomplished an inventor as he was a painter. (2)

5. In line 1 the word **quaint** most nearly means

a. old-fashioned   b. picturesque   c. odd   (d. ingenious)

Two-Word Completions

Circle the pair of words that best complete the meaning of each of the following sentences.

See pages T38–48 for explanations of answers.

1. Just as a surgeon might remove a(n) _____ tumor from our bodies, we must _____ the cancer of racial and religious prejudice from our hearts and minds.

a. fugitive . . . singe
b. wayward . . . germinate

c. indispensable . . . void
(d. malignant . . . eradicate)

2. She used to be a very cheerful and confident young woman, but she has been so _____ of late by ill health and financial worries that she has lost a good deal of her _____ good humor and optimism.

a. disheartened . . . sullen
b. unscathed . . . virtual

(c. plagued . . . customary)
d. frustrated . . . vicious

3. Eventually, I _____ them from attempting to retaliate for the wrong done to them by reminding them of a famous passage in the Bible, in which God says, "_____ is mine; I will repay."

a. animated . . . Truce
(b. dissuaded . . . Vengeance)

c. culminated . . . Homicide
d. seethed . . . Recompense

4. Gaius Julius Caesar's rivals in the Senate bitterly criticized the political _____ he formed with Pompey and Crassus as a thinly veiled attempt to overthrow the Republic and _____ the Roman world by becoming its undisputed masters.

a. dynasty . . . eradicate
(b. alliance . . . dominate)

c. regime . . . hurtle
d. iota . . . disrupt

5. The _____ of Cicero's reputation as one of the foremost public speakers of his day shines as bright today as it did on the day he first delivered that famous _____ more than 2000 years ago.

(a. luster . . . oration)
b. uncertainty . . . anecdote

c. radiance . . . ingredient
d. prominence . . . résumé

Enriching Your Vocabulary

Read the passage below. Then complete the exercise at the bottom of the page.

Once Upon a Time . . .

Stories have been called the building blocks of knowledge and the foundation of learning. The hearing and telling of stories has been an essential part of life for as far back in human history as we can imagine. Stories allow us to pass on accumulated wisdom, beliefs, and values. Stories can instruct, entertain, amaze, prompt, and inspire us.

At their core, all stories are words linked together to convey ideas. Because there are so many kinds of stories and purposes for their telling, our language has evolved to include a range of story-related words. An *anecdote* (Unit 5) is a short account of an incident in someone's life. A biography is the true story of someone's lifetime. What would you expect to hear in a saga?

Have you even been chatting with others when someone says, "That reminds me of the time . . ." and the pleasant give-and-take of storytelling begins? Perhaps your cousin recalls the occasion of catching a trout last

A whopper!

summer. As the story is retold and embellished, the modest one-pound fish soon evolves into a ten-pound whopper! Now, that's a fish story! After you stop rolling your eyes, you may counter with the instructive fable about the boy who cried wolf. Or you may seek out a scientific article that provides facts about the largest fish ever measured.

In Column A below are 10 more story-related words. With or without a dictionary, match each of these words with its meaning in Column B.

Column A

_g_	**1.** fable
_f_	**2.** allegory
_h_	**3.** tall tale
_e_	**4.** memoir
_a_	**5.** yarn
_b_	**6.** vignette
_c_	**7.** parable
_d_	**8.** legend
_j_	**9.** narrative
_i_	**10.** saga

Column B

a. an informal story "spun" out in a casual way

b. a short literary scene or description

c. a story that illustrates a moral or religious lesson

d. a story about a memorable character—real or fictional

e. a recollection of events in a writer's own life

f. a symbolic story told to represent principles or ideas

g. a story, often with animal characters, that teaches a moral

h. a hard-to-believe story filled with exaggeration

i. a long story of adventure and heroic events

j. a recounting of events and experiences in story form

See page T21 for information.

Definitions

Note carefully the spelling, pronunciation, part(s) of speech, and definition(s) of each of the following words. Then write the word in the blank space(s) in the illustrative sentence(s) following. Finally, study the lists of synonyms and antonyms given at the end of each entry.

1. amiss
(ə mis′)

(*adj.*) faulty, imperfect, not as it should be; (*adv.*) in a mistaken or improper way, wrongly

Under the circumstances it would not be
_____ **amiss** _____ to offer our congratulations.

SYNONYM: (*adj., adv.*) awry
ANTONYM: (*adv.*) properly

2. brawl
(brôl)

(*n.*) a noisy quarrel or fight; (*v.*) to quarrel or fight noisily

The noise coming from the classroom sounded more like a
_____ **brawl** _____ than a debate.

SYNONYMS: (*n.*) scuffle, donnybrook; (*v.*) spar, scrap

3. detest
(di test′)

(*v.*) to hate, dislike very much, loathe

Children who dislike green vegetables often
_____ **detest** _____ spinach.

SYNONYMS: despise, abhor
ANTONYMS: relish, love, admire, esteem

4. domestic
(də mes′ tik)

(*adj.*) native to a country, not foreign; relating to the life or affairs of a household; (*n.*) a household servant

The newspaper is filled with information about our country's
_____ **domestic** _____ affairs.

When my grandmother first came to this country, she took a
job as a _____ **domestic** _____ .

SYNONYMS: (*adj.*) household, native; (*n.*) servant
ANTONYMS: (*adj.*) foreign, alien

5. flagrant
(flā′ grənt)

(*adj.*) extremely bad, glaring; scandalous, notorious

Crossing against the light shows a
_____ **flagrant** _____ disregard for the law.

SYNONYMS: blatant, gross, outrageous
ANTONYMS: petty, piddling, trifling, inconsequential

6. flaw
(flô)

(*n.*) a slight fault, defect, crack

We noticed a _____ **flaw** _____ in the plan to start building the house before the spring rains.

SYNONYMS: imperfection, blemish
ANTONYMS: faultlessness, perfection

7. fledgling
(flej′ liŋ)

(*n.*) an inexperienced person, beginner; a young bird about to leave the nest; (*adj.*) inexperienced, budding

We placed the _____fledgling_____ back in its nest.

A _____fledgling_____ police officer appeared on the scene and wisely called for assistance.

SYNONYMS: (*n.*) novice, tyro, neophyte
ANTONYMS: (*n.*) pro, expert, veteran

8. fluster
(fləs′ tər)

(*v.*) to make or become confused, agitated, or nervous; (*n.*) a state of confusion or agitation

During the trial, the judge told the attorney not to _____fluster_____ the witness.

SYNONYMS: (*v.*) agitate, rattle, disconcert
ANTONYMS: (*v.*) reassure, soothe, quiet

9. foremost
(fôr′ mōst)

(*adj.*) chief, most important, primary; (*adv.*) in the first place

Music is _____foremost_____ among my interests.

First and _____foremost_____ , you must call home to let your family know you'll be late.

SYNONYMS: (*adj.*) leading, principal, paramount
ANTONYMS: (*adj.*) hindmost, last, secondary

10. momentum
(mō ment′ əm)

(*n.*) the force or speed with which something moves

The presidential campaign gained _____momentum_____ once the first primary was over.

SYNONYMS: drive, thrust, impetus

11. notable
(nōt′ ə bəl)

(*adj.*) striking, remarkable; (*n.*) a person who is well known, distinguished, or outstanding in some way

Being chosen for the team was a _____notable_____ event in our lives.

The party was attended by _____notables_____ from the film world.

SYNONYMS: (*adj.*) noteworthy, impressive
ANTONYMS: (*adj.*) undistinguished, unremarkable; (*n.*) unknown

12. nurture
(nər′ chər)

(*v.*) to bring up, care for, train, nourish; (*n.*) rearing, training, upbringing

It is wonderful to watch chimpanzees _____nurture_____ their young.

The _____nurture_____ they received as children served them well as they grew into adulthood.

SYNONYMS: (*v.*) raise, rear, foster
ANTONYMS: (*v.*) neglect, ignore, discourage, hinder

13. paradox
(par′ ə däks)

(*n.*) a self-contradictory statement that on closer examination proves true; a person or thing with seemingly contradictory qualities

It is a _____ paradox _____ to say that youth is wasted on the young.

SYNONYMS: riddle, enigma, anomaly, absurdity

14. perjury
(pər′ jə rē)

(*n.*) the act of swearing to a lie

The witness was convicted of _____ perjury _____ and was sentenced to serve two years in prison.

SYNONYM: false witness

15. presume
(pri züm′)

(*v.*) to take for granted, assume or suppose; to dare, take upon oneself, take liberties

The counselors _____ presume _____ that the job they had last summer will be theirs this summer as well.

SYNONYMS: surmise, trespass, infringe

16. prior
(prī′ ər)

(*adj.*) earlier, former

Unfortunately, the governor had a _____ prior _____ appointment and could not meet with the class.

SYNONYMS: previous, anterior
ANTONYMS: subsequent, later, ensuing, following

17. proficient
(prə fish′ ənt)

(*adj.*) skilled, expert, or capable in any field or activity

Dad knows his way around the kitchen and is quite a _____ proficient _____ cook.

SYNONYMS: competent, adept, able
ANTONYMS: incompetent, inept, unskilled, ignorant

18. salvo
(sal′ vō)

(*n.*) a burst of gunfire or cannon shot, often as a tribute or salute; a sudden burst of anything; a spirited verbal attack

The audience erupted in a _____ salvo _____ of laughter.

SYNONYMS: barrage, volley

19. vigilant
(vij′ ə lənt)

(*adj.*) wide-awake, alert, watchful

The _____ vigilant _____ guards paced back and forth in front of the barracks.

SYNONYMS: attentive, on one's toes
ANTONYMS: sleepy, inattentive, unobservant

20. wrath
(rath)

(*n.*) intense anger

In Greek and Roman myths characters fear the _____ wrath _____ of the gods.

SYNONYMS: rage, fury, ire, choler, indignation
ANTONYMS: favor, approval, pleasure, blessing

Completing the Sentence

From the words for this unit, choose the one that best completes each of the following sentences. Write the word in the space provided.

1. In the old days, wooden battleships saluted their victorious admiral by repeatedly firing _____ **salvos** _____ of cannon shot from their decks.

2. It's a fact that some important battles of the American Revolution occurred _____ **prior** _____ to the signing of the Declaration of Independence.

3. I must warn you again that if you fail to tell the truth, you may lay yourself open to a charge of _____ **perjury** _____.

4. I wouldn't call such a(n) _____ **flagrant** _____ and premeditated lie merely a "minor lapse of memory."

5. The minister saw from the statistics that imported goods were cutting into the _____ **domestic** _____ market.

6. Her parents _____ **nurtured** _____ her musical talents by hiring the finest teachers and taking her to hear the performances of great musicians.

7. Some people truly love the music of such modern composers as Arnold Schoenberg or Igor Stravinsky; others absolutely _____ **detest** _____ it.

8. We must be _____ **vigilant** _____ in recognizing the early signs of decay in our community and move quickly to improve conditions.

9. I have no way of knowing for sure why she left, but I _____ **presume** _____ that she had a good reason for doing so.

10. I well remember how often during my childhood I felt the full force of my parents' _____ **wrath** _____ when I had done something wrong.

11. In most respects she is a fine person, but excessive stubbornness is the one important _____ **flaw** _____ in her character.

12. We suspected that something was _____ **amiss** _____ when he did not return home from school at the usual time.

13. Like a(n) _____ **fledgling** _____ eagle about to leave the nest for the first time, our son is preparing to spend his first summer away from home.

14. At what point does a spinning top lose sufficient _____ **momentum** _____ to topple over?

15. When two players suddenly started to throw punches at each other during last night's game, an ugly bench-clearing _____ **brawl** _____ ensued.

16. The speaker went right on with his speech, in no way _____ **flustered** _____ or disturbed by the jeers and catcalls of a few rowdy hecklers.

17. Though his career as a whole was not particularly distinguished, he did score one _____ **notable** _____ success on Broadway a few years ago.

18. How do you explain the fact that some students who do poorly in math are highly _____proficient_____ in figuring out batting averages?

19. _____Foremost_____ among her many outstanding qualities is her ability to understand the points of view of other people.

20. That terrible instruments of war should in fact prove useful as guardians of the peace is one of the _____paradoxes_____of modern life.

Synonyms

*Choose the word from this unit that is **the same** or **most nearly the same** in meaning as the **boldface** word or expression in the given phrase. Write the word on the line provided.*

1. felt his enemy's **fury** _____wrath_____

2. continued to roll due to its own **force** _____momentum_____

3. under the eye of the **watchful** officer _____vigilant_____

4. did not **rattle** the experienced pilot _____fluster_____

5. was responsible for a variety of **household** chores _____domestic_____

6. witnessed a violent street **scuffle** _____brawl_____

7. committed the act of **lying** during the trial _____perjury_____

8. a really **impressive** effort _____notable_____

9. became a **skilled** gymnast after much practice _____proficient_____

10. not trust the script to **inexperienced** screenwriters _____fledgling_____

11. was **supposed** to be an expert on dolphins _____presumed_____

12. sought to **foster** the fragile relationship _____nurture_____

13. a philosophy steeped in **enigma** _____paradox_____

14. suspected that something had gone **awry** _____amiss_____

15. released a **barrage** of rockets _____salvo_____

Antonyms

*Choose the word from this unit that is **most nearly opposite** in meaning to the **boldface** word or expression in the given phrase. Write the word on the line provided.*

16. began to **admire** the new leader's policies _____detest_____

17. had no **subsequent** arrests _____prior_____

18. noticed the **perfection** in her character _____flaw_____

19. committed a **petty** violation of the law _____flagrant_____

20. an issue of **secondary** importance _____foremost_____

Choosing the Right Word

*Circle the **boldface** word that more satisfactorily completes each of the following sentences.*

1. Under the American system of justice, any person accused of a crime is (**presumed,** flawed) to be innocent until proven guilty.

2. She may have given wrong information in court, but this was an honest mistake and certainly does not make her guilty of (**perjury,** wrath).

3. How can you expect the court to excuse your repeated and (**flagrant,** vigilant) violations of the traffic laws?

4. As support for our candidate continued to gain (**momentum,** salvo), it soon became clear that she would win the election by a landslide.

5. Please don't take it (**amiss,** notably) if I suggest that your French accent sounds more like Paris, Texas, than Paris, France.

6. I can forgive an honest mistake, but I (presume, **detest**) any attempt to cover up errors by lying.

7. I am disturbed by the (momentum, **paradox**) of impoverished people in the richest land on Earth.

8. Since there had been no (**prior,** proficient) notice of the scholarship competition, we had practically no time to prepare for it.

9. *Romeo and Juliet* opens with members of the rival houses of Montague and Capulet (**brawling,** perjuring) in the streets of Verona.

10. Abraham Lincoln had very little formal schooling, but his mind was (**nurtured,** flawed) by such great works as the Bible and the plays of Shakespeare.

11. The easternmost tip of Cuba was the first populated area in the region to feel the (paradox, **wrath**) of Hurricane Zelda.

12. She worked so easily and quietly that at first we did not realize how remarkably (**proficient,** amiss) she was in the laboratory.

13. It was hard to believe that the small, rather ordinary-looking person who was standing before us was a world-famous (**notable,** fledgling).

14. The charges of incompetence the candidate leveled at her opponent were but the opening (brawl, **salvo**) in her campaign to become mayor.

15. No parent can ever be (**vigilant,** amiss) enough to prevent a small child from taking many a painful tumble.

16. The rather skinny boy whom we had noticed only two years before as a (prior, **fledgling**) quarterback was now an all-American!

17. A happy (**domestic,** nurture) life can afford an executive a great deal of relief from the everyday strains of running a large company.

18. To say that the U.S. Constitution is one of the greatest documents of all time does not mean that it is entirely without (momentum, **flaws**).

19. Though I hadn't expected to be treated quite so unkindly by the audience, I didn't become (**flustered,** nurtured) or lose my professional cool.

20. (**Foremost,** Flagrant) among the reasons that so many millions of immigrants have come to the United States is the desire for freedom.

*Read the following passage, in which some of the words you have studied in this unit appear in **boldface** type. Then complete each statement given below the passage by circling the letter of the item that is **the same** or **almost the same** in meaning as the highlighted word.*

The Space Race

(Line)

Have you ever heard of the Cold War? If so, then you are familiar with one of the greatest **paradoxes** of the twentieth century: from 1948 to 1989, a war without warfare existed between the United States and the Soviet Union.

A **notable** feature of the Cold War was the race to explore space. On October 4, 1957, the Soviets launched the space race by putting the world's first satellite, *Sputnik*, into orbit around the earth. Not to be outdone, the United States retaliated by sending into space a satellite of its own. Also in 1958, Congress established the National Aeronautics and Space Administration (NASA). The main task of the **fledgling** agency was to keep up with the Soviets in the space race. (5)

NASA faced its first great challenge in 1961. In April the Soviet cosmonaut Yuri Gagarin became the first person to orbit the earth, giving the space race new **momentum**. (10)

Less than a month after Gagarin's flight, Alan Shepard became the first American to make a space flight. Nine months later, John Glenn made three orbits of the earth. During this time, President John F. Kennedy proclaimed that the **foremost** goal of the nation's space program was to land a man on the moon before the end of the decade. The question in the minds of Americans was, could the nation meet the President's challenge? Americans also wondered if (15)

(20)

Buzz Aldrin on the moon, July 20, 1969

(25)

NASA could land an astronaut on the moon *before* the Soviets.

Then just as the decade was ending, NASA achieved its greatest triumph. On July 20, 1969, the spacecraft *Eagle* landed on the surface of the moon. With millions watching around the world, Neil Armstrong took his famous moonwalk. With Armstrong's first step, the Americans had won the space race. (30)

---

1. The meaning of **paradoxes** (line 2) is
  a. statements   c. contradictions
  b. lies   d. donnybrooks

2. Notable (line 4) is best defined as
  a. trifling   c. petty
  b. noteworthy   d. foreign

3. Fledgling (line 9) most nearly means
  a. budding   c. birdlike
  b. high-flying   d. experienced

4. Momentum (line 14) is best defined as
  a. perfection   c. importance
  b. minute   d. impetus

5. The meaning of **foremost** (line 20) is
  a. paramount   c. last
  b. secondary   d. valued

Definitions

Note carefully the spelling, pronunciation, part(s) of speech, and definition(s) of each of the following words. Then write the word in the blank space(s) in the illustrative sentence(s) following. Finally, study the lists of synonyms and antonyms given at the end of each entry.

1. abnormal
(ab nôr′ məl)

(*adj.*) not usual, not typical, strange

For my sister, who is always late, being early for an appointment would constitute an **abnormal** situation.

SYNONYMS: freakish, unnatural, irregular, anomalous
ANTONYMS: normal, usual, regular, typical

2. capsize
(kap′ sīz)

(*v.*) to turn bottom side up, upset

Anyone watching could see that it was our inexperience that caused us to **capsize** the canoe.

SYNONYMS: overturn, upend, tip over
ANTONYM: remain upright

3. catastrophe
(kə tas′ trə fē)

(*n.*) a large-scale disaster, misfortune, or failure

During the Cold War, the United States did everything possible to avoid a nuclear **catastrophe** .

SYNONYMS: calamity, tragedy, cataclysm
ANTONYMS: triumph, victory, success

4. decrease
(*v.*, di krēs′;
n., dē′ krēs)

(*v.*) to become or make less; (*n.*) a lessening

The manager hopes that theft will **decrease** once the new security system is installed.
Because of a sharp **decrease** in sales, the company had to lay off two-thirds of its workers.

SYNONYMS: (*v.*) lessen, reduce, dwindle, diminish
ANTONYMS: (*v.*) increase, grow, develop, wax

5. disputatious
(dis pyü ta′ shəs)

(*adj.*) inclined to argue or debate; provoking debate

The **disputatious** senator had engaged in filibusters to block the passage of many a bill.

SYNONYMS: argumentative, quarrelsome, contentious
ANTONYMS: nonargumentative, peaceable, pacific

6. eject
(i jekt′)

(*v.*) to drive or throw out, evict

The security guards arrived to **eject** the troublesome spectator from the stands.

SYNONYMS: oust, expel, kick out
ANTONYMS: admit, let in, insert

7. flourish
(flər' ish)

(*v.*) to grow, thrive, be prosperous; to wave in the air;
(*n.*) a dramatic gesture; a fanfare of horns

It is fortunate for lovers of the arts that painting and opera still _____ **flourish** _____ in Italy.

Actors often enter the stage with a _____ **flourish** _____ .

SYNONYMS: (*v.*) prosper, burgeon, increase
ANTONYMS: (*v.*) wither, die, fade, shrivel up

8. incentive
(in sen' tiv)

(*n.*) a reason for doing something; something that stimulates action

Because career advancement is such a strong _____ **incentive** _____, adults are usually eager and hard-working students.

SYNONYMS: stimulus, spur, motive, inducement
ANTONYMS: curb, check, restraint, hindrance

9. insubordinate
(in sə bôrd' ən ət)

(*adj.*) disobedient, rebellious

The _____ **insubordinate** _____ soldier repeatedly interrupted his commanding officer.

SYNONYMS: defiant, unruly, mutinous
ANTONYMS: obedient, submissive, docile, tractable

10. legible
(lej' ə bəl)

(*adj.*) easily read

In keeping with the jokes, pharmacists will tell you that most doctors' handwriting is barely _____ **legible** _____ .

SYNONYMS: readable, clear, decipherable
ANTONYMS: unreadable, indecipherable

11. nub
(nəb)

(*n.*) the central point or heart of a matter; a knob

After seemingly endless digressions, the speaker finally got to the _____ **nub** _____ of his argument.

SYNONYMS: core, kernel, nucleus, crux
ANTONYMS: fringe, periphery, edge

12. onslaught
(än' slôt)

(*n.*) a violent attack; a sudden rush of something

To prepare for the _____ **onslaught** _____ of winter, we replenished our supply of firewood and rock salt.

SYNONYMS: assault, charge, foray, onset

13. ordain
(ôr dān')

(*v.*) to establish by law; to order or command; to appoint as a priest or minister; to destine

Ancient astrologers believed that the stars could _____ **ordain** _____ one's future.

SYNONYMS: anoint, consecrate, enact, decree
ANTONYMS: forbid, veto, cancel

14. outstrip
(aút strip')

(*v.*) to get ahead of, do better than, exceed

By offering customers low prices and good terms, the new store hopes to _____ **outstrip** _____ the competition.

SYNONYMS: outdo, outperform, outdistance, surpass
ANTONYMS: trail, lag behind

15. pervade
(pər vād')

(*v.*) to spread throughout

Pollutants _____ **pervade** _____ the atmosphere of many of our nation's large cities.

SYNONYMS: saturate, permeate, diffuse, imbue

16. prudent
(prüd' ənt)

(*adj.*) cautious, careful, showing good sense

It pays to make _____ **prudent** _____ investments.

SYNONYMS: wary, sensible, judicious
ANTONYMS: foolish, unwise, rash, reckless

17. quench
(kwench)

(*v.*) to put out, extinguish, end

The firefighters will _____ **quench** _____ the flames with water.

SYNONYMS: douse, stifle, slake
ANTONYMS: ignite, kindle

18. remnant
(rem' nənt)

(*n.*) a small part remaining behind

By the end of the war, the rebels had but a _____ **remnant** _____ of their former strength.

SYNONYMS: remainder, residue, leftover, fragment

19. simultaneous
(si məl tā' nē əs)

(*adj.*) happening or existing at the same time

The diplomats put on headphones so that they could listen to a _____ **simultaneous** _____ translation of the speech.

SYNONYM: occurring at the same time, concurrent
ANTONYM: occurring at different times

20. swerve
(swərv)

(*v.*) to turn aside sharply; (*n.*) a sharp or sudden turn

Be aware that if you _____ **swerve** _____ too sharply, you may lose control of the car.
The sudden _____ **swerve** _____ of the bus caused some passengers to fall out of their seats.

SYNONYMS: (*v.*) veer, digress, sheer off

From the words for this unit, choose the one that best completes each of the following sentences. Write the word in the space provided.

1. Even the most _____**prudent**_____ businessperson knows that there are times when it is necessary to take chances.

2. American farms continue to produce more and more food, even though the number of people working on them has actually _____**decreased**_____.

3. Though we are still the leading producers of various industrial products, other countries are catching up fast and may soon _____**outstrip**_____ us.

4. Do you really believe that making money is the only _____**incentive**_____ that leads people to work hard and try to excel?

5. Let's ignore minor side issues and get to the _____**nub**_____ of the problem as quickly as possible.

6. The secret of the trick is to remove the first card and pick up the second so quickly that the two actions seem to be _____**simultaneous**_____.

7. Trying to avoid an argument with that _____**disputatious**_____ fellow is like trying to nail oatmeal to the wall.

8. By landing the damaged plane in an open field, the pilot prevented a major _____**catastrophe**_____ from occurring.

9. When my canoe unexpectedly hit a tree stump and _____**capsized**_____, I suddenly found myself neck-deep in some very cold and dirty water.

10. The writing on the curious old document had faded badly, but it was still perfectly _____**legible**_____ when held up to the light.

11. As the holidays approached, a feeling of excitement and anticipation seemed to _____**pervade**_____ the entire school.

12. The only thing that ever really _____**quenches**_____ my thirst on a stifling summer afternoon is a glass of ice-cold lemonade.

13. Although we are used to severe winters, a heavy snowfall this early in the season is quite _____**abnormal**_____.

14. My brother was _____**ordained**_____ a priest after he had completed his studies at the seminary.

15. At the first shock of the enemy's _____**onslaught**_____, our lines wavered a bit, but they soon recovered and held firm.

16. "If that _____**insubordinate**_____ young hothead had followed my orders to the letter," the general remarked sourly, "we wouldn't be in this fix!"

17. When you want to remove the cassette from the tape deck, just push this button, and the cartridge will _____**eject**_____ automatically.

18. When a deer suddenly ran onto the road, the car _____ swerved _____ quickly to avoid hitting it.

19. After I had eaten my fill, I threw the _____ remnants _____ of my dinner into the dog's bowl.

20. After our team won the last big game of the season, we all ran out onto the field, _____ flourishing _____ our pennants and banners jubilantly.

Synonyms

*Choose the word from this unit that is **the same** or **most nearly the same** in meaning as the **boldface** word or expression in the given phrase. Write the word on the line provided.*

1. finally got to the **core** of the matter — nub

2. would **outdo** our competitors — outstrip

3. no **stimulus** to continue her studies — incentive

4. was forced to **veer** to the right — swerve

5. wants to **oust** the corrupt officials — eject

6. two events that were **happening at the same time** — simultaneous

7. witnessed the **calamity** of war — catastrophe

8. has **readable** handwriting — legible

9. tried to **slake** her thirst with water — quench

10. strong winds that could **overturn** the boat — capsize

11. had nothing left but a **fragment** of her pride — remnant

12. a chance meeting that only fate could **decree** — ordain

13. clothing **saturated** with the liquid — pervaded

14. held their ground after the initial **assault** — onslaught

15. was reprimanded for being **disobedient** — insubordinate

Antonyms

*Choose the word from this unit that is **most nearly opposite** in meaning to the **boldface** word or expression in the given phrase. Write the word on the line provided.*

16. a treaty marked by **peaceable** negotiations — disputatious

17. began to **increase** in size — decrease

18. was **reckless** in managing her affairs — prudent

19. plants that will **wither** under your care — flourish

20. exhibits **natural** behavior — abnormal

Choosing the Right Word

*Circle the **boldface** word that more satisfactorily completes each of the following sentences.*

1. To get a good grade, make sure that your composition is interesting in content, correct in grammar and spelling, and (**abnormal, legible**).

2. The high spirits with which we had begun the hike were soon (**pervaded, quenched**) when it began to rain.

3. The only advice I can give you is to take the problems one at a time and deal with each in a sensible and (**prudent, disputatious**) way.

4. After the officials had put a stop to the fight that had broken out, they (**ejected, ordained**) the offending players from the game.

5. As we returned to the dressing room after that terrible first half, the whole atmosphere seemed to be (**pervaded, capsized**) by defeat.

6. "We have become so engrossed in the minor details of the situation that we have left no time to consider the (**nub, incentive**) of the matter," I said.

7. Two of the more (**abnormal, disputatious**) members of the committee soon got into an argument about where to build the new facility.

8. We have made some progress in cleaning up the slums in our community, but that is certainly no reason to (**decrease, eject**) our efforts.

9. The train and the car approached the crossing almost (**simultaneously, prudently**), and a terrible accident seemed unavoidable.

10. When the musicians failed to arrive and the air-conditioning conked out, we realized that the party was becoming a (**nub, catastrophe**).

11. As (**ordained, flourished**) in the U.S. Constitution, the President must be a native-born American at least 35 years old when he or she takes office.

12. The possibility of getting a summer job in an office is all the (**incentive, onslaught**) I need to improve my computer skills.

13. All our hopes and plans were (**capsized, outstripped**) when we learned that we would not be able to attend the music festival.

14. The first (**onslaught, remnant**) of the disease is marked by a severe fever and the appearance of an ugly rash all over the body.

15. With eager students and able teachers, learning will (**flourish, decrease**), even though the school building may be old and shabby.

16. When the elderly pianist began to play, we were saddened to observe that he had only a(n) (**incentive, remnant**) of his once great skill.

17. Even though you may think your supervisor is wrong, you won't be able to hold your job if you act (**simultaneously, insubordinately**).

18. I'm following a very strict study schedule, but I must admit that I (**swerved, flourished**) from it when the play-offs were televised.

19. Doesn't it seem (**abnormal, insubordinate**) for a bright young person to show no interest in taking part in any school activities?

20. Has the ability of human beings to produce new inventions (**quenched, outstripped**) our ability to use them wisely?

96 ■ *Unit 8*

Vocabulary in Context

Read the following passage, in which some of the words you have studied in this unit appear in **boldface** type. Then complete each statement given below the passage by circling the letter of the item that is **the same** or **almost the same** in meaning as the highlighted word.

(Line)

Also a Woman's War

By almost any standards, the Civil War was the greatest **catastrophe** in U.S. history. Destruction **pervaded** the South and led to its economic ruin. More than 600,000 soldiers died in the conflict, and the war left a **disputatious** legacy of racial and sectional bitterness that would last for more than a century. Yet the Civil
(5) War also left another legacy. It opened the way for American women to serve with honor in war. For the first time in U.S. history, scores of women, from the North and the South, actively took part in the war effort.

With the **onslaught** of battle, women came forward in droves to pitch in on the soldiers' behalf. Some, like Sally
(10) Tompkins, established small hospitals. Others, like Mary Livermore and Mary Ann Bickerdyke, organized or ran chapters of soldiers' aid societies.
(15) Even the famous Dorothea Dix, known for being **prudent** in her care of the mentally ill, took charge of the nursing services for all the Federal armies. A great number of women
(20) also looked after their farms or took jobs formerly held by men.

Women caring for wounded Civil War soldiers

Many women, particularly nurses, came dangerously close to the fighting. Clara Barton, who later founded the American Red Cross, regularly put
(25) her life on the line while tending a wounded soldier. Some Northern women disguised themselves as men so that they could fight with Union regiments. For some, the **incentive** was patriotism. For other women, it was to be with their husbands.

Regardless of the role they played in the war, women demonstrated loyalty, bravery,
(30) and skill. They also showed that the Civil War was not just a man's war. It was also a war in which women could serve both on the battlefield and on the home front.

---

1. The meaning of **catastrophe** (line 1) is
a. triumph
c. tragedy
b. success
d. battle

2. Pervaded (line 2) most nearly means
a. ignited
c. outdid
b. trailed
d. permeated

3. Disputatious (line 3) is best defined as
a. peaceable
c. burgeoning
b. contentious
d. triumphant

4. Onslaught (line 8) is best defined as
a. onset
c. slaughter
b. ending
d. horrors

5. The meaning of **prudent** (line 16) is
a. rash
c. lagging
b. sensible
d. successful

6. Incentive (line 27) most nearly means
a. pressure
c. hindrance
b. restraint
d. inducement

Definitions

Note carefully the spelling, pronunciation, part(s) of speech, and definition(s) of each of the following words. Then write the word in the blank space(s) in the illustrative sentence(s) following. Finally, study the lists of synonyms and antonyms given at the end of each entry.

1. accelerate
(ak sel' ə rāt)

(*v.*) to speed up, cause to move faster; to bring about more quickly

The hikers needed to _____accelerate_____ their pace once it became clear that it would soon rain.

SYNONYMS: step up, quicken, hasten
ANTONYMS: slow down, retard, decelerate

2. bystander
(bī' stan dər)

(*n.*) one who looks on or observes, a person present but not taking part

The _____bystander_____ who had witnessed the collision gave his statement to the police.

SYNONYMS: observer, spectator, onlooker
ANTONYM: active participant

3. canvass
(kan' vəs)

(*v.*) to go through an area in order to procure votes, sales, or opinions; to go over in detail; to discuss

The students volunteered to _____canvass_____ the neighborhood for our candidate.

SYNONYMS: poll, survey, solicit

4. casual
(kazh' ə wəl)

(*adj.*) happening by chance or on an irregular basis; showing little concern; informal

A _____casual_____ remark made by the mayor was taken out of context and used against him by the press.

SYNONYMS: accidental, haphazard, offhand
ANTONYMS: formal, serious, premeditated, intentional

5. downtrodden
(daùn' träd ən)

(*adj.*) treated unfairly and cruelly, oppressed

Most of the immigrants at Ellis Island represented the _____downtrodden_____ masses yearning to be free.

SYNONYMS: mistreated, ground underfoot
ANTONYMS: uplifted, liberated

6. entice
(en tīs')

(*v.*) to attract, tempt

To _____entice_____ shoppers into the store, salespersons were giving away coupons for free gifts.

SYNONYMS: lure, beguile
ANTONYMS: nauseate, sicken, revolt, repel

7. erode
(i rōd′)

(*v.*) to wear away gradually, eat away

Storms and mud slides _____eroded_____ the road so that eventually it became impassible.

SYNONYMS: corrode, abrade
ANTONYMS: nurture, promote, encourage

8. flounder
(flaủn′ dər)

(*v.*) to thrash about in a clumsy or ineffective way

After suffering much damage in the storm, the small craft was left to _____flounder_____ about helplessly.

SYNONYMS: wallow, struggle

9. graphic
(graf′ ik)

(*adj.*) lifelike, vivid; relating to the pictorial arts

A witness gave the reporter a _____graphic_____ account of the destruction caused by the tornado.

SYNONYMS: lively, colorful, descriptive
ANTONYMS: dull, boring, unrealistic, colorless

10. gruesome
(grü′ səm)

(*adj.*) horrible, revolting, ghastly

The _____gruesome_____ crime rocked the ordinarily quiet neighborhood.

SYNONYMS: gory, hideous, grisly
ANTONYMS: pleasant, delightful, appealing

11. melancholy
(mel′ ən käl ē)

(*adj.*) sad, gloomy, unhappy; (*n.*) sadness, gloominess

It must have been the gloom of the house and the steady rain that made me feel so _____melancholy_____.

The tune and the lyrics of the song were filled with _____melancholy_____.

SYNONYMS: (*adj.*) depressed, dejected; (*n.*) dejection, depression
ANTONYMS: (*adj.*) merry, happy, cheerful; (*n.*) joy, elation

12. ordeal
(ôr dēl′)

(*n.*) a difficult or painful experience, a trial

The climbers were exhausted by the _____ordeal_____.

SYNONYMS: test, hardship
ANTONYMS: pleasure, cinch

13. parch
(pärch)

(*v.*) to make dry and thirsty; to shrivel with heat

The fields of Oklahoma were _____parched_____ by drought in the 1930s.

SYNONYMS: dry up, dehydrate, desiccate
ANTONYMS: soak, drench, saturate, waterlog

14. persist
(pər sist′)

(*v.*) to continue steadily in a course of action, refuse to stop or be changed; to last, remain

Despite stern warnings from their doctor, the brothers _____**persist**_____ in their bad habits.

SYNONYMS: persevere, keep at it, endure
ANTONYMS: give up, discontinue

15. puny
(pyü′ nē)

(*adj.*) of less than normal strength or size; of no importance

The wrestler let out a coarse burst of laughter when his _____**puny**_____ opponent entered the ring.

SYNONYMS: undersized, pint-size, small, weak
ANTONYMS: robust, brawny, mammoth, gigantic

16. quibble
(kwib′ əl)

(*v.*) to evade or belittle a point by twisting words or raising minor objections; (*n.*) a petty objection

Let's not _____**quibble**_____ over details.
The buyer's _____**quibble**_____ notwithstanding, the parties soon came to an agreement.

SYNONYMS: (*v.*) nitpick, split hairs, cavil; (*n.*) squabble

17. ratify
(rat′ ə fī)

(*v.*) to approve, give formal approval to, confirm

The legislatures of three fourths of the states must _____**ratify**_____ an amendment to the U.S. Constitution.

SYNONYMS: endorse, sanction, uphold
ANTONYMS: cancel, repeal, annul, veto

18. regal
(rē′ gəl)

(*adj.*) royal, kinglike; fit for a king

The two families pooled their resources to give the bride and groom a truly _____**regal**_____ wedding.

SYNONYMS: majestic, stately, princely, august
ANTONYMS: lowly, humble, abject, servile

19. stifle
(stī′ fəl)

(*v.*) to smother, prevent from breathing; to hold back or choke off

Unable to _____**stifle**_____ her anger, the sculptor lashed out at her harshest critic.

SYNONYMS: strangle, suppress, snuff
ANTONYMS: nurture, promote, encourage

20. vital
(vīt′ əl)

(*adj.*) having life, living; necessary to life, essential; key, crucial

The treaty is of _____**vital**_____ importance to the security of our nation.

SYNONYMS: indispensable, fundamental
ANTONYMS: nonessential, unnecessary

Completing the Sentence

From the words for this unit, choose the one that best completes each of the following sentences. Write the word in the space provided.

1. In our environment class, we learned that in much of the United States, the topsoil has been badly **eroded** by natural forces.

2. She gave us a clear, detailed, and **graphic** picture of what is likely to happen if we fail to come to grips with the pollution problem.

3. As we fought the forest fire, we were practically **stifled** by the extreme heat and heavy smoke.

4. The President's powers in foreign affairs are limited by the fact that any treaty he may negotiate must be **ratified** by a two-thirds vote of the Senate.

5. When the inexperienced swimmer realized that he was in very deep water, he panicked and began to **flounder** about wildly.

6. According to Greek mythology, the Sirens used their remarkable singing voices to **entice** unwary sailors to watery graves.

7. Some poets are at their best when dealing with happy events, while others seem to prefer the more **melancholy** side of life.

8. A group of reporters from the local TV station **canvassed** our district for reactions to the proposed changes in the law.

9. As soon as he learned that he was to play the king in the play, his whole personality took on an almost **regal** air.

10. The **gruesome** sight that greeted my eyes at the scene of that awful traffic accident gave me nightmares for weeks.

11. He now claims that he was just an innocent **bystander**, but I saw him actually taking part in the fight.

12. If you were spending your own money, rather than mine, you would be more inclined to **quibble** over the price of the repairs.

13. Though the new halfback looked a little **puny** to us, he managed to hold his own against players twice his size and build.

14. Regular visits to the dentist are **vital** if you wish to have healthy, good-looking teeth.

15. How can he **persist** in denying that he was at the scene of the crime when several people saw him there?

16. Since the twins' birthday party is by no means a formal affair, **casual** clothing is in order.

17. The sled **accelerated** with alarming speed as it went down the steep slope.

18. At that tender age I was so shy that I found it a(n) _____ordeal_____ to be introduced to people I'd never met before.

19. After an hour of trudging along the dusty road under the hot sun, we were so _____parched_____ that all we could think of was cold water.

20. Although these workers were _____downtrodden_____ in their native land, in the United States they are entitled to a fair wage and safe working conditions.

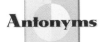

Synonyms

Choose the word from this unit that is **the same** or **most nearly the same** in meaning as the **boldface** word or expression in the given phrase. Write the word on the line provided.

1. described the devastation in **vivid** detail _____graphic_____

2. a blistering sun that will **desiccate** the land _____parch_____

3. attempted to **hold back** a sob _____stifle_____

4. a meeting that seemed **accidental** _____casual_____

5. chastised for a **weak** effort _____puny_____

6. horrified by the **grisly** sight _____gruesome_____

7. pain that will **endure** despite medication _____persist_____

8. acids that **corrode** its strength _____erode_____

9. could always **tempt** them with homemade cookies _____entice_____

10. was just a **spectator**, not a participant _____bystander_____

11. would **nitpick** over the smallest details _____quibble_____

12. to **poll** voters for their opinion _____canvass_____

13. survived the painful **test** _____ordeal_____

14. will **hasten** the growth of industry _____accelerate_____

15. would **wallow** about in the mud _____flounder_____

Antonyms

Choose the word from this unit that is **most nearly opposite** in meaning to the **boldface** word or expression in the given phrase. Write the word on the line provided.

16. was in a **cheerful** mood after the play _____melancholy_____

17. expected Congress to **repeal** the legislation _____ratify_____

18. read about the **liberated** masses _____downtrodden_____

19. is a **humble** affair from beginning to end _____regal_____

20. thought those details **unnecessary** _____vital_____

Choosing the Right Word

Circle the **boldface** word that more satisfactorily completes each of the following sentences.

1. With her (**regal,** graphic) bearing and imperious manner, Elizabeth I looked every inch the queen she in fact was.

2. The soundness of the basic ideas of the U.S. Constitution has been (**ratified,** enticed) by the experience of more than 200 years.

3. "How can you compare a union employee," the factory owner asked, "to the (**downtrodden,** melancholy) serfs and slaves of earlier times?"

4. In a democracy, the average citizen should be an active participant in public affairs, not just a quiet (**bystander,** enticer).

5. She made what proved to be a (**vital,** parched) mistake when she gave the job to one of the applicants without checking his references.

6. In spite of all the setbacks we have had, we must (**persist,** quibble) in our efforts to achieve the goal we have set for ourselves.

7. Aided by diagrams on the chalkboard, she gave a summary of her plan so clear and (**graphic,** regal) that it won the full support of the audience.

8. I find your offer most (gruesome, **enticing**), but my better judgment tells me to have nothing to do with it.

9. Do her efforts to (**accelerate,** flounder) our departure mean that she is trying to help us, or just get rid of us?

10. You will never do well in school so long as your attitude toward your studies remains (downtrodden, **casual**) and unconcerned.

11. If you have prepared properly for the exams, there will be no reason to regard them as a terrible (quibble, **ordeal**).

12. Instead of continuing to (**flounder,** accelerate), we must decide on a goal and start to move toward it.

13. It is hard to believe that this sturdy, six-foot basketball star was a (vital, **puny**) 100-pounder only a few years ago.

14. No doubt he has our best interests at heart, but my faith in him has been (**eroded,** persisted) by repeated evidence of his poor judgment.

15. In spite of the bright sunshine and the happy crowds, a strange mood of (ordeal, **melancholy**) seemed to take possession of me.

16. The dictator used fear and violence to (**stifle,** canvass) discontent among the people he ruled.

17. After weeks of no rain, the (**parched,** graphic) earth turned to dust that was blown away by the strong winds.

18. When I asked you what you meant by those words, I wasn't (**quibbling,** ratifying) but trying to discover what the problem was.

19. I think it showed bad judgment on your part to tell such a (**gruesome,** puny) story to a child who is so easily frightened.

20. The assistant principal (**canvassed,** quibbled) the faculty for ways of improving the educational standards of the school.

Vocabulary in Context

*Read the following passage, in which some of the words you have studied in this unit appear in **boldface** type. Then complete each statement given below the passage by circling the letter of the item that is **the same** or **almost the same** in meaning as the highlighted word.*

Giants of the Desert

(Line)

Visitors to the **parched** Sonoran Desert of southern Arizona and northern Mexico marvel at the many-armed giants that give the landscape its unique appearance. These are the giant saguaro cacti. In the dry, rugged desert a saguaro cactus can live for more than 200 years, grow to a height of 60 feet, and have as many as 50 arms.

Amazingly, saguaro cacti **persist** despite the harsh, unforgiving desert climate. Those (5) that have grown to old age have survived drought, freezes, flash floods, and brush fires,

as well as the pack rats that eat their seedlings. Like all desert plants, saguaros hoard water. These leafless plants absorb the water through their long roots and store it for use during the desert's long (10) dry spells.

Naturally, the mighty saguaro is a **vital** part of desert life. In fact, this giant may be home to many animals, including woodpeckers, owls, doves, bats, and insects. In addition, after a (15) saguaro reaches the age of fifty or so, hardy flowers appear at the top of the plant once a year. These flowers **entice** birds, bats, and bees, who come for the nectar and for the tasty flowers with their black seeds. (20)

Although the **regal** saguaros are plentiful in the Southwest, they are, unfortunately, in danger. These giant cacti have great value in landscape gardening, and poachers can earn thousands of dollars by uprooting them and selling them to (25)

Saguaro cactus in bloom

nurseries. To protect these Southwestern treasures from poachers, agents for the Arizona Department of Agriculture patrol the desert. Theirs is a hard but important job, for without the saguaro many desert creatures would suffer food shortages and loss of nesting sites. The Southwest, too, would lose something of unique importance, since these desert giants have come to symbolize the very essence of this rugged region. (30)

---

1. The meaning of **parched** (line 1) is
a. saturated   c. enclosed
b. rugged   d. dry

2. Persist (line 5) most nearly means
a. expire   c. give up
b. persevere   d. fight

3. Vital (line 12) is best defined as
a. useless   c. crucial
b. humble   d. unique

4. Entice (line 18) most nearly means
a. lure   c. sicken
b. repel   d. uproot

5. The meaning of **regal** (line 21) is
a. tall   c. majestic
b. hardy   d. lowly

Visit us at **www.sadlier-oxford.com**
for interactive puzzles and games.

REVIEW UNITS 7–9

Vocabulary for Comprehension

*Read the following passage, in which some of the words you have studied in Units 7–9 appear in **boldface** type. Then answer questions 1–12 on page 106 on the basis of what is stated or implied in the passage and in the introductory statement.*

This passage describes the significant impact of the Civilian Conservation Corps on America's landscape and economy during the Great Depression.

(Line)

During the Great Depression of the 1930s, the **domestic** economy was all but destroyed. Joblessness was widespread, and millions of
(5) Americans were hungry. In an effort to address the economic **catastrophe** gripping the nation, President Franklin D. Roosevelt created several ambitious programs
(10) under a policy known as the New Deal. These programs were aimed not only at building the nation's economy but also at uplifting the American spirit.
(15) Although the New Deal provided help to banks, farmers, and failing businesses, perhaps its most **notable** achievement was in the creation of programs to **decrease** the
(20) number of the nation's unemployed. By 1932, 12 million people were jobless, and Roosevelt knew he had to put Americans back to work. Promising "direct, vigorous action" in
(25) his Inaugural Address, the President created a variety of programs to help the jobless and **downtrodden**.

One of the first and most successful of these programs was
(30) the Civilian Conservation Corps, or CCC, which operated from 1933 to 1942. This was a massive public works project that addressed two of

the President's interests: promoting
(35) conservation and providing jobs for the nation's unemployed youths. Calling the CCC a civilian "tree army," Roosevelt put the program under the Army's control. Guided by
(40) engineers and experts in forestry and agriculture, nearly 3 million young men between the ages of 17 and 28 went to work. They planted trees, dug canals, conserved soil, cleared
(45) beaches and campgrounds, stocked lakes and rivers with fish, and even restored historic battlefields. And they did it for just thirty dollars a month, warm clothing, and three
(50) meals a day.

Although the CCC proved an **ordeal** for some, it gave others a lifeline. Unexpectedly, it also proved to be a boon for the nation. As the
(55) future would show, it gave the Army much-needed experience in managing large numbers of recruits, while it also prepared the nation's young men for the military discipline
(60) they would soon face in the Second World War.

1. Which of the following would make the best title for this passage?
   a. FDR's New Deal Programs
   b. $30 and Three Meals a Day
   c. High Marks for the CCC
   d. Saving the Environment
   e. A History of the Great Depression

2. The meaning of **domestic** (line 2) is
   a. national
   b. foreign
   c. household servant
   d. agricultural
   e. industrial

3. **Catastrophe** (line 7) most nearly means
   a. problem
   b. disaster
   c. success
   d. instability
   e. debate

4. **Notable** (line 18) is best defined as
   a. competent
   b. mammoth
   c. well-known person
   d. attentive
   e. impressive

5. **Decrease** (line 19) most nearly means
   a. reduce
   b. increase
   c. assist
   d. employ
   e. recruit

6. **Downtrodden** (line 27) is best defined as
   a. uplifted
   b. needy
   c. oppressed
   d. homeless
   e. sickly

7. The function of paragraphs 1 and 2 is to provide
   a. a historical context for the founding of the CCC
   b. detailed information about the CCC
   c. biographical information about Franklin D. Roosevelt

d. an analysis of Roosevelt's New Deal policies
e. a complete history of the Great Depression

8. The CCC was founded mainly to benefit
   a. unemployed fathers
   b. unemployed young men
   c. college students needing a summer job
   d. women and men in rural areas
   e. engineers and experts in forestry

9. From paragraph 3 (lines 28–50), you can infer that the main reason for joining the CCC was
   a. to have a job
   b. to leave home
   c. to see the country
   d. to join the army
   e. to be outdoors

10. The meaning of **ordeal** (line 52) is
    a. pleasant experience
    b. challenging game
    c. new adventure
    d. easy time
    e. hardship

11. The writer's attitude toward the subject can best be described as
    a. disinterested
    b. sarcastic
    c. critical
    d. respectful
    e. ironic

12. The CCC had all of the following beneficial effects EXCEPT
    a. providing jobs for unemployed young men
    b. promoting conservation by planting trees and improving the environment
    c. giving the U.S. Army experience managing large numbers of recruits
    d. giving young men experience with military discipline
    e. creating several new national parks in the West

Grammar in Context

In the opening sentence "During the Great Depression of the 1930s, the domestic economy was all but destroyed" (lines 1–3 on page 105), the author of the passage has made sure that the **singular subject** "economy" has the **singular verb** "was." There are two basic rules of **subject-verb agreement**: A **singular subject** must have a **singular verb**. A **plural subject** must have a **plural verb**.

All verbs must agree with their subjects even when words come between them. Verbs must agree with compound subjects (linked by *and*, *or*, or *nor*) and with subjects that are collective nouns (such as *team* and *class*). They must agree with indefinite pronouns (such as *each*, *anyone*, or *several*), with nouns that are singular in meaning although plural in form (such as *acoustics* or *politics*), and with measurements and amounts. Verbs must also agree with their subjects when those subjects are confusing, as is the case when the subject follows the verb in a sentence.

Choose the verb in parentheses that agrees with the subject of each sentence, and write it on the line provided.

1. Would you agree that the New Deal programs (**was, were**) very important for improving the American economy and lifting people's spirits?
were

2. Along with food and clothing, thirty dollars a month (**was, were**) what a CCC worker earned.
was

3. Many Americans today (**has, have**) relatives who once worked for the CCC.
have

4. Neither the CCC nor the WPA, the Works Progress Administration, (**is, are**) in existence today.
is

5. Would either of these federal programs (**passes, pass**) through Congress today?
pass

6. Politics (**plays, play**) a key role in the passage of legislation authorizing government projects.
plays

7. Roosevelt's efforts on behalf of the jobless and the poor (**sets, set**) a high standard for future administrations.
set

8. Today men and women often (**works, work**) side by side on huge public construction projects.
work

Two-Word Completions

Circle the pair of words that best complete the meaning of each of the following passages.

See pages T38–T48 for explanations of answers.

1. As we _____ violently to the right to avoid some rocks that suddenly sprang into view, our canoe _____ and pitched us headlong into the churning waters of the river.
a. flourished . . . flustered
b. canvassed . . . ejected
c. swerved . . . capsized
d. brawled . . . nurtured

2. If you want to stop your automobile, apply the brakes. If you want it to gain _____, step on the _____.
a. momentum . . . accelerator
b. salvo . . . nub
c. wrath . . . flaw
d. incentive . . . paradox

3. When prices go up, the value of our money _____. The higher the cost of living climbs, the more deeply inflation _____ the purchasing power of the dollar.
a. accelerates . . . entices
b. decreases . . . erodes
c. persists . . . perjures
d. flourishes . . . parches

4. My throat became so _____ during that long trek over dusty trails on the hottest day of summer that I firmly believed nothing would ever _____ my thirst!
a. flawed . . . nurture
b. puny . . . decrease
c. parched . . . quench
d. flagrant . . . pervade

5. "An experienced worker doesn't usually have trouble handling a new job with _____," the personnel manager observed. "A beginner, however, will normally _____ around until he or she learns the ropes."
a. prudence . . . quibble
b. proficiency . . . flounder
c. incentive . . . flourish
d. vigilance . . . swerve

6. "It isn't _____ to spend more than you make," I observed. "Only a fool would allow expenses to _____ income."
a. vital . . . fluster
b. amiss . . . stifle
c. abnormal . . . nurture
d. prudent . . . outstrip

Choosing the Right Meaning

Read each sentence carefully. Then circle the item that best completes the statement below the sentence.

See pages T38–T48 for explanations of answers.

Heavy losses during the Battle of Britain sometimes forced the Royal Air Force to send fledglings up against the German formations. (2)

1. In line 2 the word **fledglings** is best defined as

a. young birds   (b. novice pilots)   c. veteran flyers   d. damaged fighters

According to the principle of Manifest Destiny, first advanced in the 1840s, the United States was ordained to expand westward to the Pacific. (2)

2. In line 2 the word **ordained** is used to mean

a. ordered   b. appointed   c. enacted   (d. fated)

I think that the chairperson is doing me an injustice by dismissing my contribution to the project as "puny." (2)

3. The word **puny** in line 2 most nearly means

a. sickly   (b. unimportant)   c. undersized   d. off the wall

Far from being only casual acquaintances, as they claimed, the two had secretly been in cahoots for years. (2)

4. The word **casual** in line 1 most nearly means

(a. occasional)   b. personal   c. unconcerned   d. accidental

"There will be no response to the proposal," remarked the diplomat, "until my government has had an opportunity to canvass the terms and conditions." (2)

5. The best definition for the word **canvass** in line 2 is

a. gather   b. solicit   (c. examine)   d. poll

Antonyms

*In each of the following groups, circle the word or expression that is most nearly the **opposite** of the word in **boldface** type.*

1. foremost
a. chief
(b. last)
c. first
d. most popular

2. abnormal
a. strange
b. new
c. interesting
(d. commonplace)

3. decrease
a. shrivel
b. dwindle
c. change
(d. grow)

4. fledgling
(a. veteran)
b. wealthy
c. painless
d. clumsy

5. ratify
a. honor
(b. cancel)
c. write
d. endorse

6. nurture
a. beguile
b. esteem
(c. neglect)
d. foster

7. detest
(a. adore)
b. notice
c. avoid
d. loathe

8. notable
a. experienced
b. up-to-date
(c. unimpressive)
d. demanding

9. vital
(a. unimportant)
b. interesting
c. difficult
d. life-or-death

11. prudent
a. sensible
b. wealthy
c. demanding
(d. foolish)

13. melancholy
a. sleepy
b. sad
(c. happy)
d. weird

15. proficient
a. fast
(b. unskilled)
c. expert
d. fearless

10. puny
(a. brawny)
b. wise
c. intelligent
d. small

12. flagrant
a. youthful
(b. petty)
c. serious
d. unexplained

14. legible
a. elegant
(b. unreadable)
c. childish
d. neat

16. wrath
(a. favor)
b. intelligence
c. position
d. anger

Word Families

A. *On the line provided, write the word you have learned in Units 7–9 that is related to each of the following nouns.*
EXAMPLE: persistence—**persist**

1. proficiency, proficientness   **proficient**
2. priority, prioress, priory   **prior**
3. flagrancy, flagrance   **flagrant**
4. ratification, ratifier   **ratify**
5. detester, detestastion, destestability, detestableness   **detest**
6. vigil, vigilance, vigilantness, vigilante, vigilantism   **vigilant**
7. presumption, presumer, presumptuousness   **presume**
8. erosion, erodibility, erosiveness, erosivity   **erode**
9. enticement   **entice**
10. abnormality, abnormalness, abnormalcy   **abnormal**
11. ejection, ejector, ejectment, ejecta   **eject**
12. insubordination   **insubordinate**
13. legibility   **legible**
14. prudence   **prudent**
15. simultaneity, simultaneousness   **simultaneous**

B. *On the line provided, write the word you have learned in Units 7–9 that is related to each of the following verbs.*
EXAMPLE: pervade—**pervasive**

16. note   **notable**
17. perjure   **perjury**
18. domesticate   **domestic**
19. vitalize   **vital**
20. dispute   **disputatious**

Word Associations

In each of the following groups, circle the word that is best defined or suggested by the given phrase.

1. fit for a king
   a. vital   (b. regal)   c. proficient   d. disputatious

2. be ever watchful
   a. flagrant   b. persistent   (c. vigilant)   d. domestic

3. the heart of the problem
   a. ordeal   b. onslaught   (c. nub)   d. remnant

4. to outdo the competition
   (a. outstrip)   b. eject   c. erode   d. nurture

5. a sudden or violent attack
   (a. onslaught)   b. incentive   c. ordeal   d. paradox

6. what is left over
   a. bystander   b. nub   (c. remnant)   d. incentive

7. something essential
   a. abnormal   (b. vital)   c. prudent   d. puny

8. could not find a defect
   (a. flaw)   b. perjury   c. paradox   d. quibble

9. trial by fire or water
   a. incentive   b. quibble   (c. ordeal)   d. paradox

10. a noisy quarrel or fight
   a. ordeal   b. incentive   c. catastrophe   (d. brawl)

11. to wear away one's confidence
   a. swerve   (b. erode)   c. stifle   d. fluster

12. to permeate the house with cooking smells
   a. entice   (b. pervade)   c. flourish   d. quench

13. to take their innocence for granted
   (a. presume)   b. pervade   c. quench   d. persist

14. to suppress a yawn
   a. detest   (b. stifle)   c. entice   d. capsize

15. to douse the flames with water
   a. parch   b. eject   c. outstrip   (d. quench)

16. a burst of laughter, cheers, or applause
   (a. salvo)   b. fledgling   c. catastrophe   d. brawl

17. the oppressed masses
   a. fledgling   (b. downtrodden)   c. insubordinate   d. melancholy

18. has gone awry
   a. abnormal   b. prudent   (c. amiss)   d. vital

19. an inducement to make one work harder
   a. salvo   b. momentum   c. nub   (d. incentive)

20. to bring up and care for a child
   a. ratify   (b. nurture)   c. ordain   d. flourish

graph, graphy—to write

This root appears in **graphic** (page 99), literally "having to do with writing." The word now means "lifelike or vivid," "relating to graphs or diagrams," or "having to do with the visual arts." Some other words based on the same root are listed below.

autobiography	**biography**	**graphite**	**pictograph**
autograph	**geography**	**graphology**	**seismograph**

From the list of words above, choose the one that corresponds to each of the brief definitions below. Write the word in the blank space in the illustrative sentence below the definition.

1. an account of a person's life written by another person; such writings, collectively
Carl Sandburg wrote a famous _____**biography**_____ of Abraham Lincoln.

2. to write in one's own handwriting; to write one's signature on or in; a signature
Fans hounded the actor for his _____**autograph**_____.

3. the study of handwriting
Police investigators often rely on _____**graphology**_____ to help them unlock clues to a criminal's personality.

4. an instrument that records the direction, force, and duration of earthquakes and other earth tremors
A _____**seismograph**_____ measures the intensity of an earthquake.

5. the story of one's own life written by oneself
Helen Keller's _____**autobiography**_____ is entitled *The Story of My Life*.

6. the study of the earth's surface, climate, plants, animals, natural resources, people, and industries; the physical features of a place or region
Maps are important tools in the study of _____**geography**_____.

7. a picture or symbol used to represent an idea in a system of picture writing; a diagram using pictures to represent data
The Lakota used _____**pictographs**_____ to record important events from their past.

8. a soft, black form of carbon
The "lead" in lead pencils is actually _____**graphite**_____.

From the list of words above, choose the one that best completes each of the following sentences. Write the word in the blank space provided.

1. On Career Day our teacher's handwriting was analyzed by a guest speaker who had studied _____**graphology**_____.

2. The ___autobiography___ of Frederick Douglass, covering his early years, became an instant bestseller.

3. The university's ___seismograph___ detected that a moderate earthquake had occurred in the Pacific Ocean.

4. ___Graphite___ can be used as a lubricant when mixed with oil.

5. The young woman begged the star of the musical to ___autograph___ her program.

6. A good ___biography___ of Ulysses S. Grant or Robert E. Lee can provide valuable information about the important battles of the Civil War.

7. Our teacher advised us to draw a ___pictograph___ to help us chart the latest information about population growth in Asia.

8. The ___geography___ of Central America includes rugged mountains.

---

*Circle the **boldface** word that more satisfactorily completes each of the following sentences.*

1. Certain ancient peoples, such as the Egyptians, used (**pictographs,** autographs) in their written messages.

2. Although vacationers might not realize it, they are studying our country's (autobiography, **geography**) when they take to the roads in the summer.

3. (**Autographs,** Graphologies) of famous people such as Abraham Lincoln can fetch high prices at auctions.

4. Networks of (pictographs, **seismographs**) can sometimes help to warn of approaching tidal waves, which are caused by earthquakes.

5. "This (**biography,** geography) gives an accurate history of Leo Tolstoy's life," the librarian said.

6. Old school desks often had a groove into which hot liquid (**graphite,** seismograph) could be poured and then used for writing when cooled.

7. An expert in (**graphology,** geography) once told me that my signature showed me to be a very generous person.

8. *The Diary of a Young Girl* is an example of a(n) (biography, **autobiography**) because it was written by Anne Frank herself.

Analogies

In each of the following, circle the item that best completes the comparison.

See pages T38–48 for explanations of answers.

1. foretaste is to **preview** as
a. luster is to radiance
b. recompense is to ingredient
c. salvo is to snare
d. iota is to nub

2. incentive is to **goad** as
a. potential is to mortify
b. quibble is to dishearten
c. flaw is to entice
d. hazard is to dissuade

3. drought is to **parched** as
a. deluge is to sodden
b. blizzard is to transparent
c. trickle is to drenched
d. heat wave is to unscathed

4. paradox is to **bewilder** as
a. pleasure is to wince
b. failure is to animate
c. triumph is to brood
d. mishap is to fluster

5. plague is to **catastrophe** as
a. operation is to entertainment
b. vacation is to danger
c. cross-examination is to ordeal
d. appointment is to emergency

6. perjury is to **lie** as
a. forgery is to kidnap
b. robbery is to cheat
c. larceny is to envy
d. homicide is to kill

7. substantial is to **weight** as
a. dynamic is to momentum
b. trivial is to importance
c. makeshift is to solidity
d. marginal is to leeway

8. counterfeit is to **inimitable** as
a. douse is to inflammable
b. replace is to indispensable
c. continue is to interminable
d. see is to inaudible

9. eradicate is to **nurture** as
a. germinate is to flourish
b. browse is to maul
c. stifle is to foster
d. dupe is to hoodwink

10. notable is to **prominent** as
a. tactful is to spirited
b. barren is to void
c. graphic is to simultaneous
d. sullen is to poised

Choosing the Right Meaning

Read each sentence carefully. Then circle the item that best completes the statement below the sentence.

See pages T38–48 for explanations of answers.

Though Lee's surrender brought to an end the terrible bloodshed of the Civil War, hard feelings between North and South persisted for generations. (2)

1. The best definition for the word **persisted** in line 2 is
a. were unchanged
b. slowly disappeared
c. stubbornly endured
d. flared up

In the plays of Shakespeare, the entrance of a king is often announced by a flourish of trumpets. (2)

2. In line 1 the word **flourish** most nearly means
a. prosperity   b. gesture   c. waving   d. fanfare

"May I presume upon your patience," I inquired of my boss, "to ask you to explain once again why I can't have that raise?" (2)

3. In line 1 the phrase **presume upon** most nearly means

a. safely assume

~~b. take liberties with~~

c. dare

d. completely exhaust

The gunnery officer concluded the drill by ordering the launching crew to fire at a drone.

4. In line 1 the word **drone** is used to mean

a. swarm of bees

~~b. remote-control target~~

c. loud humming noise

d. loafer

Try as they might, negotiators could not persuade the hostile parties to sit down and talk, much less patch up their differences.

(2)

5. The word **hostile** in line 1 is best defined as

~~a. warring~~
b. unfavorable
c. suspicious
d. restless

Two-Word Completions

Circle the pair of words that best complete the meaning of each of the following sentences.

See pages T38–48 for explanations of answers.

1. The little camper's _____ expression and mournful voice told me more eloquently than words could ever have just how much she _____ for home.

a. fickle . . . canvassed

b. anonymous . . . scurried

~~c. melancholy . . . yearned~~

d. prudent . . . catered

2. Sometimes, public opinion is so _____ and unpredictable that a candidate who is the darling of the crowd one day may find himself or herself roundly _____ the next.

~~a. fickle . . . detested~~

b. miscellaneous . . . presumed

c. proficient . . . prescribed

d. orthodox . . . dominated

3. The violence of the enemy's _____ at first threatened to turn our position and drive us from the field, but we quickly regrouped and _____ a stunning defeat on the foe.

a. vengeance . . . entreated

~~b. onslaught . . . inflicted~~

c. wrath . . . eroded

d. remnant . . . consolidated

4. When police _____ the man about his movements on that night, he claimed to have been at a ball game. But officials have failed to _____ his alibi.

a. indulged . . . ratify

b. ordained . . . swerve

c. canvassed . . . pelt

~~d. interrogated . . . verify~~

5. The study of history teaches us that laziness and indifference may slowly _____ the rights and privileges of a free people. For that reason, we must be ever _____ in protecting and defending our liberties.

a. hurtle . . . transparent

~~b. erode . . . vigilant~~

c. eradicate . . . docile

d. nurture . . . tactful

Read the passage below. Then complete the exercise at the bottom of the page.

Our Debt to the Greeks

In Greek mythology, Atlas was one of the Titans, a race of mythical giants characterized by brute strength and primitive force. Atlas stood atop a mountain

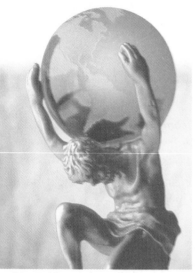

separating the earth from the heavens. This myth inspired the great 16th-century Flemish geographer Gerhardus Mercator to illustrate the cover of his new book of maps with a drawing of the mighty Atlas balancing a globe on his shoulders.

Classical Greek was the language of ancient Greece. The English language owes a tremendous debt to the Greeks for hundreds of words that have become part of our living language. A *dynasty* (Unit 1) is a powerful family or group of rulers that maintains its position or power for some time. A critic who describes a dance performance as *dynamic* (Unit 6) is conveying that it was vigorous and forceful. Both of these words are based on the Greek root *dyna-* (from the Greek word *dynamikos*), which means power.

Greek mythology has been the source of many English words. For example, Hygeia was the Greek goddess of vigor and well-being. What weakness could you claim as your Achilles heel?

Atlas holding up the world

In Column A below are 9 more words borrowed from the Greeks. With or without a dictionary, match each word with its meanings in Column B.

Column A

__h__	**1.** tyrant
__i__	**2.** titanic
__e__	**3.** hygiene
__b__	**4.** tragedy
__g__	**5.** monopoly
__f__	**6.** mosaic
__c__	**7.** strategy
__a__	**8.** sphere
__d__	**9.** chorus

Column B

a. a round, solid figure in which any point on its surface is the same distance from its center; an area of interest

b. a serious play that has a sad ending; any event that is disastrous or terrible

c. a plan of action intended to attain a specific goal

d. a group of people trained to sing together; the part of a song repeated after each verse

e. the science that deals with maintaining good health

f. a decorative picture or pattern made from the artful arrangement of small pieces of tile, glass, wood, or stone

g. total control of a service or product by one company

h. one who exercises power unfairly or cruelly

i. having great size, power, or strength; colossal, gigantic

Definitions

Note carefully the spelling, pronunciation, part(s) of speech, and definition(s) of each of the following words. Then write the word in the blank space(s) in the illustrative sentence(s) following. Finally, study the lists of synonyms and antonyms given at the end of each entry.

1. bellow
(bel' ō)

(*v.*) to make a sound similar to that of a bull, roar; (*n.*) a loud, angry roar

The wounded buffalo began to _____**bellow**_____ in pain.

The troop commander's _____**bellow**_____ could be heard a mile away.

SYNONYMS: (*v.*) yell, bawl, holler; (*n.*) howl
ANTONYMS: (*v.*) whisper; (*n.*) murmur

2. beneficiary
(ben ə fish' ē er ē)

(*n.*) one who benefits from something; a person who is left money or other property in a will or the like

The _____**beneficiary**_____ of the dead man's will was the main suspect in the murder case.

SYNONYMS: recipient, heir

3. botch
(bäch)

(*v.*) to repair or patch poorly; make a mess of; (*n.*) a hopelessly bungled job

The unsupervised laborers proceeded to _____**botch**_____ the job badly.

SYNONYMS: (*v.*) foul up, bungle, mangle

4. clutter
(klət' ər)

(*v.*) to fill or cover in a disorderly way; (*n.*) a state of disorder, mess

When we moved into our new house, we unloaded the truck and began to _____**clutter**_____ up the dining room with boxes.

Attics are often filled with _____**clutter**_____.

SYNONYMS: (*v.*) litter; (*n.*) confusion
ANTONYMS: (*n.*) order, tidiness, neatness

5. dilapidated
(də lap' ə dā tid)

(*adj.*) falling apart or ruined, run-down

The old house had become so _____**dilapidated**_____ that no one could live in it anymore.

SYNONYMS: in disrepair, deteriorated, gone to seed
ANTONYMS: shipshape, trim

6. dismantle
(dis man' təl)

(*v.*) to take apart; to strip of something

After the final performance, all the actors worked with the stagehands to _____**dismantle**_____ the set.

SYNONYM: disassemble
ANTONYMS: put together, assemble, construct

7. farce
(färs)

(*n.*) a play filled with ridiculous or absurd happenings; broad or far-fetched humor; a ridiculous sham

The humor in the play was so broad and the plot so ridiculous that the critic termed the play a _____farce_____.

SYNONYMS: buffoonery, mockery
ANTONYMS: tragedy, melodrama, tearjerker

8. futile
(fyüt′ əl)

(*adj.*) not successful, failing to have any result; useless; unimportant, frivolous

After several _____futile_____ attempts to save it, the captain ordered the ship abandoned.

SYNONYMS: fruitless, vain, ineffective
ANTONYMS: successful, effective

9. grueling
(grü′ liŋ)

(*adj.*) very tiring, calling for an extreme effort

After the _____grueling_____ climb, two of the mountaineers collapsed, exhausted.

SYNONYMS: exhausting, punishing, taxing
ANTONYMS: easy, effortless

10. hospitable
(häs pit′ ə bəl)

(*adj.*) offering friendly or generous treatment to guests; open to anything new or strange

Known for their generosity to strangers, the local inhabitants offered a _____hospitable_____ welcome to our tour group.

SYNONYMS: gracious, cordial, courteous
ANTONYMS: unfriendly, cold, icy, chilly

11. lair
(lâr)

(*n.*) the home or den of a wild animal; any hideout

The police were making careful preparations to trap the smugglers in their _____lair_____.

SYNONYMS: nest, burrow, hideaway

12. lavish
(lav′ ish)

(*adj.*) overly generous, extravagant; abundant; (*v.*) to spend or give freely or without limit

The couple received _____lavish_____ wedding gifts from their closest friends.

SYNONYMS: (*adj.*) excessive, profuse
ANTONYMS: (*adj.*) stingy, meager; (*v.*) begrudge, stint, deny

13. morbid
(môr′ bid)

(*adj.*) in an unhealthy mental state, extremely gloomy; caused by or related to disease, unwholesome

The police captain was afraid that the officer was taking a _____morbid_____ interest in the crime.

SYNONYMS: depressed, unsound, "sick"
ANTONYMS: wholesome, healthy, cheerful, blithe

14. notorious
(nō tôr′ ē əs)

(*adj.*) widely known because of bad conduct

Chicago had its share of _____notorious_____ gangsters in the 1930s.

SYNONYMS: disgraceful, infamous, disreputable
ANTONYMS: unknown, obscure, respectable

15. pamper
(pam′ pər)

(*v.*) to allow too many privileges, be too generous and easygoing toward

If my aunt continues to _____pamper_____ that child, he may grow into an irresponsible adult.

SYNONYMS: coddle, cater to, indulge
ANTONYMS: abuse, maltreat, mistreat, discipline

16. parasite
(par′ ə sīt)

(*n.*) an organism that lives in or on another organism; one who lives off another person

Uninvited, he hung around with the players so much that the team considered him a real _____parasite_____.

SYNONYMS: sponger, freeloader, leech

17. shirk
(shərk)

(*v.*) to avoid or get out of doing work, neglect a duty; to sneak, slink

People who tend to _____shirk_____ their responsibilities are not to be relied upon.

SYNONYMS: duck, sidestep
ANTONYMS: fulfill, perform, shoulder, take on

18. surplus
(sər′ pləs)

(*n.*) an amount beyond what is required, excess; (*adj.*) more than what is needed or expected

Dad was relieved to find that his business had a _____surplus_____ at the end of the year.

The Army decided to sell its _____surplus_____ goods to a group of manufacturers.

SYNONYMS: (*n.*) glut, surfeit, overage
ANTONYMS: (*n.*) shortage, lack, dearth, paucity

19. timidity
(tə mid′ ə tē)

(*n.*) the state of being easily frightened

The shy child's natural _____timidity_____ had made her afraid to try out for the team.

SYNONYMS: fearfulness, faintheartedness
ANTONYMS: fearlessness, boldness, intrepidity

20. veto
(vē′ tō)

(*n.*) the power to forbid or prevent; (*v.*) to prohibit, reject

The President decided to _____veto_____ the bill presented to him by Congress.

SYNONYMS: (*v.*) turn down, nix, forbid
ANTONYMS: (*v.*) approve, endorse, ratify, confirm

Completing the Sentence

From the words for this unit, choose the one that best completes each of the following sentences. Write the word in the space provided.

1. All the members of that family are such _____**hospitable**_____ people that we are always completely at ease whenever we visit them.

2. They gave me so _____**lavish**_____ a helping of dinner that for the first time in my life I was unable to polish off the food on my plate.

3. As a child she was so _____**pampered**_____ by her parents that she still seems to think that her wishes should be instantly granted.

4. The practice session was so _____**grueling**_____ that we scarcely had the strength to get to the dressing room and take our showers.

5. It is a curious fact of nature that most _____**parasites**_____ are unable to survive when they are separated from the organisms they feed on.

6. The _____**surplus**_____ of food produced each year in the United States is desperately needed to feed hungry people all over the world.

7. The President can _____**veto**_____ a measure passed by a majority of Congress, but his _____**veto**_____ may be overridden.

8. It is hard to believe that a teenager so courageous and able on a camping trip can show so much _____**timidity**_____ when invited to a dance.

9. Though the cabin was a little _____**dilapidated**_____ when we bought it, we were able to spruce it up without going to a great deal of expense.

10. The animals in the zoo are kept in quarters that are designed to imitate their _____**lairs**_____ in the wild state.

11. When he realized that he had been tricked by his opponent, he let out a _____**bellow**_____ of rage that could be heard all over the gym.

12. Unfortunately, the brave lifeguard's valiant attempts to rescue the drowning swimmer proved _____**futile**_____.

13. He is such a _____**notorious**_____ liar that no one takes anything he says seriously anymore.

14. Since the defendant was never given a chance to prove his innocence, his so-called "trial" was nothing more than a _____**farce**_____.

15. The inexperienced assistant _____**botched**_____ the business letter he was trying to compose and had to rewrite it.

16. Many people both here and abroad seem to have a _____**morbid**_____ fascination with the tragic fate of the Russian royal family.

17. When I accepted the invitation to join them on the vessel, I didn't realize that I had agreed to help _____**dismantle**_____ the ship.

18. Ever since the new tax laws went into effect, there has been speculation as to who the real _____**beneficiaries**_____ of the changes will be.

19. Why must you _____**clutter**_____ up your mind with so many trivial and useless scraps of information?

20. I know what it is that I have to do, and you may be certain that I will not _____**shirk**_____ my duty.

Synonyms

*Choose the word from this unit that is **the same** or **most nearly the same** in meaning as the **boldface** word or expression in the given phrase. Write the word on the line provided.*

1. cautiously inspected the **ruined** old building _____dilapidated_____

2. would **spend** time and money on her favorite hobby _____lavish_____

3. took up acting to overcome their **fearfulness** _____timidity_____

4. will **disassemble** the tent before leaving the campsite _____dismantle_____

5. may **bungle** the assignment if not careful _____botch_____

6. was reluctant to **coddle** the spoiled child any further _____pamper_____

7. received a truly **gracious** welcome _____hospitable_____

8. cleaned up the **mess** in Dad's workroom _____clutter_____

9. a meeting that turned into a **sham** _____farce_____

10. a **punishing** race to the finish line _____grueling_____

11. stared at the **infamous** figures in the wax museum _____notorious_____

12. suspected that the wolf had returned to its **den** _____lair_____

13. would inherit the estate as his father's **heir** _____beneficiary_____

14. dwelt on the **gloomy** details of the story _____morbid_____

15. would hang on like a **leech** _____parasite_____

Antonyms

*Choose the word from this unit that is **most nearly opposite** in meaning to the **boldface** word or expression in the given phrase. Write the word on the line provided.*

16. planned to **endorse** the amendment _____veto_____

17. would **whisper** orders to his assistant _____bellow_____

18. produced a **shortage** of wheat that year _____surplus_____

19. a **successful** effort by any account _____futile_____

20. will **shoulder** each and every responsibility _____shirk_____

Choosing the Right Word

Circle the **boldface** word that more satisfactorily completes each of the following sentences.

1. When I think back to my days of basic training, I can almost hear the drill sergeant (**pampering, bellowing**) commands across the field.

2. The campaign to eliminate pollution will prove (**futile, grueling**) unless it has the understanding and full cooperation of the public.

3. Since I was led to believe that she would approve my proposal, I was very much taken aback when it was (**lavished, vetoed**) out of hand.

4. He amazed us by reaching into the pile of (**clutter, lair**) on his desk and pulling out exactly the piece of paper he wanted.

5. The modern TV sitcom developed from the type of broad (**surplus, farce**) that slapstick comedians served up in the 1920s and 1930s.

6. What a difference between the (**timidity, farce**) of the typical freshman and the know-it-all confidence of a senior!

7. The best way to avoid those (**grueling, bellowing**) cram sessions just before the exams is to do your work steadily all term long.

8. When he said he would "beard the lion in his (**lair, clutter**)," he merely meant that he was going to have it out with the boss.

9. Even the toughest critics have been (**lavish, dilapidated**) in their praise of the new movie.

10. He is (**hospitable, notorious**) for his habit of taking small loans from his best friends and then conveniently forgetting about them.

11. It would be impossible to (**pamper, dismantle**) our system of governmental checks and balances without destroying American democracy.

12. The courts of many Renaissance princes were jammed with (**parasites, lairs**), toadies, and other idle hangers-on.

13. I sometimes think that he enjoys being sick and having everyone wait on him, sympathize with him, and (**shirk, pamper**) him.

14. Their record is 100% consistent—they have managed to (**botch, clutter**) every job they have undertaken.

15. We who live in the United States today are the chief (**beneficiaries, parasites**) of the rich heritage of freedom left us by the framers of the Constitution.

16. My experience has been that people who cut corners on small matters will also (**shirk, botch**) their obligations.

17. Ever since I was bitten by a stray mutt, I have had a (**morbid, lavish**) fear of dogs.

18. Beneath the (**dismantled, dilapidated**) body of the getaway car, there was a powerful, finely tuned motor, capable of reaching high speeds.

19. She was indeed fortunate to find herself working under a person who was (**notorious, hospitable**) to her novel ideas.

20. After buying all the supplies for the club party, we were delighted to find that we had a grand (**surplus, veto**) of 65 cents.

Vocabulary in Context

*Read the following passage, in which some of the words you have studied in this unit appear in **boldface** type. Then complete each statement given below the passage by circling the letter of the item that is **the same** or **almost the same** in meaning as the highlighted word.*

The Great Chicago Fire

(Line)

Chicago was a sprawling metropolis in 1871. Yet it was also a city ripe for disaster. First, Chicago was built almost entirely of wood. Wooden grain elevators, lumber mills, hotels, **dilapidated** houses and barns, bridges, and even streets, paved with pine blocks, were perfect sources of kindling. Second, Chicago also
(5) made, stored, bought, and sold a **surplus** of inflammable goods. As a result, in the hot, dry summer of 1871, Chicagoans had a right to be concerned.

By early October, Chicago's crack firefighters were exhausted, having spent a **grueling** week extinguishing 24 fires. However, on the evening of October 8,
(10) the firefighters' stamina would be tested again. It is rumored that at 8:30 in the evening, Mrs. O'Leary's cow kicked over a lantern in the barn, starting the Great Chicago Fire. In just
(15) a few minutes the barn was ablaze. In an hour the entire block was burning. In the street the **bellow** of trapped cows could be heard, as building after building burned. The flames simply
(20) could not be stopped; all efforts proved **futile**. By the following morning, much of Chicago lay in ashes.

Chicago after the Great Fire, 1871

The Great Chicago Fire was finally checked by rainfall and by the use of gunpowder. Yet the losses were staggering. In all, 300 deaths were reported. More
(25) than 100,000 people were left homeless, and 17,500 buildings were demolished. But nothing could destroy the will of the people to rebuild the city.

Soon, the rebuilding began. Architects flocked to the city in droves, eager for the chance to build high into the sky. City planners also came. As a result, Chicago became the **beneficiary** of bold new ideas in construction, city planning, and
(30) technology. In just a few years the city became the open-air gallery of skyscrapers, grand boulevards, and parks that it still is today.

---

1. The meaning of **dilapidated** (line 3) is
a. messy
b. shipshape
c. confused
d. run-down

2. Surplus (line 5) most nearly means
a. lack
b. shortage
c. surfeit
d. dearth

3. Grueling (line 8) is best defined as
a. eating
b. taxing
c. long
d. fearful

4. Bellow (line 17) most nearly means
a. roar
b. whisper
c. murmur
d. cough

5. The meaning of **futile** (line 21) is
a. fruitless
b. difficult
c. fruitful
d. successful

6. Beneficiary (line 29) most nearly means
a. official
b. recipient
c. target
d. enemy

 **Definitions**

Note carefully the spelling, pronunciation, part(s) of speech, and definition(s) of each of the following words. Then write the word in the blank space(s) in the illustrative sentence(s) following. Finally, study the lists of synonyms and antonyms given at the end of each entry.

1. **adequate**
   (ad′ ə kwət)

   (*adj.*) sufficient, enough

   Be sure to allow _____ **adequate** _____ time to check in at the airport.

   SYNONYMS: satisfactory, sufficing
   ANTONYM: insufficient

2. **ajar**
   (ə jär′)

   (*adj., adv.*) partly open

   That night, the children foolishly left the back gate _____ **ajar** _____ , and the dog escaped.

   ANTONYMS: (*adj., adv.*) closed tight, shut, open wide

3. **dialogue**
   (dī′ ə läg)

   (*n.*) a conversation between two or more people; an interchange of opinions and ideas, free discussion

   The witty _____ **dialogue** _____ in the play kept the audience amused.

   SYNONYM: exchange of ideas
   ANTONYMS: monologue, soliloquy

4. **emblem**
   (em′ bləm)

   (*n.*) a symbol, sign, token

   Like the heart, the red rose is an _____ **emblem** _____ of love.

   SYNONYMS: badge, insignia

5. **gigantic**
   (jī gan′ tik)

   (*adj.*) huge, giant, immense

   When it fell to earth, the meteorite made a _____ **gigantic** _____ hole in the ground.

   SYNONYMS: enormous, colossal, mammoth
   ANTONYMS: tiny, infinitesimal, diminutive

6. **havoc**
   (hav′ ək)

   (*n.*) very great destruction, ruin; great confusion and disorder

   The monkey created _____ **havoc** _____ at the fair as soon as it broke from its leash.

   SYNONYMS: devastation, harm, disarray
   ANTONYMS: peace and quiet, calm, order

7. **hearth**
   (härth)

   (*n.*) the floor of a fireplace; the fireside as a symbol of the home and family

   It was our custom to sit by the _____ **hearth** _____ and listen to my grandfather's stories.

   SYNONYM: chimney corner

8. implore
(im plôr')

(*v.*) to beg earnestly for

The attorney proceeded to _____**implore**_____ the judge to show his client mercy.

SYNONYMS: entreat, beseech, pray
ANTONYMS: demand forcefully, clamor for

9. infamous
(in' fə məs)

(*adj.*) very wicked; disgraceful, shameful

Because of the outlaw's _____**infamous**_____ deeds, the town was offering a large bounty for his capture.

SYNONYMS: scandalous, villainous, flagrant, heinous
ANTONYMS: glorious, splendid, illustrious, praiseworthy

10. innumerable
(i nüm' ə rə bəl)

(*adj.*) too many to count, without number

The landlord heard _____**innumerable**_____ complaints about the noisy new tenant.

SYNONYMS: countless, beyond reckoning
ANTONYMS: countable, few in number

11. lax
(laks)

(*adj.*) not strict, careless; lacking discipline; not tense, relaxed

Some players took advantage of the new coach's somewhat _____**lax**_____ control of the team.

SYNONYMS: slack, negligent, remiss
ANTONYMS: strict, vigilant, conscientious, scrupulous

12. mar
(mär)

(*v.*) to spoil, damage, injure

Spilled cleaning fluid will surely _____**mar**_____ the wooden table top.

SYNONYMS: scar, disfigure, deface
ANTONYMS: beautify, embellish, repair

13. misdemeanor
(mis di mē' nər)

(*n.*) a crime or offense that is less serious than a felony; any minor misbehavior or misconduct

He was not only fined for the _____**misdemeanor**_____ but also sentenced to serve 30 days in jail.

SYNONYMS: misdeed, petty offense or transgression
ANTONYMS: felony, serious crime

14. mull
(məl)

(*v.*) to think about, ponder; to grind or mix; to heat and flavor with spices

The governor had some time to _____**mull**_____ over the bill before signing it into law.

SYNONYMS: consider, reflect on

15. narrative
(nar' ə tiv)

(*n.*) a story, detailed report; (*adj.*) having the quality or the nature of a story

The _____ narrative _____ of the West African captive gives us a vivid picture of the horrors aboard a slave ship.

Henry Wadsworth Longfellow is considered a _____ narrative _____ poet because of the stories he tells in his poems.

SYNONYMS: (*n.*) tale, chronicle

16. overture
(o' vər chŭr)

(*n.*) an opening move toward negotiation or action; a proposal or offer; an introductory section or part

Our family enjoyed the _____ overture _____ to the opera better than the rest of it.

SYNONYMS: prelude, tender
ANTONYMS: finale, postlude

17. pact
(pakt)

(*n.*) an agreement, treaty

All the nations signed the _____ pact _____ after the war in an effort to ensure world peace.

SYNONYMS: compact, alliance, deal

18. stalemate
(stāl' māt)

(*n.*) a situation in which further action by either of two opponents is impossible; (*v.*) to bring to a standstill

The negotiations ended in _____ stalemate _____, as both sides refused to budge on the main issue.

Recent aggression on the part of one nation threatened to _____ stalemate _____ the peace talks.

SYNONYMS: (*n.*) standoff, draw; (*v.*) deadlock
ANTONYMS: (*n.*) victory; (*v.*) defeat

19. vindictive
(vin dik' tiv)

(*adj.*) bearing a grudge, feeling or showing a strong tendency toward revenge

The mayor was so _____ vindictive _____ that he threatened to sue the newspaper for its unflattering remarks about his administration.

SYNONYMS: vengeful, spiteful, malicious
ANTONYMS: forgiving, relenting

20. wilt
(wilt)

(*v.*) to become limp and drooping (as a flower), wither; to lose strength and vigor

Intense heat or lack of water will _____ wilt _____ the flowers.

SYNONYMS: sag, weaken, shrivel up
ANTONYMS: flourish, bloom, sprout, perk up, revive

Completing the Sentence

From the words for this unit, choose the one that best completes each of the following sentences. Write the word in the space provided.

1. The smoke from the logs burning on the _____**hearth**_____ curled slowly upward into the chimney.

2. "The Highwayman" by Alfred Noyes is a(n) _____**narrative**_____ poem that tells the story of a woman who sacrifices her life for her sweetheart.

3. In most operettas, the musical numbers are connected to one another by spoken _____**dialogue**_____ .

4. Though some of Verdi's operas begin with short preludes, for others he composed full-length _____**overtures**_____ .

5. The flood had wrought such _____**havoc**_____ that the governor of the state declared the stricken region a disaster area.

6. The U.S. entry into World War I broke the _____**stalemate**_____ on the Western Front and tipped the balance in favor of an Allied victory.

7. Though Hitler's Germany and Stalin's Russia were bitter enemies, the two countries signed a nonaggression _____**pact**_____ in 1939.

8. Can any punishment be too severe for someone who has been guilty of such a(n) _____**infamous**_____ crime?

9. Who has not gazed with awe at the _____**innumerable**_____ stars that fill the sky on a clear summer night!

10. Since I have never done him any harm, I don't understand why he should take such a(n) _____**vindictive**_____ attitude toward me.

11. Before you leave, be absolutely sure that your supplies of food and water are _____**adequate**_____ for an eight-day journey across the desert.

12. The dove is often used as a(n) _____**emblem**_____ of peace.

13. No one questions the honesty and good intentions of the mayor, but he has been criticized for being _____**lax**_____ in carrying out his duties.

14. Though my sister started out looking as fresh as a daisy, she began to _____**wilt**_____ noticeably after only five minutes in that humidity.

15. On our trip to northern California, we felt very small and unimportant as we stood beside the _____**gigantic**_____ redwood trees.

16. She _____**implored**_____ the doctor to tell her frankly how badly her son had been hurt.

17. You cannot discipline a group of teenagers by making a capital offense of every _____**misdemeanor**_____ .

18. Because the front door was _____ ajar _____ , the cat strolled into the living room.

19. One careless mistake can seriously _____ mar _____ an otherwise perfect record.

20. Let me have some time to _____ mull _____ over your proposal before I give you a definite answer.

Synonyms

*Choose the word from this unit that is **the same** or **most nearly the same** in meaning as the **boldface** word or expression in the given phrase. Write the word on the line provided.*

1. committed a **vengeful** crime against his accuser   vindictive

2. a peaceful scene by the **fireplace**   hearth

3. tall buildings that would **spoil** the view   mar

4. started to **droop** from the heat   wilt

5. will **beg** the officer not to arrest her son   implore

6. a match that ended in a **standoff**   stalemate

7. wears an **insignia** on his collar   emblem

8. refused to make the first **offer**   overture

9. signed the **treaty** that would end the fighting   pact

10. was spellbound by the play's opening **conversation**   dialogue

11. **negligent** in her duties   lax

12. to treat the crime as a **petty offense**   misdemeanor

13. a flock of birds that seemed **beyond reckoning**   innumerable

14. picked up where the **tale** left off   narrative

15. would **think** over the new proposal   mull

Antonyms

*Choose the word from this unit that is **most nearly opposite** in meaning to the **boldface** word or expression in the given phrase. Write the word on the line provided.*

16. photographed the **diminutive** species   gigantic

17. created **calm** with his music   havoc

18. left the windows **shut**   ajar

19. has **insufficient** funds to complete the job   adequate

20. met the **illustrious** politician   infamous

Choosing the Right Word

*Circle the **boldface** word that more satisfactorily completes each of the following sentences.*

1. As long as the door to compromise is even slightly (**ajar,** vindictive), there is a chance that we will be able to reach an understanding.

2. Some parents are quite strict with their children; others are somewhat (**lax,** adequate) and permissive.

3. I was a little miffed when my polite (stalemates, **overtures**) of friendship were so rudely and nastily rejected.

4. The facts of history cannot always be arranged in the form of a smooth and logical (pact, **narrative**).

5. British enlistment posters in World War I assured young men that they would be fighting for "king and country, (**hearth,** havoc) and home."

6. In spite of all the criticism, our flag still stands throughout most of the world as a(n) (pact, **emblem**) of justice and freedom.

7. After World War II the United States was not (**vindictive,** lax) toward its former enemies but tried to help them recover and rebuild.

8. Instead of resorting at once to armed force, the two nations entered into a diplomatic (**dialogue,** havoc) that eventually resolved the conflict.

9. For many years Benedict Arnold served his country faithfully, but then he disgraced his name for all time by an (ajar, **infamous**) act of treason.

10. Our high hopes for an easy victory (**wilted,** mulled) away to nothing as we watched our opponents steadily increase their lead over us.

11. I will not allow our long friendship to be (**marred,** implored) by this unfortunate misunderstanding.

12. Contract talks have been stalled for weeks, and nothing either side has suggested can seem to break the (**stalemate,** dialogue).

13. The man has such a (vindictive, **gigantic**) ego that absolutely nothing ever seems to fluster, faze, or deflate him.

14. Instead of continuing to (**mull,** implore) over the injustices that people have done to you, forget about the past and concentrate on the future.

15. Though jaywalking may be considered a(n) (**misdemeanor,** overture), murder is definitely not!

16. As I look over your record, I get the impression that your background in math and science is not (**adequate,** ajar) for an engineering course.

17. Her insistence on studying the terms of our tutoring agreement made me think that I'd signed a (**pact,** hearth) with a lawyer.

18. Since I am willing to contribute to any worthy cause, there is no need to (wilt, **implore**) me for aid in such an emotional way.

19. The blustery winds on that cold November day played (**havoc,** pact) with my hair all during our sight-seeing tour.

20. The wonders of nature are as (**innumerable,** adequate) as the grains of sand on a seashore or the leaves on the trees in a forest.

Vocabulary in Context

*Read the following passage, in which some of the words you have studied in this unit appear in **boldface** type. Then complete each statement given below the passage by circling the letter of the item that is **the same** or **almost the same** in meaning as the highlighted word.*

"Our Flag Was Still There"

(Line)

Every American has sung "The Star-Spangled Banner" **innumerable** times, but not everyone knows the history of the song. Here is a brief **narrative** of the events that led to the writing of the words to our national anthem.

During the War of 1812, a District of Columbia lawyer named Francis Scott Key boarded a British truce ship in Chesapeake Bay to **implore** the British to release (5) Dr. John Beanes, who had been arrested by British troops after they had sacked Washington, D.C. On the night of September 13, 1814, while Key was aboard the ship during a heavy rain, the British bombarded Fort McHenry, a stronghold guarding Baltimore, causing **havoc** in the fort. (10)

The American cannons returned fire; Key was detained on the British ship overnight. Afraid that Fort McHenry would fall, and with it the new American republic, Key spent the night worrying. At dawn the rain stopped, and (15) the British warships sailed away. Much to his relief, Key saw in the "dawn's early light" that the American flag was still flying over the fort. However, it was not the small storm flag that Fort McHenry's commander, Maj. George (20) Armistead, had flown during the rain, but a **gigantic** flag he had recently purchased from a Baltimore flag maker.

Fourth of July fireworks in Washington, D.C.

Key, an amateur poet, was so inspired by the sight of the "star-spangled banner," a sign that (25) the British had not captured the fort, that although he was still aboard the truce ship, he wrote a poem on the back of a letter he had in his pocket. Key called the poem "In Defense of Fort M'Henry" and had it published anonymously in Baltimore. A little later, he renamed the poem "The Star-Spangled Banner." In the same year the poem was set to the music of a popular English tune, and in 1931 Congress adopted the (30) song as our national anthem.

---

1. The meaning of **innumerable** (line 1) is
a. numbered c. several
(b.) countless d. countable

2. Narrative (line 2) is best defined as
a. dialogue (c.) story
b. essay d. prelude

3. Implore (line 5) most nearly means
(a.) entreat c. allow
b. demand d. signal

4. Havoc (line 10) is best defined as
a. worry c. indifference
b. disfavor (d.) disorder

5. Gigantic (line 22) most nearly means
a. tiny (c.) enormous
b. sufficient d. diminutive

Definitions

Note carefully the spelling, pronunciation, part(s) of speech, and definition(s) of each of the following words. Then write the word in the blank space(s) in the illustrative sentence(s) following. Finally, study the lists of synonyms and antonyms given at the end of each entry.

1. abound
(ə baùnd´)

(*v.*) to be plentiful, be filled

Lush fruit trees _____ abound _____ in the orchards of Central California.

SYNONYMS: burst with, overflow with, teem with
ANTONYMS: lack, want

2. braggart
(brag´ ərt)

(*n.*) a boaster; (*adj.*) boastful in a loud, annoying way

There seems to be a _____ braggart _____ in every family, who boasts about his or her achievements and worth.
Greek Mythology is filled with _____ braggart _____ gods and heroes who take more than a little pride in their deeds and skills.

SYNONYMS: (*n.*) bigmouth, blowhard

3. cache
(kash)

(*n.*) a hiding place; something hidden or stored

We found a _____ cache _____ of canned food hidden under the stairs in the cellar.

SYNONYMS: stockpile, hoard, store

4. clarification
(klar ə fə kā´ shən)

(*n.*) the act of making clear or understandable, an explanation

Reporters asked for a _____ clarification _____ of the politician's statement so that they could accurately report her position.

SYNONYMS: elucidation, explication

5. despondent
(di spän´ dənt)

(*adj.*) sad, without hope, discouraged

The doctor was _____ despondent _____ over the loss of his patient and dear friend.

SYNONYMS: dejected, depressed, forlorn
ANTONYMS: jubilant, elated

6. embezzle
(em bez´ əl)

(*v.*) to steal property entrusted to one's care

The senator's aide lost his job when he was caught trying to _____ embezzle _____ campaign funds.

SYNONYMS: swindle, defraud

7. heartrending
(härt´ ren diŋ)

(*adj.*) causing mental pain or grief

The survivor told a _____ heartrending _____ story about the shipwreck and the days she spent alone on the island.

SYNONYMS: moving, sad, heartbreaking, poignant
ANTONYMS: amusing, funny, hilarious

8. leisurely
(lē' zhər lē)

(*adj.*) unhurried, taking plenty of time; (*adv.*) in an easygoing or unhurried way

My parents enjoy taking a _____**leisurely**_____ stroll through the park on Sunday afternoon.

We ate _____**leisurely**_____ and spent hours talking about old times.

SYNONYMS: (*adj.*) slow, relaxed
ANTONYMS: (*adj.*) hasty, hurried, rushed, hectic

9. lethargic
(lə thär' jik)

(*adj.*) unnaturally sleepy; dull, slow moving; indifferent

The twins often become _____**lethargic**_____ after eating a large meal at their grandmother's house.

SYNONYMS: lazy, sluggish, listless
ANTONYMS: wide-awake, alert, energetic, dynamic

10. malady
(mal' əd ē)

(*n.*) a sickness, illness, disease, disorder

Rheumatic fever, usually a childhood _____**malady**_____, can cause permanent damage to the heart.

SYNONYMS: ailment, indisposition
ANTONYMS: health, well-being

11. mellow
(mel' ō)

(*adj.*) ripe, well-matured; soft, sweet, and rich; gentle, pleasant; (*v.*) to become gentle and sweet

Hawaii is known for its _____**mellow**_____ fruit, all of which is soft, sweet, ripe, and juicy.

Mom continued to hope that her upstart brother would _____**mellow**_____ with age and experience.

SYNONYMS: (*adj.*) dulcet, creamy
ANTONYMS: (*adj.*) unripe, green, harsh, grating, strident

12. nomadic
(nō ma' dik)

(*adj.*) wandering, moving about from place to place

Many groups in the desert live a _____**nomadic**_____ life, moving about in search of water and grazing land.

SYNONYMS: roving, roaming, vagrant, migratory, itinerant
ANTONYMS: stationary, settled, rooted, fixed

13. piecemeal
(pēs' mēl)

(*adj.*) one piece at a time; (*adv.*) gradually

The committee's _____**piecemeal**_____ approach to the problem was taking more time and money than the school board could afford.

Patchwork quilts are sewn _____**piecemeal**_____.

SYNONYM: (*adv.*) bit by bit
ANTONYM: (*adv.*) all at once

14. quest
(kwest)

(*n.*) a search, hunt; (*v.*) to search, seek, ask

In _____ quest _____ of a safe water route to the Pacific, Lewis and Clark journeyed more than three thousand miles.

Diplomats _____ quest _____ for peaceful solutions to global problems.

SYNONYMS: (*n.*) pursuit, venture

15. random
(ran' dəm)

(*adj.*) by chance, not planned or prearranged; irregular

According to a _____ random _____ sampling of voters, Proposition 10 seems to be the most important issue on the ballot.

SYNONYMS: haphazard, arbitrary
ANTONYMS: planned, deliberate, systematic

16. rant
(rant)

(*v.*) to speak wildly and noisily; (*n.*) loud, violent talk

When the speaker began to _____ rant _____ like a rabble-rouser, the crowd shouted him down.

Listening to the _____ rant _____ of that radio personality makes me want to give up on talk shows.

SYNONYMS: (*v.*) rave, fume, spout, harangue
ANTONYMS: (*v.*) whisper, mumble

17. reinforce
(rē in fôrs')

(*v.*) to make stronger with new materials or support

They used steel beams to _____ reinforce _____ the structure of the building.

SYNONYMS: strengthen, bolster, prop up, support
ANTONYMS: weaken, undermine, sap, impair

18. seclusion
(si klü' zhən)

(*n.*) isolation from others, solitude

Some actors choose to live in _____ seclusion _____, away from the prying eyes of journalists.

SYNONYMS: aloneness, solitariness
ANTONYM: the thick of things

19. status
(stā' təs)

(*n.*) a person's condition or position in the eyes of the law; relative rank or standing, especially in society; prestige

Winning the prestigious book award boosted the young writer's literary _____ status _____.

SYNONYMS: situation, recognition

20. turmoil
(tər' moil)

(*n.*) a state of great confusion or disorder; mental strain or agitation

For many years after the Civil War, the South remained a society in _____ turmoil _____.

SYNONYMS: upheaval, tumult, chaos
ANTONYMS: peace and quiet, order

Completing the Sentence

From the words for this unit, choose the one that best completes each of the following sentences. Write the word in the space provided.

1. After putting up all week with the noise and confusion of life in the big city, I enjoy the _____ seclusion _____ of my mountain retreat on weekends.

2. The lake so _____ abounds _____ with trout and pickerel that even a person with my limited skill in fishing can catch them easily.

3. Most detectives solve crimes in a(n) _____ piecemeal _____ fashion, as clues come to light, rather than all at once.

4. Though Ponce de León's _____ quest _____ for the Fountain of Youth proved futile, he did discover Florida.

5. The _____ turmoil _____ of the French Revolution and the Napoleonic Era was succeeded by 100 years of relative peace and quiet in Europe.

6. Apparently, the man could pay off his staggering gambling debts only by _____ embezzling _____ funds from the company that employed him.

7. The park is always full of soapbox orators _____ ranting _____ about the inequality of government or society.

8. The tenor's voice was rich and _____ mellow _____, but the baritone's sounded somewhat harsh and unpleasant.

9. Instead of trying to decide which applicants were best suited for the job, he selected two of them at _____ random _____.

10. It's natural to feel a little _____ despondent _____ over not getting the job, but don't let that prevent you from applying for other positions.

11. At first, when I couldn't make out what she wanted me to do, I asked her for some _____ clarification _____ of her instructions.

12. In order to prevent the illegal entry of aliens into the United States, it has been necessary to _____ reinforce _____ our border patrols.

13. Yesterday, I read a truly _____ heartrending _____ account of the plight of millions of Africans suffering from the effects of a severe famine.

14. The two brothers are both fine athletes, but one is quiet and modest, while the other is an awful _____ braggart _____.

15. When I first entered this country, I was classified as a "resident alien," but my _____ status _____ has changed since then.

16. Arthritis is a _____ malady _____ that attacks many millions of people, especially in middle and old age.

17. During warm months, foxes bury many animals they have killed, with the result that they have _____ caches _____ to tide them over the winter.

18. Hundreds of homeless people now lead essentially ____nomadic____ existences on the streets of our major cities.

19. Though I am always full of energy in the morning, I start to become a little ____lethargic____ as the day wears on.

20. Every once in a while, I like to take time out from my busy schedule to have a ____leisurely____ dinner with old friends.

Synonyms

Choose the word from this unit that is **the same** or **most nearly the same** in meaning as the **boldface** word or expression in the given phrase. Write the word on the line provided.

1. was among the last **roving** groups in Lapland ____nomadic____

2. achieved a high **standing** among her peers ____status____

3. students in **pursuit** of knowledge ____quest____

4. will live in **solitude** for the winter ____seclusion____

5. legal terms that will need **explication** ____clarification____

6. attempted to **steal** money from the trust fund ____embezzle____

7. began to **rave** at the hostile audience ____rant____

8. was caught up in the **chaos** left by the storm ____turmoil____

9. a **hoard** of gold bullion ____cache____

10. **dejected** over the loss of his job ____despondent____

11. to **bolster** belief in our system of government ____reinforce____

12. is just another conceited **boaster** ____braggart____

13. rehearsed the play **bit by bit** ____piecemeal____

14. suffers from a serious **illness** ____malady____

15. inventive minds that **teem with** ideas ____abound with____

Antonyms

Choose the word from this unit that is **most nearly opposite** in meaning to the **boldface** word or expression in the given phrase. Write the word on the line provided.

16. took a **rushed** trip down the Mississippi River ____leisurely____

17. is always **energetic** on Monday ____lethargic____

18. has a **strident** personality ____mellow____

19. told a **hilarious** story about their escape ____heartrending____

20. witnessed a **deliberate** act of kindness ____random____

Choosing the Right Word

*Circle the **boldface** word that more satisfactorily completes each of the following sentences.*

1. As soon as I opened the book, I realized that I had stumbled on a rich (**cache,** **braggart**) of useful information for my report.

2. Over the years I have learned one thing about rumors: Where the facts are few, fictions (**abound, clarify**).

3. Since I was in no hurry to get where I was going, I decided to set a rather (**random,** **leisurely**) pace for myself.

4. Our present policy appears to be so contradictory that I believe some (**clarification,** **turmoil**) of it is in order.

5. My experience on my summer job has (**reinforced, abounded**) many of the lessons I learned in the classroom.

6. Though he (**rants, embezzles**) and raves about the problems of the world, he has little to offer in the way of solutions to them.

7. Although she appeared calm, her mind was in (**turmoil, status**).

8. The eternal (**quest, seclusion**) for youth and beauty explains the huge sales of cosmetics, to men as well as to women.

9. For weeks a gang of muggers wandered the streets aimlessly, choosing their victims at (**random, piecemeal**) from those who happened by.

10. Only the fact that they cannot see the seriousness of the emergency can explain their (**lethargic, nomadic**) response to our appeal for help.

11. At the time when this event happened, I was very angry, but over the years my emotions have (**mellowed, reinforced**).

12. Many doctors believe that when sick people become (**heartrending, despondent**) over their health, it is more difficult for them to recover.

13. People who waste the natural resources of this country are in a sense (**embezzling,** **reinforcing**) the wealth of future generations.

14. Instead of such (**mellow, piecemeal**) efforts to prevent air pollution, we need a unified campaign that will be continued for as long as necessary.

15. The President went on the air to inform the general public of the present (**malady,** **status**) of the negotiations with the enemy.

16. (**Nomadic, Despondent**) groups of horse breeders still wander the plains of Central Asia in search of pasturage for their herds.

17. In the (**heartrending, lethargic**) conclusion of the film, the hero dies in the arms of his beloved.

18. I believe that education, understanding, and experience provide the only cure for the (**malady, status**) of racial prejudice.

19. There is a great difference between being quietly confident of your own ability and being an obnoxious (**nomad, braggart**).

20. Why would a world-famous writer choose to live in the (**quest, seclusion**) of a country village far from the "madding crowd"?

Read the following passage, in which some of the words you have studied in this unit appear in **boldface** type. Then complete each statement given below the passage by circling the letter of the item that is **the same** or **almost the same** in meaning as the highlighted word.

A Museum for Every Taste

(Line)

The United States **abounds with** museums. There are more than 8,000 of them, from the popular, like Chicago's Museum of Science and Industry, to the obscure, like the Devil's Rope Museum, which displays all types of barbed wire, in McLean, Texas. In fact, if your interest is specialized, chances are you can pursue it at one (5) of the growing number of offbeat museums in our nation.

For example, if wacky airplanes are your cup of tea, you might make your way to the Mid-America Museum, west of Hot Springs, Arkansas, where a **cache** of playful contraptions can be seen and touched. If, on the other hand, your **quest** is for the perfect wave, you can visit "the
(10) world's first surfing museum," in Santa Cruz, California.

If you happen to prefer roller skates to waves, don't be **despondent**—just head to the National Museum of Roller
(15) Skating in Lincoln, Nebraska. There you will find antique roller skates, costumes, motorized skates, and even old skate keys. However, if it's a **mellow** musical experience you're
(20) after, your choice may be the Miles Musical Museum in Eureka Springs, Arkansas. On a **leisurely** tour, the

Mid-America Museum near Hot Springs, Arkansas

owners will entertain you by cranking up any number of antique musical machines.

No matter how absurd they may seem, these offbeat museums are true
(25) American treasures. They preserve our shared past by keeping the things that matter to us and also reveal a good deal about our people and country. With these goals in mind, it shouldn't surprise you to know that there is even a museum that honors American know-how—for that's exactly the aim of the Rough and Tumble Engineers' Museum in Kinzers, Pennsylvania. There, old steam engines, threshers,
(30) and tractors are fixed to run almost like new, proving that in this country, no matter how far-out your interest, there is probably a museum just for you.

---

1. The meaning of **abounds with** (line 1) is
  a. bounces with   c. is supplied with
  b. lacks   (d.) overflows with

2. Cache (line 7) most nearly means
  a. case   c. cave
  (b.) store   d. cellar

3. Quest (line 8) is best defined as
  a. desire   (c.) search
  b. need   d. find

4. Despondent (line 13) is best defined as
  a. elated   (c.) discouraged
  b. irresponsible   d. hopeful

5. The meaning of **mellow** in (line 19) is
  (a.) dulcet   c. colorful
  b. harsh   d. funny

6. Leisurely (line 22) most nearly means
  a. hasty   c. hectic
  (b.) unhurried   d. playful

REVIEW UNITS 10-12

Visit us at www.sadlier-oxford.com
for interactive puzzles and games.

Vocabulary for Comprehension

*Read the following passage, in which some of the words you have studied in Units 10–12 appear in **boldface** type. Then answer questions 1–11 on page 139 on the basis of what is <u>stated</u> or <u>implied</u> in the passage and in the introductory statement.*

Long before the civil rights movement of the 1950s and 1960s, African Americans worked to end racial discrimination and segregation. This passage describes some of their efforts.

(Line)

Have you ever heard the term the *Great Migration*? If so, you may know that between 1870 and 1920, hundreds of thousands of African

(5) Americans moved from rural areas in the Southeast to the industrialized urban areas in the Northeast and Midwest. For most, this huge migration meant an escape from

(10) poverty and the **malady** of discrimination, of being treated unfairly. To these African Americans, the movement north was a **quest** for a better life, as northern factory jobs were

(15) a great improvement over farmwork.
As more industrial jobs became available during World War I, about half a million African Americans went north. Although their economic

(20) **status** improved during the war years, African Americans in both the North and the South were still denied many basic rights. As a result, some notable African Americans rose to

(25) the challenge of righting injustices and achieving equal opportunity.
One African American who fought to end injustice was Booker T. Washington. Born enslaved,

(30) Washington taught himself to read. Years later, in 1891, he founded the Tuskegee Institute in Alabama. There African Americans were taught skills

such as bricklaying, printing, and

(35) teaching, which would help them improve their lives as they worked peacefully toward equality.
African American women also struggled for justice. Ida B. Wells, for

(40) example, strove to end the **notorious** practice of segregation—that is, of separating African Americans from other groups in society—and other forms of racial injustice. For Wells,

(45) her pen and her resolve were her only weapons. As editor of the newspaper *Free Speech*, which she founded in Memphis, Tennessee, Wells fought to end **random** acts of

(50) violence against African Americans. "Can you remain silent," she wrote ". . . when such things are done in your own community and country?"
As these African American leaders

(55) and others lectured across the country, they inspired the growth of the civil rights movement. In fact, even today, their words and deeds still motivate organizations to

(60) continue the struggle for justice.

1. The primary purpose of the passage is to
  a. entertain the reader with several fictional anecdotes
  b. describe African American life in the North from 1870 to 1920
  c. give information about African Americans' early struggles to end injustice
  d. persuade the reader to take action
  e. tell a personal story about the writer's ancestors

2. The question in lines 1–2 functions as the focus for
  a. the entire passage
  b. paragraph 1
  c. paragraph 2
  d. paragraphs 3 and 4
  e. paragraph 5

3. Malady (line 10) most nearly means
  a. stigma
  b. humiliation
  c. crime
  d. oppression
  e. sickness

4. Quest (line 13) is best defined as
  a. hope
  b. victory
  c. search
  d. request
  e. competition

5. In lines 12–15 you learn that the main motivation for African Americans moving to the North from the South was their search for
  a. a college education
  b. a better life
  c. better housing
  d. family and friends
  e. political representation

6. Status (line 20) most nearly means
  a. condition
  b. education
  c. successes
  d. opportunities
  e. skills

7. Notorious (line 40) is best defined as
  a. haphazard
  b. disgraceful
  c. widespread
  d. official
  e. cruel

8. The meaning of **random** (line 49) is
  a. brutal
  b. shocking
  c. shameful
  d. arbitrary
  e. planned

9. The author's attitude toward the achievements of Booker T. Washington and Ida B. Wells can best be described as one of
  a. indifference
  b. hostility
  c. disbelief
  d. sympathy
  e. admiration

10. From the sentence "For Wells, her pen and her resolve were her only weapons (lines 44–46), you can infer that Wells
  a. wrote countless articles expressing her opinions
  b. kept her opinions to herself
  c. had to defend herself against many enemies
  d. was weak and easily intimidated
  e. finally gave in to pressure to stop writing her articles

11. Which of the following describes something that both Booker T. Washington and Ida B. Wells had in common?
  a. They wrote best-selling books.
  b. They founded educational institutions.
  c. They founded newspapers.
  d. They visited the White House.
  e. They lectured all across the country.

Grammar in Context

In the sentence "One African American who fought to end injustice was Booker T. Washington" (lines 27–29 on page 138), the author of the passage has taken care to use the **subject pronoun** *who* rather than the **object pronoun** *whom*.

Who, the subject pronoun, can introduce a question, as in the sentence "Who was Ida Wells?" Or, as in the sentence above, it can introduce a subordinate clause. *Whom* is an object pronoun, as in the sentence "To whom did the African American leaders make their speeches?" Remember that *whom* can be the object of a preposition or a verb, or it can be an indirect object.

One way to help you decided whether *who* or *whom* is the correct pronoun to use is to replace the pronoun in question with *she* or *her*. If *she* sounds right in the sentence, them *who* (the subject pronoun) is correct. If *her* sounds right, then *whom* (the object pronoun) is the one to use.

Choose the pronoun in parentheses that correctly completes each of the following sentences, and write it on the line provided.

1. (**Who, whom**) was Ida B. Wells, and what made her famous?
   Who

2. For (**who, whom**) did Booker T. Washington fight?
   whom

3. Harriet Tubman, (**who, whom**) guided many slaves to freedom, was known as "Moses" to her followers.
   who

4. With (**who, whom**) was Frederick Douglass meeting secretly on that morning?
   whom

5. The abolitionists decided (**who, whom**) would speak firmly to the president about freeing the slaves.
   who

6. The thousands of African Americans (**who, whom**) migrated to the North in the twentieth century sought better jobs and better lives there.
   who

7. To (**who, whom**) was Dr. Martin Luther King, Jr., speaking when he gave his "I have a dream" speech?
   whom

8. (**Who, whom**) would know the locations of the "stations" on the Underground Railroad?
   Who

Two-Word Completions

Circle the pair of words that best complete the meaning of each of the following passages.

See pages T38–T48 for explanations of answers.

1. As he sat by the fire that glowed in the _____, the old sailor entertained the children with a(n) _____ of his adventures on the high seas, beginning when he was a boy of twelve, almost sixty years before.
a. lair . . . farce
b. cache . . . dialogue
c. hearth . . . narrative
d. clutter . . . overture

2. Since the soil is so remarkably rich and fertile, a variety of crops can be grown in _____. The farmers keep what they need for themselves and sell off the _____ at a handsome profit.
a. abundance . . . surplus
b. seclusion . . . reinforcements
c. lavishness . . . hospitality
d. leisure . . . adequacy

3. Before we can even think about renovating this _____ old house, we must remove all the worthless _____ that is strewn around the rooms and blocking the entrances.
a. gigantic . . . cache
b. dilapidated . . . clutter
c. mellow . . . havoc
d. futile . . . surplus

4. "I am still _____ the matter over in my mind," the President told the press. "When I have reached a decision, I will either sign the bill or _____ it."
a. mellowing . . . botch
b. narrating . . . dismantle
c. mulling . . . veto
d. clarifying . . . mar

5. The earliest inhabitants of North America lived _____ lives. They were constantly moving from place to place in search of the game that made up the greater part of their diet. This endless _____ for food eventually took them to all parts of the continent.
a. nomadic . . . quest
b. grueling . . . cache
c. pampered . . . malady
d. lethargic . . . status

*Read each sentence carefully. Then circle the item that
best completes the statement below the sentence.*

See pages T38–T48 for explanations of answers.

Her lax smile told me that she had not found the vocabulary test as difficult as she had
feared. (2)

1. In line 1 the word **lax** most nearly means

a. undisciplined   b. negligent   (c. relaxed)   d. sarcastic

Edgar Allan Poe's story "The Black Cat" ends with the discovery of the cache in which the
narrator has walled up the animal he has slain. (2)

2. In line 1 the word **cache** is used to mean

(a. hiding place)   b. grave   c. hoard   d. buried coffin

The last words of the 16th-century French author François Rabelais are reported to have
been "Draw the curtain; the farce is played." (2)

3. The best definition for the word **farce** in line 2 is

a. sham   (b. comedy)   c. humor   d. melodrama

As the park rangers approached the carcass left behind by poachers, a few jackals went
shirking into the brush. (2)

4. In line 2 the word **shirking** is used to mean

a. neglecting   b. avoiding   c. sidestepping   (d. sneaking)

Am I guilty of "conspicuous consumption" if I purchase something solely for the status it
is supposed to lend me? (2)

5. The word **status** in line 1 is best defined as

a. fame   (b. prestige)   c. condition   d. position

Antonyms

*In each of the following groups, circle the word or expression that is
most nearly the **opposite** of the word in **boldface** type.*

1. veto
a. forbid
b. cancel
(c. approve)
d. suggest

2. dialogue
a. conversation
b. discussion
c. whisper
(d. monologue)

3. dismantle
a. explode
(b. assemble)
c. design
d. destroy

4. shirk
a. describe
b. ignore
c. understand
(d. do)

5. lethargic
a. dreamy
b. agreeable
c. nasty
(d. energetic)

6. leisurely
a. well-organized
b. easygoing
(c. hasty)
d. artistic

7. pamper
(a. mistreat)
b. educate
c. coddle
d. adopt

8. turmoil
a. flames
b. haste
c. secrecy
(d. peace)

9. grueling
a. easy
b. tiring
c. long
d. interesting

11. implore
a. demand
b. beg
c. love
d. defend

13. heartrending
a. funny
b. sad
c. modern
d. typical

15. futile
a. large
b. tiring
c. successful
d. new

10. reinforce
a. paint
b. construct
c. test
d. weaken

12. despondent
a. jubilant
b. gloomy
c. unusual
d. sour

14. wilted
a. faded
b. spoiled
c. died
d. bloomed

16. gigantic
a. shaggy
b. tiny
c. fierce
d. new

Word Families

A. *On the line provided, write the word you have learned in Units 10–12 that is related to each of the following nouns.*
EXAMPLE: dilapidation—**dilapidated**

1. despondency, despondence, despond — despondent
2. futility, futileness — futile
3. adequacy, adequateness — adequate
4. hospitality, hospitableness — hospitable
5. randomness, randomization, randomizer — random
6. embezzlement, embezzler — embezzle
7. vindictiveness — vindictive
8. leisure, leisureliness — leisurely
9. abundance — abound
10. reinforcement, reinforcer — reinforce
11. notoriety, notoriousness — notorious
12. lethargy — lethargic
13. nomad, nomadism — nomadic
14. infamy — infamous
15. mellowness — mellow

B. *On the line provided, write the word you have learned in Units 10–12 that is related to each of the following verbs.*
EXAMPLE: seclude—**seclusion**

16. plagiarize — plagiarism
17. waste — wastrel
18. indulge — indulgent
19. lament — lamentable
20. contend — contentious

Word Associations

In each of the following groups, circle the word that is best defined or suggested by the given phrase.

1. a run-down old building
a. despondent b. morbid (c. dilapidated) d. hospitable

2. to create confusion
a. rant (b. havoc) c. clutter d. pact

3. got the information a bit at a time
(a. piecemeal) b. leisurely c. lethargically d. ajar

4. like stars that are too many to count
a. mellow (b. innumerable) c. lax d. dilapidated

5. a person named in a will
a. stalemate b. braggart (c. beneficiary) d. parasite

6. the search for world peace
a. malady (b. quest) c. havoc d. cache

7. constantly on the move
a. piecemeal b. random (c. nomadic) d. despondent

8. to rave or talk wildly
a. veto (b. rant) c. implore d. bellow

9. extra goods or material
a. clutter (b. surplus) c. emblem d. cache

10. to ponder their suggestions
a. pamper b. clutter c. dismantle (d. mull)

11. needs a clear explanation of your remarks
a. pact (b. clarification) c. overture d. narrative

12. a symbol that stands for something else
a. beneficiary (b. emblem) c. pact d. overture

13. to litter shelves with books and papers
a. mar b. dismantle c. rant (d. clutter)

14. a sufficient supply
(a. adequate) b. random c. surplus d. morbid

15. with the window slightly open
a. dilapidated (b. ajar) c. piecemeal d. lax

16. a very generous gift
(a. lavish) b. adequate c. grueling d. gigantic

17. living off someone else
(a. parasite) b. braggart c. beneficiary d. emblem

18. a dulcet tone
a. leisurely b. lavish (c. mellow) d. lethargic

19. "Don't bungle the job."
a. embezzle b. dismantle c. mar (d. botch)

20. to shout a command
a. veto b. quest c. implore (d. bellow)

Building with Classical Roots

note, not—to know, recognize

This root appears in **notorious** (page 119), "widely and unfavorably known." Some other words based on the same root are listed below.

connote	notary	noteworthy	notion
denote	notation	notify	notoriety

From the list of words above, choose the one that corresponds to each of the brief definitions below. Write the word in the blank space in the illustrative sentence below the definition.

1. remarkable, outstanding because of some special excellence ("*worthy of being recognized*")

The senator made _____ **noteworthy** _____ remarks about the importance of reducing air pollution.

2. an idea; a foolish idea or opinion; a small useful item

She has the odd _____ **notion** _____ that no one in her class likes her.

3. to point out, give notice of, inform

We will _____ **notify** _____ our attorney of your intention to sue us.

4. to indicate, be the sign of, mean exactly

The child's high temperature and chills _____ **denote** _____ severe illness.

5. to suggest or imply in addition to giving an exact meaning

The name *Angela* means "angel," but it also _____ **connotes** _____ goodness.

6. a public official who certifies statements and signatures

The _____ **notary** _____ public witnessed the signing of Grandfather's will.

7. ill fame; being famous for something bad

Jesse James achieved _____ **notoriety** _____ as an outlaw in the Old West.

8. a record; a note to assist memory, memorandum; a set of symbols or expressions

Good students often write _____ **notations** _____ in the margins of books.

From the list of words above, choose the one that best completes each of the following sentences. Write the word in the space provided.

1. The letter I received this morning _____ **notified** _____ me that I had been accepted at one of the colleges to which I had applied.

2. Place a _____ **notation** _____ on her medical record card to remind the nurse to call her in two months for a follow-up appointment.

3. The deed became a legal document when it was signed by all parties in the presence of a _____**notary**_____.

4. Do you have any _____**notion**_____ of what he is attempting to do?

5. All the _____**notoriety**_____ she had received after being a witness in the bribery trial caused her to move to another city.

6. The flashing signals at the crossing _____**denote(d)**_____ the approach of a train.

7. Isn't it fascinating how certain colors have come to _____**connote**_____ strong feelings, such as red for anger?

8. What do you think was the most _____**noteworthy**_____ achievement on behalf of humanity during the past 25 years?

Circle the **boldface** word that more satisfactorily completes each of the following sentences.

1. The Vikings' (**notation,** **notoriety**) as bloodthirsty invaders has lasted for more than a thousand years.

2. All the (**noteworthy, notorious**) painters of the Italian Renaissance are represented in the current exhibit at the museum.

3. Symbols such as the plus sign and the minus sign are used in mathematical (**notation, notary**).

4. An inventor has the ability to transform a fleeting (**notation, notion**) into a useful product.

5. Gathering clouds and a dark gray sky (**denote, connote**) rain.

6. In 19th-century novels dark clouds usually (**denote, connote**) that something bad is about to happen.

7. One of the duties of a (**notation, notary**) is to witness the signing of an important document.

8. Please (**denote, notify**) us when the next tryout for the team will be.

 **Analogies**

In each of the following, circle the item that best completes the comparison.

See pages T38–48 for explanations of answers.

1. puny is to **gigantic** as
a. foremost is to prominent
(b. lethargic is to dynamic)
c. grueling is to graphic
d. vicious is to malignant

2. jaywalking is to **misdemeanor** as
a. forgery is to vice
(b. homicide is to felony)
c. embezzlement is to blunder
d. perjury is to error

3. ratify is to **veto** as
a. mar is to disfigure
b. fluster is to bewilder
c. procure is to ordain
(d. renovate is to dilapidate)

4. fruitless is to **futile** as
(a. spirited is to animated)
b. rural is to urban
c. orthodox is to quaint
d. amiss is to upright

5. buffoon is to **farce** as
a. doctor is to patient
b. farmer is to plow
(c. acrobat is to circus)
d. bystander is to accident

6. innumerable is to **count** as
a. indispensable is to employ
b. interminable is to begin
(c. illegible is to read)
d. inflammable is to kindle

7. despondent is to **melancholy** as
a. indifferent is to enthusiasm
b. peevish is to courtesy
c. sullen is to joy
(d. indignant is to wrath)

8. implore is to **entreat** as
(a. interrogate is to question)
b. parch is to quench
c. accelerate is to decrease
d. nurture is to stifle

9. alliance is to **pact** as
(a. truce is to cease-fire)
b. dynasty is to brawl
c. anecdote is to oration
d. regime is to onslaught

10. reinforce is to **more** as
a. flourish is to less
b. shirk is to more
(c. erode is to less)
d. eradicate is to more

 **Choosing the Right Meaning**

Read each sentence carefully. Then circle the item that best completes the statement below the sentence.

See pages T38–48 for explanations of answers.

The story was so predictable and the characters so dull that it's no wonder the audience's reaction was so lethargic. (2)

1. The word **lethargic** in line 2 is best defined as
(a. indifferent)   b. lazy   c. enthusiastic   d. critical

One side of the packing material was molded to form a pattern of tiny plastic nubs to absorb shock. (2)

2. In line 1 the word **nubs** most nearly means
a. cores   b. cruxes   c. hearts   (d. knobs)

The death of Stonewall Jackson in 1863 left a void in the ranks of Lee's generals that no other officer was able to fill. (2)

3. In line 1 the word **void** is used to mean

a. annulment   b. cancellation   c. vacancy   d. promotion

It was the custom in many American homes in the late nineteenth century to serve mulled beverages to guests at holiday time. (2)

4. The best definition for the word **mulled** in line 1 is

a. pondered   c. heated and flavored
b. chilled and diluted   d. homemade

The current was swift in the shallows along the bank, but once we paddled into deeper water, the river turned quite sullen. (2)

5. The word **sullen** in line 2 is used to mean

a. silent   b. sluggish   c. morose   d. surly

Two-Word Completions

Circle the pair of words that best complete the meaning of each of the following sentences.

See pages T38–48 for explanations of answers.

1. Though modern medicine can _____ remedies for many of the _____ that afflict us, it still hasn't found a surefire cure for cancer.

a. prescribe . . . maladies   c. ordain . . . narratives
b. verify . . . remnants   d. presume . . . surpluses

2. The sudden wail of the air-raid siren and the ominous _____ of airplanes overhead sent dozens of civilians _____ for cover.

a. luster . . . floundering   c. rant . . . yearning
b. drone . . . scurrying   d. brood . . . hurtling

3. "Staircases and hallways that are _____ with all kinds of junk constitute a real fire _____," the fire marshal told us when he inspected our plant recently.

a. disrupted . . . ingredient   c. cluttered . . . hazard
b. inflicted . . . momentum   d. retarded . . . stalemate

4. The hunters set various kinds of traps to _____ the beast when it left its mountain lair in _____ of food and water for its young.

a. goad . . . uncertainty   c. plague . . . vengeance
b. snare . . . quest   d. frustrate . . . foretaste

5. During the African dry season the land becomes so _____ that even a mighty river can be reduced to a mere _____.

a. sodden . . . résumé   c. lubricated . . . iota
b. wilted . . . nub   d. parched . . . trickle

Enriching Your Vocabulary

Read the passage below. Then complete the exercise at the bottom of the page.

Bravo!
Words from Italian

It is true that the Roman Empire declined and fell, but it left behind a legacy that includes the five Romance languages: French, Spanish, Portuguese, Romanian, and Italian. English borrowings from Italian are few, but tend to be concentrated in the arts.

Italian words go to the very foundations of the musical arts. *Opera* is an Italian word meaning work or composition (opera was developed in Florence, the center of the Italian Renaissance), as are *piano* and *violin*. The best violins ever created were made not long after the instrument was developed, by Amati and Stradivari (the famous *Stradivarius* violins); a few of these violins still exist today and are extremely valuable. A *soprano* (a very high voice) and a *basso* (a very low voice) make an effort to keep to the *tempo,* or pace, of the music. And the *prima donna* is the female star of an opera.

La Scala opera house in Milan

In the visual arts we find the words *gouache,* for a brilliant opaque water-based paint used in graphics, and *fresco*, for a technique of painting in wet plaster; famous paintings such as *The Last Supper,* by Leonardo Da Vinci, are frescoes.

Other Italian words are scattered throughout English. A *salvo* (Unit 7) is a burst of cannon fire or gunfire, often as a salute, or a spirited verbal attack. To *trill* is to warble, to sing with a fluttering sound like some birds.

In Column A below are 9 more words from Italian. With or without a dictionary, match each word with its meaning in Column B

Column A

e	**1.** espionage
i	**2.** inferno
f	**3.** svelte
c	**4.** extravaganza
g	**5.** cavalcade
a	**6.** corsair
h	**7.** manifesto
b	**8.** vista
d	**9.** maestro

Column B

a. a pirate or pirate ship

b. a distant view, especially from a good viewing point, as from a window or from up high

c. a very large or elaborate display or entertainment

d. a master in an art, especially a musical art

e. the act or practice of spying or of operating a spy network

f. slim or graceful

g. a ceremonial procession; a dramatic series of events

h. a public announcement of aims or intentions

i. a situation or condition of great suffering, resembling hell

Definitions

Note carefully the spelling, pronunciation, part(s) of speech, and definition(s) of each of the following words. Then write the word in the blank space(s) in the illustrative sentence(s) following. Finally, study the lists of synonyms and antonyms given at the end of each entry.

1. agitation
(aj i tā' shən)

(*n.*) a violent stirring or movement; noisy confusion, excitement; a stirring up of public enthusiasm

The _____ agitation _____ for campaign finance reform was gaining widespread support in Congress.
SYNONYMS: disquiet, uneasiness, upset
ANTONYMS: peace of mind, composure, calm

2. blurt
(blərt)

(*v.*) to say suddenly or without thinking

The detective was fairly certain that after hours of interrogation, the suspect would _____ blurt _____ out the truth.
SYNONYMS: blab, let slip

3. chronological
(krän əl äj' i kəl)

(*adj.*) arranged in order of time of occurrence

The importance of a time line is that it arranges historical events in _____ chronological _____ order.
SYNONYMS: in time sequence, consecutive

4. countenance
(kaůn' tə nəns)

(*n.*) a face, facial expression; (*v.*) to tolerate or approve

The teacher's smiling _____ countenance _____ reassured us that the rehearsal was going well.
The new boss does not _____ countenance _____ lateness or absenteeism.
SYNONYMS: (*v.*) support, condone
ANTONYM: (*v.*) disapprove of

5. diminish
(di min' ish)

(*v.*) to make or become smaller, reduce in size

It takes no time at all for a fad to _____ diminish _____ in popularity.
SYNONYMS: lessen, decrease, dwindle
ANTONYMS: increase, enlarge, augment

6. enchant
(en chant')

(*v.*) to please greatly; to charm, put under a magic spell

The singer proceeded to _____ enchant _____ the audience with her beautiful voice and engaging style.
SYNONYMS: delight, thrill, bewitch
ANTONYMS: bore, nauseate, disgust

7. fluctuate
(flək′ chü āt)

(*v.*) to change continually; to move up and down

Stock prices _____ **fluctuate** _____ daily.

SYNONYMS: waver, seesaw, oscillate
ANTONYMS: stay put, remain unchanged

8. foster
(fôs′ tər)

(*v.*) to bring up, give care to; to promote, encourage; (*adj.*) in the same family but not related by birth

The American ambassador worked to _____ **foster** _____ positive relations with the newly formed republic.

It is important for _____ **foster** _____ children to be placed with loving families.

SYNONYMS: (*v.*) support, nurture, cultivate
ANTONYMS: (*v.*) stifle, smother, quash, discourage

9. grovel
(gräv′ əl)

(*v.*) to humble oneself, act in a fearful and servile way; to lie face downward; to indulge in something base or unworthy

Afraid of punishment, the Roman slave began to _____ **grovel** _____ at the feet of the emperor.

SYNONYMS: crouch, cower, cringe, wallow

10. handicraft
(han′ dē kraft)

(*n.*) work done by hand; a trade requiring hand skill

Making apple-head dolls is a _____ **handicraft** _____ still enjoyed in the Arkansas River Valley, among other places.

SYNONYMS: handiwork, manual art

11. hilarious
(hi lâr′ ē əs)

(*adj.*) extremely funny, causing loud amusement

The comedian told a _____ **hilarious** _____ story that had the audience laughing hysterically.

SYNONYMS: highly amusing, side-splitting
ANTONYMS: boring, dull, humorless, heartrending

12. ignite
(ig nīt′)

(*v.*) to set on fire, cause to burn; to heat up, excite

We used lighter fluid to _____ **ignite** _____ the charcoal in the outdoor grill.

SYNONYMS: inflame, light, kindle
ANTONYMS: quench, extinguish, douse, put out

13. magnitude
(mag′ nə tüd)

(*n.*) the great size or importance of something

At first, the _____ **magnitude** _____ of the task seemed to be overwhelming for a group as small as ours.

SYNONYMS: extent, immensity, enormity
ANTONYMS: smallness, unimportance, insignificance

14. massive
(mas' iv)

(*adj.*) large and heavy; great in size or scope

A _____**massive**_____ boulder still blocks the entrance to the secret cave.

SYNONYMS: bulky, huge, immense, monumental
ANTONYMS: flimsy, frail, thin

15. maternal
(mə tər' nəl)

(*adj.*) of or like a mother

The kittens' mother took her _____**maternal**_____ responsibilities very seriously.

SYNONYMS: motherly, protective, sympathetic
ANTONYMS: fatherly, paternal

16. pall
(pôl)

(*v.*) to lose in interest, attraction, or effectiveness; to become tiresome; (*n.*) a dark covering, something that conceals

The archaeologist's optimism began to _____**pall**_____ when the first excavation yielded only pieces of pottery.

News of the surprise attack on Pearl Harbor cast a _____**pall**_____ over the nation on December 7, 1941.

SYNONYMS: (*v.*) bore, weary; (*n.*) gloom, shadow
ANTONYMS: (*v.*) intrigue, fascinate; (*n.*) light, brightness

17. reputable
(rep' yət ə bəl)

(*adj.*) well thought of, having a good reputation

A list of _____**reputable**_____ lawyers is available through the local bar association.

SYNONYMS: reliable, respectable, trustworthy
ANTONYMS: shady, unsavory, questionable

18. revere
(ri vēr')

(*v.*) to love and respect deeply, honor greatly

The elderly teacher was _____**revered**_____ by a whole generation of students.

SYNONYMS: admire, esteem, cherish
ANTONYMS: scorn, disdain, mock, deride

19. saga
(säg' ə)

(*n.*) a narrative of heroic exploits; a long, detailed account

Although written in Old English, *Beowulf* is very much like a Norse _____**saga**_____ in that it details the colorful deeds of a legendary hero.

SYNONYMS: heroic tale, epic, chronicle

20. stodgy
(stäj' ē)

(*adj.*) dull, boring; old-fashioned, hidebound; lumpy, thick

The _____**stodgy**_____ politician showed little inclination to listen to the speeches of junior senators.

SYNONYMS: stuffy, tiresome, blah
ANTONYMS: forward-looking, avant-garde, progressive

Completing the Sentence

From the words for this unit, choose the one that best completes each of the following sentences. Write the word in the space provided.

1. The number and the _____**magnitude**_____ of the problems faced by the President of the United States are almost beyond our imagination.

2. Our study of American history has taught us to _____**revere**_____ the great men and women who founded this nation.

3. In the _____**Saga**_____ of Eric the Red, there is a very interesting account of the Norse discovery of North America in A.D. 1000.

4. "When I was living in the Australian outback, I learned many curious skills and _____**handicrafts**_____ from the local people," the explorer said.

5. Can you imagine my _____**agitation**_____ when I was told I would have to take over the lead role in the play immediately, with no rehearsals!

6. The audience was _____**enchanted**_____ not only by the lovely voice of the soprano but also by her youthful good looks.

7. She was very fortunate to have had talented and sympathetic teachers who _____**fostered**_____ her career.

8. We will donate the proceeds of the cake sale to any _____**reputable**_____ charity you may select.

9. We had hoped to have a wonderful time at the party, but the sad news of the principal's accident cast a(n) _____**pall**_____ over the gathering.

10. Statements _____**blurted**_____ out in anger may often be regretted for a long time afterward.

11. How can you _____**countenance**_____ such rude behavior in a young child!

12. Educators report that there is often a vast difference between a child's mental age and his or her _____**chronological**_____ age.

13. The waves of laughter from the audience indicated that those around me found the clown's antics as _____**hilarious**_____ as I did.

14. The two little girls playing house down in the basement fussed over the doll with all the _____**maternal**_____ care and attention that their own mothers bestowed on them.

15. His attitudes are so incredibly _____**stodgy**_____ and hidebound that they would have been considered old-fashioned 100 years ago!

16. The pilot light of the stove will automatically _____**ignite**_____ the burner when the handle is turned to the "on" position.

17. With no money coming in and my daily expenses continuing to mount, my savings have _____**diminished**_____ at an alarming rate.

18. Even though I need a job badly, I still have my self-respect, and I am not going to _____ grovel _____ just to get work.

19. Instead of moving steadily upwards or steadily downwards, the price of oil has been _____ fluctuating _____ all year.

20. All of a sudden, from out of the fog loomed a(n) _____ massive _____ ocean liner bearing down on our small boat.

Synonyms

*Choose the word from this unit that is **the same** or **most nearly the same** in meaning as the **boldface** word or expression in the given phrase. Write the word on the line provided.*

1. an example of local **handiwork**   handicraft

2. launched a **monumental** attack   massive

3. streets filled with a **covering** of black smoke   pall

4. will **approve** the President's proposal   countenance

5. guided by her **motherly** instinct   maternal

6. to **let slip** the truth   blurt

7. an earthquake of great **size**   magnitude

8. saw hope **dwindle** with each passing day   diminish

9. would cause her emotions to **waver**   fluctuate

10. narrates events in **consecutive** order   chronological

11. would **delight** with her smile   enchant

12. will **cower** before the king   grovel

13. was left in a state of **uneasiness**   agitation

14. watched a **highly amusing** play   hilarious

15. read a medieval Icelandic **tale**   saga

Antonyms

*Choose the word from this unit that is **most nearly opposite** in meaning to the **boldface** word or expression in the given phrase. Write the word on the line provided.*

16. to **deride** the Romantic poets   revere

17. will **extinguish** the flame of rebellion   ignite

18. can **stifle** pride in their work   foster

19. is known for being **progressive**   stodgy

20. was engaged in **questionable** practices   reputable

Choosing the Right Word

*Circle the **boldface** word that more satisfactorily completes each of the following sentences.*

1. For more than a hundred years, the delightful adventures of Alice in Wonderland have been (**enchanting,** palling) readers young and old.

2. My love of reading, (**fostered,** diminished) by my parents since early childhood, has continued to grow through the years.

3. The cowboy on his trusty quarter horse plays a prominent part in the (**saga,** magnitude) of the Old West.

4. The Tea Act of 1773 was one of the sparks that helped (**ignite,** enchant) the American Revolution.

5. So many different battles took place during the Civil War that I often have difficulty remembering the correct (**chronology,** handicraft).

6. When the Wright brothers made the first successful airplane flight, few people realized the (pall, **magnitude**) of their achievement.

7. As the game proceeded, and the lead continued to change hands, our feelings (fostered, **fluctuated**) from joy to despair and back again.

8. If it were not for the strong (**maternal,** hilarious) instinct to protect the young, many species of animals could not survive.

9. Like everyone else, I want to be well liked, but I will not (**grovel,** fluctuate) before public opinion when I am firmly convinced that it is wrong.

10. The man was such a controversial figure in his own time that he was both (fostered, **revered**) as a saint and despised as a villain.

11. Her charming personality and sparkling wit brought a breath of fresh air into the (**stodgy,** hilarious) atmosphere of the stuffy old club.

12. Though there has of late been a good deal of (countenance, **agitation**) for tax reform, nothing much has come of it so far.

13. Many older people complain that the warm spirit of neighborliness has greatly (**diminished,** revered) under the conditions of city living.

14. The speaker alarmed us when he said that our whole system of handling lawbreakers has (**massive,** stodgy) faults that will be difficult to correct.

15. In my excitement, I accidentally (**blurted,** agitated) out the very thing that I was trying so hard to conceal.

16. Many professionals and executives today have made enjoyable hobbies of such (**handicrafts,** sagas) as carpentry and weaving.

17. Any editorial about pollution appearing in such a (maternal, **reputable**) newspaper is bound to make a strong impression on many citizens.

18. For a long time my favorite TV entertainment was police and detective programs, but now they are beginning to (**pall,** enchant).

19. One of the sure signs of a country that is not free is that the people in power will not (**countenance,** blurt) any criticism of their acts.

20. She kept us in stitches with her (massive, **hilarious**) jokes.

*Read the following passage, in which some of the words you have studied in this unit appear in **boldface** type. Then complete each statement given below the passage by circling the letter of the item that is **the same** or **almost the same** in meaning as the highlighted word.*

The Adams Family

(Line)

No chronicle of American history would be complete without the **saga** of the Adams family, one of our nation's most distinguished clans. Told in **chronological** order, their story begins with Samuel Adams, one of the "radicals" of the American Revolution. Although he began as a brewer, Sam Adams soon found that his true calling was politics. As a founder of the Committees of Correspondence, Adams (5) sought to **ignite** the colonists' passion for self-rule.

President John Adams

Although more moderate, John Adams, Sam Adams' cousin, was also a founder of the Committees of Correspondence. Like his cousin, John Adams believed that the committees could **foster** unity among the (10) colonists by keeping them informed about political events in each of the colonies, thus becoming a "great political engine," moving the colonies closer toward liberty. When asked some years later about the meaning of the (15) American Revolution, John Adams replied that there really had been two revolutions. One was the war itself. The other "was in the minds and hearts of the people." Indeed, by the end of the war, Adams, like many Americans, would (20) desire not only independence but also a chance to form a new kind of government. As our nation's first Vice President and second President, John Adams would get his chance.

John Adams' son, John Quincy Adams, (25) would also have an opportunity to make his mark in government. The younger Adams held many governmental posts and was our nation's sixth President.

Few families in American history are as **revered** as the Adams family. As the builders of a new nation, this family did, in the words of John Adams, "something notable and striking" that would be remembered. (30)

---

1. The meaning of **saga** (line 1) is
a. home   c. face
b. epic   d. series

2. Chronological (line 2) most nearly means
a. size   c. time
b. importance   d. wavering

3. Ignite (line 6) is best defined as
a. extinguish   c. harden
b. support   d. inflame

4. Foster (line 10) most nearly means
a. promote   c. lessen
b. quash   d. enlarge

5. The meaning of **revered** (line 28) is
a. mocked   c. esteemed
b. scorned   d. liked

Definitions

Note carefully the spelling, pronunciation, part(s) of speech, and definition(s) of each of the following words. Then write the word in the blank space(s) in the illustrative sentence(s) following. Finally, study the lists of synonyms and antonyms given at the end of each entry.

1. affliction
(ə flik′ shən)

(*n.*) a physical ailment; a cause of pain or trouble, misfortune

Lupus is a dreadful _____**affliction**_____ that kills nearly 5,000 people, mostly women, each year.

SYNONYMS: illness, woe, torment, anguish
ANTONYMS: blessing, boon, joy

2. akin
(ə kin′)

(*adj.*) related by blood; having similar qualities or character

Our neighbors seem to have ideas _____**akin**_____ to ours about landscaping.

SYNONYMS: kindred, like, comparable
ANTONYMS: unrelated, dissimilar

3. cosmopolitan
(käz mə päl′ ə tən)

(*adj.*) found in most parts of the world; having many fields of interest; of worldwide scope; sophisticated

It does not surprise us that our cousin, a magazine editor and a big-city dweller, has a _____**cosmopolitan**_____ outlook.

SYNONYMS: global, international, polished
ANTONYMS: narrow, unsophisticated, provincial

4. elongate
(i lôŋ′ gāt)

(*v.*) to grow in length, become longer; to extend the length of

The artist sought to _____**elongate**_____ the trunk of the elephant in her caricature in order to amuse the children.

SYNONYMS: lengthen, stretch, protract
ANTONYMS: shorten, abbreviate, contract, curtail

5. gala
(gā′ lə)

(*n.*) a public entertainment marking a special event, a festive occasion; (*adj.*) festive, showy

The reporter had never seen such finery as was worn at the _____**gala**_____.

The President and the First Lady attended a _____**gala**_____ performance at the Kennedy Center in Washington, D.C.

SYNONYMS: (*n.*) extravaganza, fête; (*adj.*) spectacular, grand

6. gaudy
(gô′ dē)

(*adj.*) flashy, showy; not in good taste

The singer's _____**gaudy**_____ outfit was totally inappropriate for a command performance before the queen.

SYNONYMS: garish, loud, vulgar
ANTONYMS: restrained, quiet, sober, sedate, tasteful

7. gratitude
('grat ə tüd)

(*n.*) appreciation, thankfulness

Be sure to express your _____**gratitude**_____ to your teacher for having written you a letter of recommendation.

SYNONYMS: thanks, gratefulness

8. heed
(hēd)

(*v.*) to pay careful attention to, notice; to be guided by; (*n.*) close attention or consideration

My parents are always telling me to _____**heed**_____ their advice.

Pay no _____**heed**_____ to old superstitions.

SYNONYMS: (*v.*) listen to, attend
ANTONYMS: (*v.*) ignore, disregard

9. hoax
(hōks)

(*n.*) an act intended to trick or deceive, a fraud; (*v.*) to trick, deceive

Their plan was to _____**hoax**_____ people into believing that they had found a masterpiece.

SYNONYMS: (*n.*) deception, ruse, fake; (*v.*) dupe

10. impartial
(im pär' shəl)

(*adj.*) just, unbiased, fair, not taking sides

The defense attorney knew it would be difficult to find _____**impartial**_____ jurors to serve on such a celebrated case.

SYNONYMS: disinterested, neutral, objective
ANTONYMS: one-sided, prejudiced, biased, partial

11. impostor
(im päs' tər)

(*n.*) a swindler, deceiver; one who uses a false name or character in order to cheat

After having posed as a doctor for five years, the man was finally exposed as an _____**impostor**_____.

SYNONYMS: cheat, trickster, four-flusher, pretender

12. inflate
(in flāt')

(*v.*) to fill with air or gas; to swell or puff out; to make something appear larger than it is

On the evening before the big parade, we watched the workers _____**inflate**_____ the huge balloons.

SYNONYMS: blow up, pump up, enlarge, exaggerate
ANTONYMS: deflate, flatten, diminish

13. meager
(mē' gər)

(*adj.*) poor, scant, unsatisfactory; thin, slight

My brother, a high school student, is always complaining that he cannot live on the _____**meager**_____ allowance my parents give him.

SYNONYMS: scanty, skimpy, sparse
ANTONYMS: ample, plentiful, abundant, lavish

14. meditate
(med′ ə tāt)

(*v.*) to think about deeply and quietly, reflect upon; to plan, intend

Many ancient philosophers would seek peaceful surroundings in which to _____meditate_____ on the meaning of life.

SYNONYMS: ponder, contemplate, muse, ruminate

15. nutritious
(nü trish′ əs)

(*adj.*) nourishing, valuable and satisfying as food

My mother cooks _____nutritious_____ meals to ensure that we have a balanced diet.

SYNONYMS: healthful, wholesome

16. oppress
(ə pres′)

(*v.*) to govern or rule cruelly or unjustly; to weigh heavily upon

Too many dictators have used their absolute power to _____oppress_____ the people they govern.

SYNONYMS: mistreat, persecute, grind underfoot
ANTONYMS: pamper, coddle, free, liberate

17. pedestrian
(pə des′ trē ən)

(*n.*) one who goes on foot; (*adj.*) relating to walking; on foot; ordinary, dull, unimaginative

The driver slammed on the brakes and swerved so as not to hit the _____pedestrian_____.

Critics denounced his _____pedestrian_____ literary style, but his book sales were high.

SYNONYMS: (*adj.*) commonplace, prosaic
ANTONYMS: (*n.*) driver, rider; (*adj.*) original, novel

18. transmit
(tranz mit′)

(*v.*) to send on, pass along, send out

In the Old West local sheriffs would often _____transmit_____ messages by telegraph to the marshal of the territory.

SYNONYMS: pass on, convey, relay, deliver

19. vanquish
(vaŋ′ kwish)

(*v.*) to defeat in a battle or contest, overthrow; to overcome a feeling or condition

The general's goal was to _____vanquish_____ his country's enemies.

SYNONYMS: beat, conquer, subdue
ANTONYMS: succumb to, yield to

20. wan
(wän)

(*adj.*) unnaturally pale or sickly looking; lacking vitality; dim, faint; weak, ineffectual

The patient was so weak that all she could give the nurse was a _____wan_____ smile.

SYNONYMS: ashen, pasty, pallid, bloodless, gaunt
ANTONYMS: rosy, ruddy, blooming, radiant

Completing the Sentence

From the words for this unit, choose the one that best completes each of the following sentences. Write the word in the space provided.

1. Superstars and other celebrities are usually very much in evidence at _____ **gala** _____ events such as opening night of a new Broadway show.

2. With a population made up of people from many different lands, New York City is one of the most _____ **cosmopolitan** _____ places in the world.

3. Most of us are so busy with everyday concerns that we can find little or no time to _____ **meditate** _____ on the larger issues of life.

4. Though the newspapers hailed the find as the "discovery of the century," it turned out to be nothing but an outrageous _____ **hoax** _____ .

5. The big clown's _____ **gaudy** _____ costume was in sharp contrast to the simple white outfits worn by the trapeze artists.

6. Junk food may look attractive and taste great, but it is by no means as _____ **nutritious** _____ as much plainer fare.

7. Modern medical science can do wonders for people suffering from various physical or emotional _____ **afflictions** _____ .

8. Most cities have now passed laws to discourage _____ **pedestrians** _____ from crossing against the light or jaywalking.

9. If you had only _____ **heeded** _____ my warnings, all this trouble could easily have been avoided.

10. The family lawyer proved that the young man claiming to be the missing heir was no more than a(n) _____ **impostor** _____ .

11. An earthworm moves by first _____ **elongating** _____ and then contracting its wonderfully elastic body.

12. I don't expect you to throw yourself on your knees, but I wish you'd show a little _____ **gratitude** _____ for the things I've done for you.

13. Unfortunately, the region cannot support a very large population because its natural resources are so _____ **meager** _____ .

14. "Although these two words are not related etymologically," the professor observed, "they are _____ **akin** _____ to each other in meaning."

15. Refusing to be _____ **oppressed** _____ by unjust laws, the American colonists rose in revolt against the British government.

16. After beating off the enemy's initial assault, our brave troops delivered a series of crippling counterattacks that _____ **vanquished** _____ the foe.

17. Since I am a very close friend of his, you cannot expect me to be totally _____ **impartial** _____ in judging your criticisms of him.

18. The distraught mother's _____ **wan** _____ expression reflected her sense of anxiety over her lost child.

19. Have you ever tried to _____ **inflate** _____ a bicycle tire with one of those old-fashioned hand pumps?

20. Modern technology has provided us with the computer, a device for collecting, sorting, and _____ **transmitting** _____ information quickly.

Synonyms

*Choose the word from this unit that is **the same** or **most nearly the same** in meaning as the **boldface** word or expression in the given phrase. Write the word on the line provided.*

1. will **convey** the message by e-mail _____ transmit

2. had an **exaggerated** sense of her importance _____ inflated

3. attended a **dull** series of lectures _____ pedestrian

4. will **subdue** all foes of the realm _____ vanquish

5. ate a **wholesome** meal before the game _____ nutritious

6. was taken in by the **ruse** _____ hoax

7. had light hair and a **pallid** complexion _____ wan

8. must **listen to** the captain's command _____ heed

9. would **muse** on the meaning of the universe _____ meditate

10. will comfort her in her time of **anguish** _____ affliction

11. showed our **appreciation** for their support _____ gratitude

12. had a truly **global** point of view _____ cosmopolitan

13. was taken in by the **pretender** _____ impostor

14. will **lengthen** the program by adding commercials _____ elongate

15. a **festive** celebration to honor the winners _____ gala

Antonyms

*Choose the word from this unit that is **most nearly opposite** in meaning to the **boldface** word or expression in the given phrase. Write the word on the line provided.*

16. was **dissimilar** to the views she held _____ akin

17. sought to **liberate** his subjects _____ oppress

18. was surprised by the **tasteful** furnishings in his home _____ gaudy

19. cooked with a **lavish** amount of spices _____ meager

20. would be a truly **biased** witness _____ impartial

*Circle the **boldface** word that more satisfactorily completes each of the following sentences.*

1. Education and compassion are the only weapons by which we will (**heed, vanquish**) prejudice and superstition once and for all.

2. Is there any country in the world in which the terrible (**affliction, impostor**) of poverty has been entirely overcome?

3. When she came out on the stage, she was greeted by a (**meager, gaudy**) round of applause; before she left, she had the audience cheering.

4. Each scholarship candidate was identified by a number so that the people doing the grading would be absolutely (**impartial, pedestrian**).

5. We are so accustomed to TV that we tend to forget what a marvel it is to (**oppress, transmit**) colored images from one place to another.

6. A viewing diet made up entirely of game shows may be entertaining, but it is not particularly (**meager, nutritious**), mentally speaking.

7. Try as he might, the sideshow barker couldn't convince me that the "real live mermaid" inside the tent wasn't just a clever (**hoax, gala**).

8. After a lifetime of travel in dozens of countries all over the world, she is highly (**cosmopolitan, akin**) in her tastes and ideas.

9. The man's pathetically (**wan, elongated**) personality is matched only by the hopelessly bland and lifeless statements that issue from his mouth.

10. Is it necessary for you to go into the woods to (**meditate, inflate**) every time you have to make a routine decision?

11. Such extravaganzas as the "Night of 100 Stars" are usually designed to be (**gala, wan**) charity benefits for worthy causes.

12. The speaker had important things to say, but his way of expressing himself was so unimaginative and (**nutritious, pedestrian**) that he lost our interest.

13. By continuing to praise his extremely modest accomplishments, you are helping to (**inflate, transmit**) his already oversized ego.

14. We won the game because we kept our heads and paid no (**gratitude, heed**) to the insulting remarks made by our opponents.

15. Have you ever noticed that as the sun sinks lower in the sky, shadows become (**elongated, cosmopolitan**)?

16. I'd describe nostalgia as a feeling more (**meager, akin**) to yearning than to grief.

17. My mind and body were so (**oppressed, heeded**) by the stifling heat that afternoon that I couldn't do anything at all.

18. He claimed to be a famous multimillionaire, but when he tried to borrow bus fare, we realized he was a(n) (**pedestrian, impostor**).

19. Mere words cannot express our (**affliction, gratitude**) for your splendid services to our school.

20. Shakespeare's advice about dressing—"rich, not (**gaudy, akin**)"—still holds true in today's sophisticated world.

Vocabulary in Context

*Read the following passage, in which some of the words you have studied in this unit appear in **boldface** type. Then complete each statement given below the passage by circling the letter of the item that is **the same** or **almost the same** in meaning as the highlighted word.*

"Chess on Ice"

(Line)

You step onto the **elongated** "sheet" of ice, which is twice the size of a bowling alley, push off from a "hack," then "slide" your "stone" with a "broom" and "lay it up just past the hog line." Huh? What kind of game are you playing? Is it shuffleboard on ice? No, like more than one million people worldwide, you are curling.

(5)   A subtle game, curling probably had its beginnings on a frozen lake (*loch*) somewhere in Scotland more than 400 years ago. By the 1700s curling had become Scotland's national pastime, and many curling clubs were established in that country, with numerous rules for curlers to **heed**. These rules included no wagering, swearing, or political discussions

(10)   while curling, in addition to detailed instructions for sweeping the 42-pound granite stone which, today, looks like a tea kettle, across the "keen" ice. During the French and Indian War, Scottish soldiers

(15)   brought curling to North America.

Today, particularly in the icy Midwest, curling clubs have sprung up, as has enthusiasm for the sport. Just ask residents of Mapleton, "the curling capital of southern

(20)   Minnesota." They'll tell you how they drive for hours, in bad weather, to attend curling tournaments, called "bonspiels." In Canada, curling is nearly **akin** to ice hockey in its number of supporters.

American women's curling team at Nagano

(25)   Clearly, curling has come a long way from its **meager** beginnings. In fact, in 1998 it officially became an Olympic sport. That year, in Nagano, Japan, the Canadian women's curling team **vanquished** Denmark to take the gold medal. Curling's popularity continues to grow in the United States. In fact, our nation's largest curling club, in St. Paul, Minnesota, now boasts 700

(30)   members. In an age of raucous sports, with celebrity athletes and **inflated** salaries, curling remains a game of manners, a kind of chess on ice.

---

1. The meaning of **elongated** (line 1) is
a. slippery   c. shortened
b. frozen   d. extended

2. Heed (line 8) is best defined as
a. be guided by   c. ignore
b. memorize   d. create

3. Akin (line 23) most nearly means
a. unrelated   c. similar
b. plentiful   d. dissimilar

4. Meager (line 26) is best defined as
a. slight   c. ample
b. lavish   d. ancient

5. Vanquished (line 27) most nearly means
a. succumbed to   c. tormented
b. diminished   d. defeated

6. The meaning of **inflated** (line 30) is
a. flattened   c. enlarged
b. typical   d. modest

Definitions

Note carefully the spelling, pronunciation, part(s) of speech, and definition(s) of each of the following words. Then write the word in the blank space(s) in the illustrative sentence(s) following. Finally, study the lists of synonyms and antonyms given at the end of each entry.

1. **authoritative**
   (ə thär′ ə tā tiv)

   (*adj.*) official, coming from a source that calls for obedience or belief; dictatorial

   A dictionary is an _____ authoritative _____ source for the spelling, pronunciation, and definition of words in a language.

   SYNONYMS: reliable, authoritarian
   ANTONYMS: unofficial, unreliable

2. **bankrupt**
   (baŋk′ rəpt)

   (*adj.*) in a state of financial ruin; (*v.*) to ruin financially; (*n.*) one who has been ruined financially

   The _____ bankrupt _____ company was closing its doors forever.

   Another bad sales year will _____ bankrupt _____ the failing firm.

   A _____ bankrupt _____ will have trouble getting credit.

   SYNONYMS: (*adj.*) flat broke, insolvent
   ANTONYMS: (*adj.*) financially sound, solvent

3. **clamor**
   (klam′ ər)

   (*n.*) a public outcry; any loud and continued noise; (*v.*) to call for by loud, continued outcries

   The coal miners began to _____ clamor _____ for better working conditions in the mine.

   The _____ clamor _____ of the trumpets was piercing.

   SYNONYMS: (*n.*) uproar, din, racket; (*v.*) cry out for

4. **coincide**
   (kō in sīd′)

   (*v.*) to be in full agreement; to be the same in nature, character, or function; to happen at the same time

   Our political beliefs would _____ coincide _____ with theirs on the issues of term limits and tax reform.

   SYNONYMS: agree, concur, match

5. **cynical**
   (sin′ ə kəl)

   (*adj.*) inclined to believe the worst of people; bitterly mocking or sneering

   The radio personality's _____ cynical _____ attitude made it difficult for the station manager to find sponsors for the talk show.

   SYNONYMS: skeptical, sarcastic, contemptuous
   ANTONYMS: hopeful, optimistic

6. despot
(des' pət)

(*n.*) a ruler who oppresses his or her subjects, a tyrant

That film director is known for acting like a
_____ **despot** _____ on the movie set.

SYNONYMS: dictator, autocrat, strongman

7. feud
(fyüd)

(*n.*) a bitter, long-term quarrel; (*v.*) to fight or quarrel with

A senseless _____ **feud** _____ caused the
division between the two clans.

What originally caused the clans to
_____ **feud** _____ has long been forgotten.

SYNONYMS: (*n.*) dispute, vendetta
ANTONYMS: (*n.*) pact, agreement, harmony, concord

8. haggle
(hag' əl)

(*v.*) to argue in a petty way, especially about a price

Let's not _____ **haggle** _____ over the price of
admission until we finish writing the play!

SYNONYMS: bargain with, dicker with, wrangle

9. hardy
(här' dē)

(*adj.*) able to bear up under difficult conditions or harsh
treatment; brave and tough

The saguaro is a _____ **hardy** _____ variety of the
cactus family.

SYNONYMS: rugged, sturdy, resolute, stalwart
ANTONYMS: frail, feeble, weak

10. harmonious
(här mō' nē əs)

(*adj.*) able to get along together well; combining different
elements that blend pleasingly; melodious

The two companies' negotiations were
_____ **harmonious** _____ and resulted in a merger.

SYNONYMS: agreeable, compatible, tuneful
ANTONYMS: harsh, grating, discordant

11. hoard
(hôrd)

(*v.*) to store up, save; (*n.*) a hidden store or supply

Where did the miser keep his _____ **hoard** _____
of money?

SYNONYMS: (*v.*) amass, stockpile, cache
ANTONYMS: (*v.*) waste, throw away, squander

12. indisposed
(in dis pōzd')

(*adj., part.*) slightly ill; disinclined to do something

My sister was _____ **indisposed** _____ with a bad head
cold.

SYNONYMS: (*adj.*) ailing, unwell, reluctant
ANTONYMS: (*adj.*) healthy, willing, eager

13. legacy
(leg' ə sē)

(*n.*) an inheritance; something handed down from an ancestor
or from the past

The _____ legacy _____ from her grandmother
made her a wealthy woman.
SYNONYMS: bequest, heritage

14. legitimate
(lə jit′ ə mət)

(*adj.*) lawful, rightful; reasonable, justifiable

There is a new committee that rules on whether complaints
are _____ legitimate _____.
SYNONYMS: legal, right, proper, genuine
ANTONYMS: unlawful, illegal, improper, unauthorized

15. mirth
(mərth)

(*n.*) merry fun, gaiety; laughter

The children were filled with _____ mirth _____ as
they exited the Fun House.
SYNONYMS: merriment, glee
ANTONYMS: gloom, sadness, sorrow

16. officiate
(ə fish′ ē āt)

(*v.*) to perform the duties of an office; to conduct a religious
ceremony; to referee

Will a judge _____ officiate _____ at the ceremony?
SYNONYMS: chair, preside, emcee, moderate

17. partial
(pär′ shəl)

(*adj.*) not complete; favoring one side over another; showing a
strong liking for someone or something

To say that she is _____ partial _____ to sweets
would be an understatement.
SYNONYMS: incomplete, biased, prejudiced, fond of
ANTONYMS: complete, fair, just, unbiased

18. patronize
(pa′ trə nīz)

(*v.*) to give one's business to regularly as a customer; to
support, provide financial help; to treat someone as an inferior
while making a show of being kind or gracious

We like to _____ patronize _____ the family-owned
stores in the neighborhood.
SYNONYMS: do business with, deal with, trade with
ANTONYMS: boycott, refuse to deal with

19. rite
(rīt)

(*n.*) a ceremony; the customary form of a ceremony; any formal
custom or practice

A minister will perform the marriage
_____ rites _____.
SYNONYMS: observance, ritual, liturgy

20. sagacious
(sə gā′ shəs)

(*adj.*) shrewd; wise in a keen, practical way

History has shown that _____ sagacious _____ leaders
exercise tolerance and fairness, along with good judgment.
SYNONYMS: smart, clever, astute
ANTONYMS: silly, foolish, ill-advised, dopey

Completing the Sentence

From the words for this unit, choose the one that best completes each of the following sentences. Write the word in the space provided.

1. Where can I get a(n) _____**authoritative**_____ estimate of how the population of the United States is likely to change in the years ahead?

2. The pioneers who settled the West were _____**hardy**_____ people who could cope with difficulties and dangers of all kinds.

3. We must be prepared to defend the _____**legacy**_____ of freedom that we have inherited from earlier generations of Americans.

4. Historians are still examining the deadly _____**feud**_____ that arose between the Hatfield and McCoy families more than 100 years ago.

5. Since your program for cleaning up the lakefront _____**coincides**_____ with ours, why can't we work together?

6. Nothing will be accomplished unless the members of the committee work together in a(n) _____**harmonious**_____ fashion.

7. When you say that "everyone is out to take advantage of everyone else," I think you're being much too _____**cynical**_____.

8. The pagan religions of ancient times revolved around the performance of various _____**rites**_____ designed to ensure the fertility of the land.

9. Is it true that squirrels _____**hoard**_____ nuts and other foods that they can use during the winter?

10. Although she had no previous experience as a treasurer, she showed herself to be highly _____**sagacious**_____ in the way she handled money.

11. I am making only a(n) _____**partial**_____ payment at the present time and will pay off the balance in installments.

12. I think your price for the tennis racket is too high, but since I'm in no mood to _____**haggle**_____ with you, I'll take it.

13. The students were urged to _____**patronize**_____ the local merchants who advertised in the school paper.

14. True, business has been poor, but we are covering our expenses and can assure you that there's no danger of our going _____**bankrupt**_____.

15. The fact that the baseball season is opening today is certainly not a(n) _____**legitimate**_____ excuse for being absent from school.

16. The referee who _____**officiates**_____ at a hockey game needs the stamina to keep up with the players and the patience to put up with them.

17. I like a good laugh as much as anyone, but I realized that such a solemn ceremony was not the time for _____**mirth**_____.

18. My aunt called to say that she would not be able to visit us today because she was _____**indisposed**_____ with an asthma attack.

19. Our supervisor became extremely unpopular with us because he acted like a(n) _____**despot**_____ toward everyone in the department.

20. About five minutes before feeding time, all the babies in the nursery start to _____**clamor**_____ for their bottles.

Synonyms

*Choose the word from this unit that is **the same** or **most nearly the same** in meaning as the **boldface** word or expression in the given phrase. Write the word on the line provided.*

1. broadcast **incomplete** details of the tragedy	partial
2. will undergo a **ritual** of initiation	rite
3. was behaving in a highly **dictatorial** manner	authoritative
4. would **argue** over a penny	haggle
5. asked a substitute to **preside**	officiate
6. was **ailing** with a headache	indisposed
7. proved to be the **legal** heir to the throne	legitimate
8. was filled with joy and **gaiety**	mirth
9. would **trade with** the shops in the mall	patronize
10. had taken sides in the bitter **quarrel**	feud
11. would **concur** with the judge's opinion of the case	coincide
12. a **bequest** of untold value	legacy
13. workers who will **cry out** for reform	clamor
14. to rule with the iron hand of a **tyrant**	despot
15. made one of his usual **sarcastic** remarks	cynical

Antonyms

*Choose the word from this unit that is **most nearly opposite** in meaning to the **boldface** word or expression in the given phrase. Write the word on the line provided.*

16. known to **squander** their wealth	hoard
17. makes a **grating** sound	harmonious
18. was **foolish** in the choices she made	sagacious
19. would soon be a **solvent** corporation	bankrupt
20. was a **weak** breed of cattle	hardy

Choosing the Right Word

*Circle the **boldface** word that more satisfactorily completes each of the following sentences.*

1. One reason the coach is so popular is that he is firm and even tough with his players but never acts like a (**despot,** bankrupt).

2. A good sports official pays no attention to the (**clamor,** mirth) of the crowd when a decision goes against the home team.

3. Your healthy body is a (**legacy,** rite) you have received from your parents, and you should strive to protect it from harmful influences.

4. During the winter, there are always a few (partial, **hardy**) souls who take a dip in the icy waters off Atlantic Beach.

5. No matter how efficient the new chairperson may be, the meeting will not proceed (authoritatively, **harmoniously**) unless the members cooperate.

6. We will give careful attention to (cynical, **legitimate**) complaints, but we will not be influenced by silly faultfinding.

7. The jury was impressed by the fact that the testimony of two witnesses who were complete strangers (**coincided,** clamored) in every detail.

8. A party that cannot offer new ideas to deal with the pressing problems of the day must be considered politically (legitimate, **bankrupt**).

9. She may give the impression of being a simple old woman, but we have found her to be unusually (**sagacious,** indisposed) in judging people.

10. Why (**haggle,** officiate) over minor details when we are in agreement on the main issue?

11. The (harmonious, **authoritative**) tone in which she gave the order left no doubt in anyone's mind that she expected full obedience.

12. We cannot accept the idea that capital and labor must constantly (**feud,** coincide) with each other.

13. In the period ahead there may be shortages of some foodstuffs, but we will only make things worse if we resort to (patronizing, **hoarding**).

14. Isn't it (**cynical,** feuding) of you to ask other people to support a candidate in whom you yourself have no confidence?

15. I was (hardy, **indisposed**) to accept the halfhearted invitation that reached me only a day before the party.

16. If you're looking for a witty, charming personality to (**officiate,** coincide) at the awards dinner, need I say that I'm available?

17. Life cannot be all happiness; we must expect tears as well as (legacies, **mirth**).

18. I am annoyed by the (haggling, **patronizing**) way in which they keep reminding me "how a well-bred person behaves."

19. Each answer will be considered either right or wrong; no (sagacious, **partial**) credit will be given.

20. Learning to drive, graduating from high school, and entering college or the job market are all part of the (**rites,** hoards) of passage from a teenager to an adult.

Read the following passage, in which some of the words you have studied in this unit appear in **boldface** type. Then complete each statement given below the passage by circling the letter of the item that is **the same** or **almost the same** in meaning as the highlighted word.

As American as Hot Dogs

(Line)

Have you ever wondered what a picnic would be like without hot dogs? Or a baseball game? Although the origin of the hot dog is unclear (it may be related to the wiener from Vienna, Austria, or the *frankfurter wurst* from Frankfurt, Germany), this "fun food" is a **legitimate** American phenomenon. The **clamor** for hot dogs can be heard at sports stadiums and amusement parks from coast to coast. (5)

Like its origin, the name "hot dog" is also shrouded in mystery. The National Hot Dog and Sausage Council will suggest that "hot dog" may have been coined in 1906 by Harry Stevens, a concessionaire at the old Polo Grounds ballpark in New York City. According to the council, Stevens began calling the sandwich a hot dog rather than a "dachshund sausage" as it had been known at the time. (10)

Regardless of how the hot dog got its name, it soon became the favorite patriotic fare of Americans, who were soon **patronizing** hot-dog stands and gobbling up the "dogs" just as (15) fast as they could be placed in buns.

Of course, the best way to eat a hot dog depends on one's location. In fact, for years a **feud** has been raging between Chicagoans and (20) New Yorkers, as each group claims to know the best way to cook and

Baseball fan enjoying a hot dog

"dress" a "frank." In the Windy City, people prefer their hot dogs boiled or steamed, mixed with pork, well seasoned, and piled high with relish, tomato, pickles, and peppers. In the Big Apple, people (25) are **partial to** all-beef hot dogs grilled and topped with mustard, onions, and sauerkraut.

No matter how Americans may "dress" their "dogs," it is clear that they love this food. In all, Americans eat 20 billion hot dogs a year, which proves just how much they "relish" this dish. (30)

---

1. The meaning of **legitimate** (line 4) is
- a. rugged
- (b.) genuine
- c. legal
- d. foolish

2. Clamor (line 4) is best defined as
- a. function
- b. fondness
- c. glee
- (d.) outcry

3. Patronizing (line 14) most nearly means
- a. stockpiling
- b. bargaining with
- (c.) doing business with
- d. boycotting

4. Feud (line 19) is best defined as
- (a.) dispute
- b. pact
- c. boycott
- d. din

5. Partial to (line 26) most nearly means
- a. against
- b. unbiased
- c. avoiding
- (d.) fond of

Visit us at www.sadlier-oxford.com
for interactive puzzles and games.

REVIEW UNITS 13–15

Vocabulary for Comprehension

Read the following passage, in which some of the words you have studied in Units 13–15 appear in **boldface** *type. Then answer questions 1–11 on page 172 on the basis of what is* stated *or* implied *in the passage and in the introductory statement.*

Jim Thorpe (1888–1953), the subject of this passage, was one of America's greatest and most versatile athletes.

(Line)

Voted the greatest male athlete of the first half of the twentieth century by the Associated Press in 1950, Jim Thorpe received **massive** praise and

(5) criticism in his lifetime. Thorpe was born in Indian Territory (now Oklahoma) in 1888. In 1904, Thorpe was sent to the Carlisle Indian School in Pennsylvania, where his astounding

(10) athletic ability was first discovered by Glenn S. "Pop" Warner, the legendary coach of the school. When the coach spotted Thorpe high-jumping six feet, he offered him a place on the track

(15) team, where he instantly became a star. He also became a football hero. In fact, in one of his best games, he helped the Carlisle football team **vanquish** its rival Harvard by booting

(20) four field goals. For his efforts on the football field, he was named to the All-American team.

Jim Thorpe left Carlisle in 1909 to play baseball for two seasons in the

(25) East Carolina minor league, a decision that would affect his whole life. His greatest achievement would come, however, in the 1912 Olympic Games in Stockholm, Sweden. There

(30) he would win two gold medals—in the pentathlon and the decathlon. "Sir, you are the greatest athlete in the world," said King Gustav V of

Sweden, who was **officiating** at the

(35) games. Yet as events would show, Thorpe's triumph would be only a **partial** victory.

Shortly after the Olympic games were held, a sportswriter who had

(40) seen Thorpe play baseball in the minor leagues exposed him as a professional athlete, making him ineligible for Olympic competition. The Amateur Athletic Union stripped

(45) Thorpe of his Olympic records and medals in 1913, casting a **pall** over his achievements.

Thorpe joined the baseball New York Giants in that same year. The

(50) versatile Thorpe played professionally in both baseball and football. He was named the first commissioner of the new National Football League in 1920.

(55) For his achievements in football, he was inducted into the College and Pro Football Halls of Fame. In 1982, nearly 30 years after his death, the International Olympic Committee

(60) restored Thorpe's medals, thereby preserving his status as one of the world's greatest athletes.

1. Which of the following would make the best title for this passage?
   a. Great Male Athletes of the Twentieth Century
   b. The Athletic Career of Jim Thorpe
   c. Famous Native Americans
   d. The Olympic Games of 1912
   e. "Pop" Warner and Jim Thorpe

2. The meaning of **massive** (line 4) is
   a. enthusiastic
   b. reliable
   c. unjustified
   d. great
   e. widespread

3. **Vanquish** (line 19) most nearly means
   a. welcome
   b. succumb to
   c. persecute
   d. challenge
   e. conquer

4. The criticism of Thorpe mentioned in line 5 had to do with
   a. his personal life
   b. his professional behavior as a baseball player
   c. his professional behavior as a football player
   d. his professional career before the 1912 Olympic Games
   e. his conduct as a football commissioner

5. **Officiating** (line 34) is best defined as
   a. voting
   b. observing
   c. presiding
   d. competing
   e. announcing

6. **Partial** (line 37) most nearly means
   a. elusive
   b. small
   c. incomplete
   d. instant
   e. fond of

7. Thorpe's athletic ability was first recognized when he was
   a. a student at the Carlisle Indian School
   b. a minor league baseball player

c. a professional football player
   d. a gold medal winner at the 1912 Olympic Games
   e. a baseball player for the New York Giants

8. From paragraph 3 (lines 39–47), you can infer that
   a. sportswriters were biased against Thorpe
   b. Olympic competitors had to be amateur athletes
   c. Thorpe had a spectacular career in the minor leagues
   d. Olympic competitors had to be professional athletes
   e. Thorpe did not know about the Olympic committee's rules

9. **Pall** (line 46) is best defined as
   a. shadow
   b. light
   c. bore
   d. fascination
   e. scandal

10. Jim Thorpe was all of the following EXCEPT
   a. a commissioner of the National Football League
   b. a member of the Football Hall of Fame
   c. the winner of the pentathlon in the 1912 Olympics
   d. the winner of the decathlon in the 1912 Olympics
   e. the most valuable player in the 1912 World Series

11. To organize this passage, the author has arranged information in
   a. spatial order
   b. order of importance
   c. chronological order
   d. cause-effect order
   e. comparison-contrast order

**Grammar
in Context**

The sentence "The versatile Thorpe played professionally in both baseball and football" (lines 50–52 on page 171) has a pleasing rhythm and is easy to follow because of the way it repeats a grammatical form. We say that a sentence such as this one has **parallel construction**. To better understand what this means, read the following version of the sentence, this time written without parallel structure: "The versatile Thorpe played professionally in baseball, and he was playing professional football." That no longer sounds right, does it?

Here are a few rules that will help you make sure your sentences have parallel construction: (1) Be consistent when articles, prepositions, or conjunctions precede equivalent items or items in a series. Use the preceding word before the first word in the series only ("Many track coaches, baseball coaches, and footfall coaches admired Thorpe's great athletic skills.") or before every word in the series ("Many track coaches, many baseball coaches, and many football coaches admired Thorpe's great athletic skills.") (2) When you write to compare or contrast parallel ideas, make sure to express those ideas using the same grammatical form ("For Thorpe, having success in athletics went hand in with having trouble with the Amateur Athletic Union.").

On the lines provided, rewrite each of the following sentences to eliminate any faulty parallelism. Write "correct" if the sentence is correct.

Answers may vary; sample answers given.

1. I like to play baseball, football, soccer, and to play basketball.
   I like to play baseball, football, soccer, and basketball.

2. Many would agree that sluggers Babe Ruth, Ted Williams, and the big hitter Hank Aaron are among baseball's all-time greatest players.
   Many would agree that sluggers Babe Ruth, Ted Williams, and Hank Aaron are among baseball's all-time greatest players.

3. Watching Thorpe running for a touchdown or hitting a home run was so much more exciting than watching him participate in a high-jump contest.
   correct

4. Seeing a game in person is so much better than to see one on TV.
   Seeing a game in person is so much better than seeing one on TV.

5. Many athletes compete in more than one sport, but you will not be seeing very many doing so at a high level.
   Many athletes compete in more than one sport, but not many do so at a high level.

6. The sportswriter's article about Thorpe exposed the athlete's professional experiences, and it was damaging to Thorpe's Olympic victories.
   The sportswriter's article about Thorpe exposed the athlete's professional experiences and damaged Thorpe's Olympic victories.

 **Two-Word Completions**

Circle the pair of words that best complete the meaning of each of the following passages.

See pages T38–T48 for explanations of answers.

1. "If we are to win this election," the senator said, "we must put aside our private _____ and present a truly united front. Those who _____ this advice will be helping our cause. Those who ignore it can only hurt us."

a. afflictions . . . diminish
b. legacies . . . revere

c. handicrafts . . . countenance
d. feuds . . . heed

2. The tragic news of our friend's death in an automobile accident cast a(n) _____ of gloom over our little gathering that evening and turned our _____ to tears.

a. affliction . . . rite
b. clamor . . . agitation

c. saga . . . countenance
d. pall . . . mirth

3. The referees who _____ at hockey games are like judges presiding over trials. For that reason, they and their assistants must be as _____ as possible. If they show any favoritism in their calls, they'll hear about it from the fans.

a. officiate . . . impartial
b. agitate . . . authoritative

c. clamor . . . cosmopolitan
d. haggle . . . partial

4. "I'm more than happy to shop at any establishment that is owned by a _____ businessperson," Mom declared. "But I simply refuse to _____ a store that is run by people who are out to cheat me."

a. despotic . . . bankrupt
b. reputable . . . patronize

c. cosmopolitan . . . foster
d. legitimate . . . transmit

5. "You certainly don't have to _____ your money the way a miser would," I observed, "but if you continue to throw it around quite so freely, you'll soon be _____ ."

a. transmit . . . stodgy
b. hoard . . . bankrupt

c. revere . . . pedestrian
d. foster . . . indisposed

6. "I hate to _____ over minor details," the fussy little prince remarked to the court magician. "But as long as you're pulling things out of a hat, couldn't you come up with something nourishing? I'm hungry, and bouquets of fake flowers aren't particularly _____ ."

a. haggle . . . nutritious
b. meditate . . . massive

c. grovel . . . pedestrian
d. clamor . . . gaudy

Choosing the Right Meaning

Read each sentence carefully. Then circle the item that best completes the statement below the sentence.

See pages T38–T48 for explanations of answers.

To put maximum pressure on German defenses, the Soviet Army planned a massive assault on the Eastern Front to coincide with the D-day landings in Normandy. (2)

1. In line 2 the phrase **coincide with** most nearly means

(a. occur at the same time as) c. support
b. fully agree with d. draw attention from

British comedies of the late nineteenth century are often peopled with cosmopolitan types who speak in witty, glittering epigrams. (2)

2. The best definition for the word **cosmopolitan** in line 1 is

a. global b. stock (c. sophisticated) d. international

Warned that the least agitation might cause the mixture to explode, lab technicians handled the container with extreme caution. (2)

3. In line 1 the word **agitation** most nearly means

(a. shaking) b. confusion c. excitement d. uneasiness

It is true that his is a hard-luck story, but when will he learn that it is difficult to feel sorry for someone who grovels in self-pity? (2)

4. The word **grovels** in line 2 is best defined as

a. crouches b. cringes c. cowers (d. wallows)

Evidence presented at the trial showed that far from being a "crime of opportunity," the burglary had been meditated weeks before. (2)

5. The word **meditated** in line 2 is used to mean

a. reflected upon c. discussed b. rehearsed (d. planned)

Antonyms

*In each of the following groups, circle the word or expression that is most nearly the **opposite** of the word in **boldface** type.*

1. reputable
a. well-known
b. wealthy
c. local
(d. shady)

2. partial
(a. complete)
b. scholarly
c. written
d. unfair

3. heed
a. obey
(b. ignore)
c. report
d. send

4. ignite
(a. extinguish)
b. borrow
c. offer
d. light

5. enchanted
a. pleased
b. ignored
c. surprised
(d. disgusted)

6. feud
a. quarrel
(b. harmony)
c. job
d. study

7. foster
(a. hold back)
b. encourage
c. pay for
d. expect

8. diminish
a. equal
(b. increase)
c. confirm
d. lower

9. affliction
a. experience
b. blessing
c. hardship
d. surprise

11. gratitude
a. joy
b. heed
c. thanklessness
d. fear

13. revered
a. invented
b. supported
c. honored
d. despised

15. elongate
a. shorten
b. clean up
c. clutter
d. decorate

10. indisposed
a. ill
b. unqualified
c. interested
d. healthy

12. cynical
a. optimistic
b. bitter
c. stupid
d. intelligent

14. oppressed
a. mistreated
b. reported
c. pampered
d. observed

16. sagacious
a. brief
b. silly
c. wise
d. witty

Word Families

A. *On the line provided, write the word you have learned in Units 13–15 that is related to each of the following nouns.*
EXAMPLE: gaudiness—**gaudy**

1. hilarity, hilariousness — **hilarious**
2. reverence, reverend — **revere**
3. impartiality — **impartial**
4. meditation, meditator, meditativeness — **meditate**
5. sagaciousness, sagacity — **sagacious**
6. massiveness, mass — **massive**
7. oppression, oppressor, oppressiveness — **oppress**
8. patronage, patron, patronization — **patronize**
9. reputability, reputation, repute — **reputable**
10. cynicism, cynic — **cynical**
11. nutrition, nutritionist, nutritiousness — **nutritious**
12. fluctuation — **fluctuate**
13. officiation, office, official — **officiate**
14. ignition, igniter (ignitor) — **ignite**
15. transmission, transmittance, transmitter, transmittal — **transmit**
16. coincidence — **coincide**

B. *On the line provided, write the word you have learned in Units 13–15 that is related to each of the following verbs.*
EXAMPLE: agitate—**agitation**

17. authorize, author — **authoritative**
18. harmonize — **harmonious**
19. legitimize, legitimatize — **legitimate**
20. afflict — **affliction**

Word Associations

In each of the following groups, circle the word that is best defined or suggested by the given phrase.

1. property left to children by parents
a. rite (b. legacy) c. gala d. bankruptcy

2. a loud outcry from angry people
a. gratitude (b. clamor) c. affliction d. despot

3. on a very large scale
a. chronological (b. massive) c. partial d. sagacious

4. a festive occasion or celebration
a. affliction b. mirth c. hoax (d. gala)

5. what a regular customer does
a. countenance b. transmit (c. patronize) d. foster

6. laughter and merriment
a. feud b. magnitude c. affliction (d. mirth)

7. birds of a feather
a. indisposed (b. akin) c. legitimate d. hilarious

8. a meal that supplies what the body needs
(a. nutritious) b. stodgy c. hilarious d. harmonious

9. the look on someone's face, be it happy or sad
(a. countenance) b. feud c. impostor d. clamor

10. typical of a mother
a. akin b. cynical (c. maternal) d. reputable

11. carpentry, weaving, pottery, metalwork, etc.
a. pedestrians (b. handicrafts) c. impostors d. galas

12. used to be a lot of fun, but now we're tired of it
a. heed b. transmit (c. pall) d. foster

13. what a referee would do
a. coincide (b. officiate) c. meditate d. hoard

14. greatness of size, like an earthquake or a conflict
a. agitation (b. magnitude) c. despot d. handicraft

15. like a timetable
(a. chronological) b. hilarious c. gaudy d. impartial

16. a plant that thrives even under unfavorable conditions
a. authoritative b. massive c. wan (d. hardy)

17. what a tyrant would do to the people he ruled
a. countenance b. patronize (c. oppress) d. revere

18. the story of the adventures of a Viking, such as Eric the Red
a. hoax (b. saga) c. rite d. gala

19. extremely funny
a. chronological b. impartial (c. hilarious) d. cynical

20. prices going up and down rapidly
(a. fluctuate) b. ignite c. heed d. diminish

Building with Classical Roots

rupt—to break

This root appears in **bankrupt** (page 164). Literally, the word means "bank broken," that is, "unable to pay one's debts." It also means "one who is unable to pay his or her debts" or "to ruin financially and thus make unable to pay debts." Some other words based on the same root are listed below.

abrupt	disruptive	incorruptible	irruption
corrupt	erupt	interrupt	rupture

From the list of words above, choose the one that corresponds to each of the brief definitions below. Write the word in the blank space in the illustrative sentence below the definition.

1. to break in upon; to stop, halt

All day long she has to _____**interrupt**_____ her work in order to answer the telephone.

2. sudden, short, blunt; very steep

The car made a(n) _____**abrupt**_____ stop at the crosswalk to avoid hitting the pedestrian.

3. causing disorder or turmoil ("*to break apart*")

His late arrival had a _____**disruptive**_____ influence on the meeting.

4. to burst forth ("*to break out*")

Lava _____**erupted**_____ from the exploding volcano as the population fled.

5. a breaking or bursting in; a violent invasion

The _____**irruption**_____ of the Goths into Roman territory led to the collapse of the Roman Empire.

6. a breaking; to break

The engineers worked frantically to repair the _____**rupture**_____ in the wall of the dam.

7. rotten, wicked, dishonest; to make evil; to bribe

The _____**corrupt**_____ dictatorship was replaced by a democratic republic.

8. not open to immoral behavior, honest; unbribable

He remained a(n) _____**incorruptible**_____ public official despite the many attempts of the crime boss to bribe him.

From the list of words above, choose the one that best completes each of the following sentences. Write the word in the blank space provided.

1. I was very much hurt when she made such a(n) _____**abrupt**_____ reply to my question.

2. His unwillingness to listen to my side of the story caused a serious

_____**rupture**_____ in our friendship.

3. The principal warned that the parents of _____**disruptive**_____ students would be sent for.

4. When cynics remark that "everyone has a price," they are expressing their belief that no one is truly _____**incorruptable**_____.

5. The gamblers tried to _____**corrupt**_____ the athletes by offering them large sums of money to throw the game.

6. The police feared violence would _____**erupt**_____ if the opposing groups of demonstrators were allowed to get near each other.

7. The bulkhead sprang a leak, causing a(n) _____**irruption**_____ of seawater into the ship's hold.

8. I know I shouldn't have _____**interrupted**_____ him in the middle of a sentence, but that sentence seemed as though it would never end!

---

*Circle the **boldface** word that more satisfactorily completes each of the following sentences.*

1. The scandal revealed that the social service agency was riddled with (**incorruptible,** (**corrupt**)) bureaucrats.

2. Talking in the library can have a(n) (**abrupt,** (**disruptive**)) effect on those who are attempting to read or study.

3. The doctors would need to perform surgery in order to determine whether the patient's appendix had (**interrupted,** (**ruptured**)).

4. As a(n) (**corrupt,** (**incorruptible**)) mayor of a large city, she will long be remembered for her honesty.

5. History has shown that riots sometimes (**abrupt,** (**erupt**)) during a long, hot summer in the city.

6. The valve broke off in my hand, and a(n) ((**irruption,** **rupture**) of steam filled the room.

7. The property consists of mostly flat land that makes an ((**abrupt,** **incorruptible**) rise toward the back.

8. My little sister has an annoying habit of trying to ((**interrupt,** **erupt**) me when I am on the telephone.

Review Units 13–15 ■ *179*

Analogies — In each of the following, circle the item that best completes the comparison.

See pages T38–48 for explanations of answers.

1. farce is to **hilarious** as
a. overture is to literate
b. anecdote is to interminable
c. paradox is to quaint
d. tragedy is to heartrending ✓

2. impostor is to **counterfeit** as
a. notable is to prominent ✓
b. fledgling is to proficient
c. braggart is to timid
d. parasite is to sullen

3. quibble is to **haggle** as
a. foster is to stifle
b. entreat is to implore ✓
c. grovel is to flounder
d. entice is to oppress

4. vindictive is to **vengeance** as
a. unscathed is to recompense
b. bewildered is to clarification ✓
c. hospitable is to seclusion
d. cynical is to gratitude

5. blindness is to **affliction** as
a. homicide is to ordeal
b. embezzlement is to catastrophe
c. pneumonia is to malady ✓
d. perjury is to misdemeanor

6. diminish is to **inflate** as
a. seethe is to capsize
b. enchant is to pamper
c. detest is to revere ✓
d. consolidate is to abound

7. scurry is to **feet** as
a. mull is to legs
b. snare is to eyes
c. meditate is to ears
d. bellow is to lungs ✓

8. legacy is to **beneficiary** as
a. oration is to speaker
b. gift is to recipient ✓
c. turmoil is to firebrand
d. flight is to fugitive

9. inflammable is to **ignite** as
a. graphic is to picture ✓
b. unique is to prove
c. reluctant is to plan
d. insubordinate is to produce

10. lamb is to **docile** as
a. cow is to sagacious
b. horse is to fickle
c. mule is to wayward ✓
d. sheep is to regal

Choosing the Right Meaning — Read each sentence carefully. Then circle the item that best completes the statement below the sentence.

See pages T38–48 for explanations of answers.

My favorite painting in the exhibition was an Italian still life showing a pitcher, a fruit knife, and a bowl of mellow figs. (2)

1. The best definition for the word **mellow** in line 2 is
a. gentle   b. pleasant   c. ripe ✓   d. rich

Can you name the friar who officiates at the secret wedding of the doomed lovers Romeo and Juliet? (2)

2. The phrase **officiates at** in line 1 is used to mean
a. referees   b. conducts ✓   c. moderates   d. chairs

Although A. E. Glug tried many verse forms, he was partial to narrative poetry and indeed achieved his greatest success with the epic poem *The Clodyssey* (1906). (2)

3. The phrase **was partial to** in line 1 is used to mean

a. mastered

(b. favored)

c. was biased against

d. was trained in

Once exclusive to American cities such as New York and Chicago, skyscrapers have in recent years come to dominate many a European metropolis as well. (2)

4. In line 2 the word **dominate** most nearly means

a. control

b. eclipse

(c. tower over)

d. master

With the slogan "No taxation without representation!" American colonists protested the authoritative levies imposed by the British crown. (2)

5. In line 2 the word **authoritative** most nearly means

(a. tyrannical)

b.reliable

c. obedient

d. official

Two-Word Completions

Circle the pair of words that best complete the meaning of each of the following sentences.

See pages T38–48 for explanations of answers.

1. As the police officers who had been called to the scene of the accident were _____ eyewitnesses to the incident, a large crowd of curious _____ began to collect nearby.

a. lubricating . . . buffoons

b. procuring . . . dupes

c. patronizing . . . pedestrians

(d. interrogating . . . bystanders)

2. I did everything I could to _____ them from pursuing a course of action that I firmly believed would end in disaster, but all my efforts were, unfortunately, _____ .

(a. dissuade . . . futile)

b. transmit . . . meager

c. mortify . . . spirited

d. swerve . . . disputatious

3. Though I admire the intrepid daredevils who _____ life and limb diving off towering cliffs into the sea, hundreds of feet below, I am much too _____ to try something like that myself.

a. hoard . . . hardy

(b. hazard . . . timid)

c. heed . . . stodgy

d. mar . . . lethargic

4. As I _____ idly through the curious book, my eye happened to light upon some interesting old photographs of haying and plowing and other scenes of life in _____ America at the end of the 19th century.

a. fluctuated . . . sodden

(b. browsed . . . rural)

c. tampered . . . gaudy

d. prescribed . . . radiant

5. During the 14th century, the bubonic _____, or "Black Death," suddenly swept across Europe, killing three quarters of the population and seriously _____, or even paralyzing, the social and economic life of the continent.

a. goad . . . dominating

b. luster . . . inflicting

(c. plague . . . disrupting)

d. hearth . . . renovating

Enriching Your Vocabulary

Read the passage below. Then complete the exercise at the bottom of the page.

The Language of Science

Scientific advances have not only contributed vast amounts of knowledge and data, but have also enriched our language with thousands of words. Many terms may originally have been coined to describe precise scientific concepts or phenomena. Over time and with repeated usage, science words can take on informal, nonscientific meanings that expand our ability to communicate.

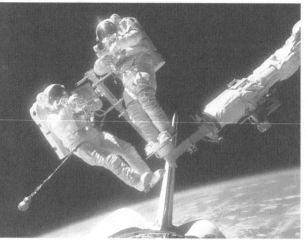

Astronauts making repairs

Modern astronomy forever changed in 1957, when *Sputnik,* the world's first earth-made satellite, was sent into orbit. This landmark achievement led to even young school children learning what it meant for a satellite to circle a larger planet. Soon people began to speak of satellite nations and satellite offices.

In biology, a *parasite* (Unit 10) is an organism that lives off another organism, taking its food from its host—usually at the host's expense. From its explicit scientific meaning, *parasite* has come to describe a person who lives off others without a fair return—a hanger-on, sponge, or deadbeat, to use popular slang. In physics, *radiant* (Unit 5) energy is sent out as rays of light or heat. But the bright, joyful smile of a blissful person can also be described as radiant, although no beams of light or heat are visible.

In Column A below are 6 more scientific words. With or without a dictionary, match each word with its meanings in Column B.

Column A

___f___ **1.** hybrid

___e___ **2.** magnetic

___b___ **3.** galaxy

___d___ **4.** eclipse

___a___ **5.** inertia

___c___ **6.** gravity

Column B

a. the tendency for an object at rest to remain at rest, or for a moving object to keep moving; resistance to change

b. a large independent system of stars and other heavenly bodies; a gathering of distinguished people

c. the natural force that tends to cause all objects to move toward the center of the earth; importance or seriousness

d. the partial or total blocking of the light of one heavenly body by another; a decline in importance or use

e. being able to attract iron; having the power to attract

f. the offspring of two distinct plants or animals of different varieties; anything of mixed origin or unlike parts

Selecting Word Meanings

*In each of the following groups, circle the word or expression that is **most nearly the same** in meaning as the word in **boldface** type in the given phrase.*

1. without any **incentive**
   a. money   b. right   c. inducement ✓   d. selfishness

2. something that we **detest**
   a. know   b. hate ✓   c. welcome   d. understand

3. **entreat** them to leave
   a. command   b. beg ✓   c. require   d. expect

4. made a **fruitless** effort
   a. strenuous   b. futile ✓   c. planned   d. successful

5. a **foretaste** of things to come
   a. return   b. result   c. anticipation ✓   d. cause

6. received **innumerable** warnings
   a. countless ✓   b. threatening   c. official   d. detailed

7. made a **cynical** comment
   a. poetic   b. long-winded   c. necessary   d. skeptical ✓

8. **gruesome** details
   a. delicious   b. novel   c. horrifying ✓   d. unexpected

9. made **lavish** preparations
   a. hasty   b. careful   c. extravagant ✓   d. stingy

10. **tamper** with the evidence
    a. begin   b. interfere ✓   c. agree   d. argue

11. carry on a **feud**
    a. machine   b. quarrel ✓   c. movement   d. alliance

12. a rather **animated** discussion
    a. scholarly   b. dull   c. useless   d. lively ✓

13. committed **homicide**
    a. embezzlement   b. theft   c. murder ✓   d. lying

14. left **ajar**
    a. alone   b. partly open ✓   c. untouched   d. sealed

15. an **impartial** decision
    a. unbiased ✓   b. incomplete   c. unhurried   d. effective

16. an **anonymous** donor
    a. innocent   b. eager   c. unnamed ✓   d. angry

17. was **available** only on Fridays
    a. obtainable ✓   b. necessary   c. needed   d. qualified

18. **bewilder** one's teammates
    a. help   b. confuse ✓   c. teach   d. please

19. capsize the vessel
a. seize   (b. overturn)   c. purchase   d. repair

20. a **cosmopolitan** point of view
a. mechanical   (b. sophisticated)   c. false   d. important

21. the **downtrodden** workers
a. well-paid   b. happy   c. skillful   (d. oppressed)

22. a grueling **ordeal**
a. race   (b. test)   c. setback   d. interview

23. guilty of **perjury**
a. kidnapping   b. stealing   c. killing   (d. lying)

24. where fish **abound**
a. leap   b. produce young   c. are protected   (d. are plentiful)

25. foster a new policy
a. plan   b. object to   (c. encourage)   d. reexamine

Antonyms

*In each of the following groups, circle the **two** words or expressions that are **most nearly opposite** in meaning.*

26. a. swerve   (b. veto)   c. maul   (d. ratify)

27. (a. reputable)   b. domestic   (c. shady)   d. humdrum

28. a. heed   (b. decrease)   c. officiate   (d. accelerate)

29. a. hostile   b. hardy   (c. hilarious)   (d. heartrending)

30. a. vital   (b. leisurely)   (c. grueling)   d. miscellaneous

31. a. remnant   (b. bystander)   c. regime   (d. participant)

32. a. graphic   (b. injured)   (c. unscathed)   d. pending

33. (a. boycott)   (b. patronize)   c. hurtle   d. grovel

34. a. quaint   (b. puny)   (c. gigantic)   d. orthodox

35. a. inflammable   (b. cheerful)   c. substantial   (d. despondent)

36. (a. indifference)   b. melancholy   c. narrative   (d. enthusiasm)

37. a. persist   (b. reinforce)   c. seethe   (d. undermine)

38. a. insinuate   (b. entice)   c. renovate   (d. dissuade)

39. (a. enchant)   b. presume   c. trickle   (d. pall)

40. (a. spotless)   b. ultimate   c. disputatious   (d. grimy)

Supplying Words in Context

In each of the following sentences, write in the blank space the most appropriate word chosen from the given list.

Group A

stifle	botch	potential	nub
dominate	meager	fledgling	impostor
nomadic	mull	malignant	flagrant
uncertainty	downright	inflict	interrogate

41. When I was just a(n) _____ **fledgling** _____ in my very first pro season, one of the veteran players took me under his wing.

42. Though the situation in that part of the world is calm now, it is a(n) _____ **potential** _____ powder keg that may go off at any moment.

43. This mistake is so _____ **flagrant** _____ that it cannot be overlooked, even though the manager's son was responsible for it.

44. Although I realize you have many interesting stories to tell, I do wish you wouldn't always _____ **dominate** _____ the conversation.

45. He decided to give up trying to become a professional writer when he realized that his talents were really very _____ **meager** _____.

46. With a great effort, I managed to _____ **stifle** _____ my anger and replied as courteously as I could.

47. Inexperienced as we were, we knew we would _____ **botch** _____ the preparation of the meal, so we decided to go out to eat.

48. Instead of giving me all those unimportant details, let's get right to the _____ **nub** _____ of the matter.

49. I know I would have to _____ **mull** _____ over the events of the evening before I could determine if I had acted inappropriately.

50. It was _____ **downright** _____ rude of her to ignore my kind offer of help.

Group B

adjacent	interminable	recompense	cache
implore	dilapidated	malady	elongate
transmit	iota	morbid	pamper
utmost	snare	preview	casual

51. Luckily, the communications officer was able to _____ **transmit** _____ an SOS signal just before the ship's radio stopped working.

52. The wait outside the operating room seemed _____ **interminable** _____ to the parents of the injured child.

53. In a tearful voice, the guilty man's wife _____ **implored** _____ the court to treat her husband leniently.

54. The smile of joy she gave me when she received the award was ample
_____ **recompense** _____ for all the time and effort I had spent in helping her.

55. If you had a(n) _____ **iota** _____ of consideration for us, you would turn down
the volume on the television set.

56. Even though he lives in a house _____ **adjacent** _____ to the school, he is often late
for his first class.

57. The trick was to _____ **snare** _____ him in his own web of lies and deceit.

58. Religious intolerance is a social _____ **malady** _____ that simply cannot be
countenanced in a democracy such as ours.

59. The deserted cabin was so _____ **dilapidated** _____ that it looked as though any
strong breeze would cause it to collapse.

60. When the younger players went in for the last few minutes of the game, we had a(n)
_____ **preview** _____ of what the team would be like next year.

Words Connected with Moods

*The words in Column A may be applied to various moods that are typical of many people. In the space before each word, write the **letter** of the item in Column B that identifies it.*

	Column A	Column B
j	**61.** docile	a. sad, depressed
c	**62.** fickle	b. filled with resentment or anger over something
k	**63.** wayward	c. changing rapidly, especially in one's affections
i	**64.** vigilant	d. not caring one way or the other
f	**65.** peevish	e. extremely cruel
g	**66.** spirited	f. irritable, cross, easily annoyed
b	**67.** indignant	g. full of life and vigor
a	**68.** melancholy	h. willing to forgive almost anything
l	**69.** lethargic	i. on the lookout, alert
d	**70.** indifferent	j. easily controlled and taught
		k. disobedient, insisting on having one's own way
		l. unnaturally sleepy or slow moving

Words That Describe Behavior

Some words that describe the way people behave are listed below. Write the appropriate word on the line next to each of the following descriptions.

dupe	parasite	insubordinate	lax
firebrand	prudent	poised	dynamic
fallible	inimitable	tactful	scrimp
regal	reluctant	proficient	vindictive

71. She shows great drive, originality, and ability to get things done.   **dynamic**

72. He uses care and good judgment in handling his affairs.   **prudent**

73. She is sensitive to the feelings of other people and careful not to hurt them.   **tactful**

74. He dances in a way that no one else can equal or even try to match.   **inimitable**

75. His speech arouses the fury of his audiences.   **firebrand**

76. She is so trusting that she is easily deceived and used by others.   **dupe**

77. He expects to live off other people.   **parasite**

78. She is motivated by revenge.   **vindictive**

79. Hours of practice have made her a skillful pianist.   **proficient**

80. Like everyone else, she makes mistakes from time to time.   **fallible**

Word Associations

*In each of the following, circle the word or expression that best completes the meaning of the sentence or answers the question, with particular reference to the meaning of the word in **boldface** type.*

81. Which of the following would be most likely to create **havoc**?
a. a summer breeze
b. a game of volleyball
c. a school assembly
d. a tornado)

82. An example of a **grim** event is
a. a graduation
b. a fatal accident)
c. a family reunion
d. a holiday

83. A person who **quibbles** during an argument is
a. winning the argument
b. splitting hairs)
c. being courteous
d. getting angry

84. Memories that have been **eroded**
a. are still bright and clear
b. have been worn away by time)
c. are painful
d. are set down in writing

85. You would probably find it **mortifying** to
    a. snack between meals
    b. earn enough money to buy your
       own clothes
    c. win a dance contest
    (d. do poorly on this Final Mastery Test)

86. If there is **mutual** admiration between two people,
    a. the admiration is not genuine
    (b. they admire each other)
    c. the admiration is one-sided
    d. the admiration won't last

87. Which of the following suggests a person who is **frustrated**?
    a. "It's a great idea!"
    (b. "Foiled again!")
    c. "I won!"
    d. "I'll do it!"

88. A customer gives a storekeeper a $1 bill that is seen to be **counterfeit**. The storekeeper will probably
    a. accept it with thanks
    b. offer $2 for it
    (c. refuse to accept it)
    d. donate the bill to charity

89. Which of the following is likely to be **sodden**?
    a. a desert
    b. toast
    (c. a rain-soaked field)
    d. a dust storm

90. A **stalemate** lacks
    (a. a solution)
    b. a sense of humor
    c. freshness
    d. opponents

91. You would be most likely to **brood** over
    a. an event of no importance
    b. tomorrow's lunch
    c. an exciting sports victory
    (d. failing an important examination)

92. Which of the following would *not* be likely to **canvass** an area?
    a. an interviewer
    (b. a homebody)
    c. a pollster
    d. a door-to-door salesperson

93. A **braggart** would be most likely to
    a. grin and bear it
    b. stick to his or her guns
    c. fly off the handle
    (d. toot his or her own horn)

94. Which of the following would *not* be found in **rural** areas?
    (a. skyscrapers)
    b. water
    c. cows
    d. people

95. Which nickname would most likely be given to a **stodgy** person?
    a. "Trickster"
    b. "Doc"
    (c. "Stuffed Shirt")
    d. "Egghead"

96. You would be most likely to **browse**
    (a. in a library)
    b. on the tennis court
    c. when you are asleep
    d. during a test

97. A person facing the **hazards** of life is
    a. making money
    b. taking risks
    c. winning victories
    d. playing golf

98. Which of the following is *not* **transparent**?
    a. a pane of glass
    b. a feeble excuse
    c. air
    d. a wooden door

99. A person who receives a **legacy** has gained something as a result of
    a. inheriting it
    b. hard work
    c. dishonesty
    d. gambling

100. Which of the following cannot be **quenched**?
    a. fire
    b. ambition
    c. a flood
    d. thirst

INDEX

The following tabulation lists all the basic words taught in the various units of this book, as well as those introduced in the *Vocabulary of Vocabulary, Working with Analogies, Building with Classical Roots,* and *Enriching Your Vocabulary* sections. Words taught in the units are printed in **boldface** type. The number following each entry indicates the page on which the word is first introduced. Exercise and review materials in which the word also appears are not cited.